M000266546

Starting the Dialogue

Perspectives on

Technology and Society

Marie Hoepfl & Brian Raichle

Appalachian State University

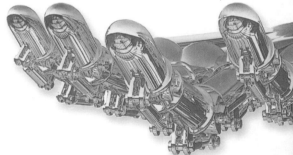

Kendall Hunt
publishing company

Cover design provided courtesy Jason David Strom.

Kendall Hunt
publishing company

www.kendallhunt.com
Send all inquiries to:
4050 Westmark Drive
Dubuque, IA 52004-1840

Copyright © 2009 by Kendall Hunt Publishing Company

ISBN: 978-0-7575-6745-2

All rights reserved. No part of this publication may be reproduced,
stored in a retrieval system, or transmitted, in any form or by any
means, electronic, mechanical, photocopying, recording, or otherwise,
without the prior written permission of the copyright owner.

Printed in the United States of America
10 9 8 7 6 5 4 3 2 1

Contents

Acknowledgments   v

Preface   vii

Section 1—Defining Technology   1

Introduction   1

Practical Ethics for a Technological World   5
Paul A. Alcorn

Section 2—Technological Decision Making   19

Introduction   19

Assessing the Risks of Technology   22
William E. Evan and Mark Manion

Big and Bad: How the S.U.V. Ran Over Automobile Safety   35
Malcolm Gladwell

Shaping the Future   45
Steven W. Popper, Robert J. Lempert, and Steven C. Bankes

While Washington Slept   53
Mark Hertsgaard

Section 3—Basic Human Needs: Rethinking Food, Water, and Shelter   71

Introduction   71

The Human Sponge   75
Fred Pearce

Taking the Water to the People   78
Fred Pearce

Hundreds of Man-Made Chemicals—In Our Air, Our Water, and Our Food—Could Be Damaging the Most Basic Building Blocks of Human Development   88
Gay Daly

The Case of the Vanishing Frogs   101
Timothy R. Halliday and W. Ronald Heyer

House Proud: High Design in a Factory-Made Home? Michelle Kaufmann Believes She Holds the Key   109
William Booth

Building Materials: What Makes a Product Green?   113
Alex Wilson

   Environmental Building News' Checklist for Environmentally Responsible Design and Construction   120
   Building Green, Inc.

Section 4—Fueling the Technological Revolution   125

Introduction   125

Razing Appalachia   128
Maryanne Vollers

Lights Out: Approaching the Historic Interval's End   138
Richard Heinberg

Global Oil Production about to Peak? A Recurring Myth   150
Red Cavaney

Powering the Future   155
Michael Parfit

Section 5—Perspectives on Transportation Technologies   169

Introduction   169

Transportation's Perennial Problems   171
W. Wayt Gibbs

Charter of the New Urbanism   178
Congress for the New Urbanism

Section 6—Perspectives on Communication Technologies   185

Introduction   185

Surveillance Nation   188
Dan Farmer and Charles C. Mann

Television Addiction Is No Mere Metaphor   198
Robert Kubey and Mihaly Csikszentmihalyi

Get Me Rewrite!   206
Michael Hirschorn

Section 7—Perspectives on Biological and Medical Technologies   213

Introduction   213

The Ideology of Machines: Medical Technology   215
Neil Postman

Section 8—Perspectives on Military and Security Technologies   225

Introduction   225

Technology Studies for Terrorists: A Short Course   227
Langdon Winner

Section 9—Perspectives on Workplace and Leisure Technologies   243

Introduction   243

From Ford to Dell: Mass Production to Mass Customization   244
Roger Alcaly

Section 10—Wild Promises: Anticipating Our Technological Future   253

Introduction   253

The Future: What Is the Problem?   256
Susan Greenfield

A Robot in Every Home   264
Bill Gates

The Quest for Mars   272
W. Henry Lambright and Debora L. VanNijnatten

The Nanotechnology Revolution   282
Adam Keiper

Acknowledgments

We extend thanks to the editors and staff at Kendall Hunt Publishers, in particular Angela Puls and Ray Wood, for their support for this project and for their patience; to our colleague Jerianne Taylor, who assisted with the planning of this project; and to the students in the Department of Technology at Appalachian State University, whose insights, passion, and commitment to a sustainable future provide inspiration to us all.

Preface

Introduction

The idea for this book has percolated for several years, during which time we have both taught university courses focusing on the interactions between technology and society. Part of the joy in teaching these courses has been the opportunity to introduce our students to the wealth of excellent books, articles, and other media that delve into the issues surrounding the development and use of technology. These resources range from very philosophical examinations of technology as an expression of human creativity to very technical treatments of specific technologies, and everything in between. To borrow a distinction made by a former colleague, we can talk about "big T" technology, meaning the *phenomenon* of technological activity and its implications; or we can talk about "little T" technology, meaning the myriad specific tools, objects, systems, and processes that comprise the human-made world. This book strives to provide a mix of these two perspectives, using articles and excerpts that have been specifically chosen for their capacity to illustrate—and spur discussions on—societal issues associated with technology.

For readers unfamiliar with the interdisciplinary field of the study of technology, a definition is in order. Specifically, we define technology as the artifacts and processes that make up the human-made world. From an academic perspective, one could say that technology is *the study of* those artifacts and processes. Most importantly, we wish for readers of this book to view technology from the broad range of human technological activity, rather than from the narrowly constrained view of computer technologies often intended when the word "technology" appears in common usage. In addition, readers are encouraged to remember that they use and interact daily with these technological artifacts and systems, and that understanding these technologies will benefit them personally, and society collectively.

A number of books have been published that are similar in structure to this one; these edited compilations are evidence of the broad literature on, and growing interest in, society and technology interactions. We have used and appreciated these edited volumes, but over the years continued to believe that there was room for another text that offers a broader mix of topical readings, including some with a heavier technical emphasis and with a particular emphasis on sustainability. In addition, we have provided background information on each topic, discussion questions, and suggestions for activities and additional resources, all of which we hope will make for a very user-friendly, and useful, book.

This is a far-ranging book in the sense that we have selected a diverse set of examples to illustrate the many technological choices we face on a daily basis. The key word is *choice*; all of us make daily decisions about which technologies we will use, buy, promote, support, and/or ignore. Sometimes, these decisions are thrust upon us as we react to the negative impacts of a particular technology; sometimes, our choices are very constrained. No matter the case, we believe that all of us share a responsibility for becoming as informed as possible about technologies and their impacts, both good and bad.

The Structure of This Book

This book is divided into six sections. Section One offers a more comprehensive definition of technology, one that provides a framework for discussing the topical issues covered in the remainder of this text. The excerpt from work by Paul Alcorn looks at the process of technological change from an evolutionary perspective, essentially outlining the ways that technological development by humans contrast with evolutionary change in other species. He further introduces the topic of ethics as it relates to technology. This introductory discussion allows us to identify some of the fundamental arguments surrounding the characteristics of technology.

Section Two extends the discussion started in the first section by illustrating the factors that enter into technological choice. Beginning the section is an excerpt on risk assessment by William Evan and Mark Manion, who describe some of the accepted strategies for calculating risks associated with new technologies. Although risk assessment is an important component of the decision making process, as these authors point out our ability to identify (let alone quantify) risks in complex systems is limited at best. Malcolm Gladwell, who in his role as a staff writer at *The New Yorker* has written very accessible and entertaining case studies about technological decision-making, uses the example of choice related to the personal automobile. Through this example we see that decisions about technology are sometimes based more on *perceptions* of the way things are than they are on more factual information, and thus are not always well reasoned. Steven Popper, Robert Lempert, and Steven Bankes describe new approaches to decision making that take into account how humans reason when significant uncertainties about the future exist, which is certainly the case when new technologies are being considered. Their version of exploratory modeling allows decision makers to consider multiple scenarios that balance social, environmental, and economic considerations. Finally, we include an article by Mark Hertsgaard, which uses a modern-day debate over global climate change to illustrate the difficulties of implementing governmental policy to address a large-scale problem associated with technological development. Through this example, we hope that readers will understand that technological choice is not strictly an abstract endeavor, but that it is also a daily activity with increasingly wide-ranging consequences.

In Section Three, we turn attention to technologies that address our fundamental needs for food, water, and shelter. Out of all the technological dilemmas we face, those associated with meeting these basic needs are, surprisingly, often the least widely discussed. Fred Pearce offers some sobering statistics about water usage worldwide, and describes several large-scale projects designed to meet the growing demand for fresh water for irrigation and residential and commercial use. Access to fresh water is increasingly being understood as the global crisis it may soon become, and efforts to exploit existing freshwater resources can often lead to massive environmental and cultural disruptions. Gay Daly describes another concern associated with pollutants in our water and air supplies: the growing body of evidence that ubiquitous human-made chemical compounds may in fact be disrupting the reproductive capacity of animals, including humans. The problem of pollution is further examined by Timothy Halliday and Ronald Heyer, who first report on the declining populations of amphibian species. They then offer a cogent rationale for why humans should respond to such environmental disruptions. On a more positive note, the section moves on to three articles that highlight new approaches to the design of buildings, detailing the many elements of structures that can lead to a healthier and more efficient built environment.

Section Four focuses on the resource that fuels all of human technology: energy. More specifically, the excerpts in this section examine the variety of energy resources upon which we rely as well as some of the issues related to energy utilization. Generally, when we speak of energy we are actually referring to two forms of energy: the conversion technologies that bring us electricity in usable forms to power our appliances, lights, and machines; and petroleum products that provide the liquid fuel to power our automobiles and other transport devices. In the first article of this section, Maryanne Vollers provides a poignant look at the way our appetite for coal-based electricity has affected the rural communities of Appalachia. Richard Heinberg tackles the problem of oil and challenges notions about supplies by explaining in careful detail the concept of "peak oil" and its ramifications for a society that is so dependent on this fuel source. Red Cavaney's article examines this issue from the supply side, challenging peak oil theories and advocating for continued exploration of petroleum resources. The last selection by Michael Parfit gives a balanced overview of a variety of energy resources and wisely concludes that, where energy is concerned, there is no single, best approach for meeting our energy demands.

Sections Five through Nine are linked conceptually in that each of these sections offers selected perspectives on different technological contexts, including transportation technologies, communication technologies, biological and medical technologies, military technologies, and workplace and leisure technologies. Each of these sections includes readings that highlight the social, cultural, environmental, or economic questions posed by various technologies, and the questions raised provide opportunities for further study and discussion about technology's effects. The readings included here were selected because they offer both technical details as well as exploration of the larger context in which the technologies are used. For example, in *Surveillance Nation* Dan Farmer and Charles Mann describe the tools being used to monitor public spaces, but the larger topics this leads to include privacy, government policy, and the implications of widespread use of surveillance tools.

We complete the book in Section Ten with four articles that illustrate the perspectives on technology introduced in Section One, but as applied to the future. Science fiction novels, television dramas, and movies have long painted visions of what our technological future might look like, and these visions generally share some common features: we'll be smarter; own more labor-saving devices; and be able to further overcome the constraints of space, time, and biological heritage. But what's not often discussed, or even acknowledged as discussion-worthy, are the impacts these technologies will have on societal relationships and the environment. If you could design the technological future, what would it look like? Susan Greenfield looks into the future, noting that the scientific breakthroughs of the 21st Century will lead to higher levels of technical feasibility, but also reminding us of the hard-earned lessons of the past: that technological advancement comes at a price. Bill Gates offers a not-surprisingly optimistic prediction about the future by describing how cheap, powerful computing will lead to a robotics revolution and a robot in every home. Henry Lambright and Debora VanNijnatten outline a plan for achieving a goal that has long captured the human spirit: human space travel to distant planets. We close this section with a reading by Adam Keiper, who describes the emerging field of nanotechnology. Taken together, these readings provide a launching point for discussion about the technological issues of the future.

Defining Technology

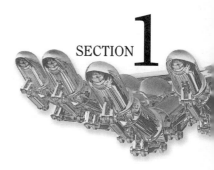

Any examination of the relationship between society and technology must start by establishing a context that helps frame the nature of that examination. Much has been written and said about the nature and impacts of technology, although curiously the formal study of this field has gained modest traction in traditional educational circles. French writer Jacques Ellul, whose work *The Technological Society* has been one of the most influential in the genre, stated four decades ago: "No social, human, or spiritual fact is so important as the fact of technique in the modern world. And yet no subject is so little understood."[1] The situation is little changed today.

Why is this so? We could point to any number of reasons, but will highlight just a few. First, technology encompasses such a vast array of human activity that its scope is difficult to grasp. If technology represents the totality of the tools and systems that make up the human-made environment, it's difficult to place technology within the disciplinary boundaries that often define our formal educational institutions. Second, for many who adhere to the purity of what might be called a "classical" education, technology is often dismissed as an "applied science," the study of which is the provenance of mechanics, engineers, or technicians. Third, even among those who do focus their attention

on the phenomenon of technology, some are more drawn to the details of the tools and techniques, while others are more inclined to theorize about the social and environmental impacts of technology and care less about technical details. Few of us have, in other words, all the information necessary for a comprehensive understanding.

Nevertheless, there is a growing belief that all members of modern society, dependent as we are on technological tools and systems, must achieve what has been termed *technological literacy*. The characteristics of this literacy include knowing about the concepts, benefits, and risks associated with technology; exhibiting a willingness to learn about new technologies; participating in decision making about technology; and having the capabilities to use, design, and evaluate technologies. The benefits of technological literacy to the individual include the ability to make better-informed choices, to become a more actively engaged citizen, to contribute to the workforce, and to function more effectively in society.[2]

There is yet another reason to promote the goal of technological literacy for all, having to do with the changing nature of our technological development. From an evolutionary perspective, one does not have to look too far into our past to find a time when the technological tools and systems we employed were relatively simple and relatively small-scale. As recently as 1900, for example, 41 percent of U.S. citizens were employed in agriculture and 60 percent of the population lived in rural areas; by 2000 less than 2 percent of the U.S. workforce was employed in agriculture.[3] This is just one piece of evidence pointing to an overall shift in our technological development. While agrarian activity decreased in importance, industrial activity, with its associated resource implications, advanced. According to DeVore, the types of changes that took place in society as the result of industrialization were important in three ways.[4] Because industrial activity is so capital and resource intensive, it requires a hierarchical organizational structure. Furthermore, industrialization "presupposes mass consumption," rapidly altering the size of the production system and the scope of its reach (presaging globalization). Finally, production of this size and scope demands an emphasis on production efficiency. Whereas once we toiled with simple tools to produce food, shelter, and basic amenities for the survival of ourselves and our families, today we engage in increasingly specialized work with highly evolved tools to create and manage complex, often centralized systems of manufacturing, energy production, transportation, communication, and beyond. The key characteristics of this technological evolution, for purposes of this discussion, are two: technologies have become harder to understand (and thus to evaluate and control), and the potential reach of these technologies has expanded far beyond the level of local impact to, in some cases, *global* impact. Tools of war and global climate change represent just two examples of this characteristic.

These last points are worthy of some additional examination. With regard to the first—the greater complexity and the emphasis on hi-erarchical, centralized organizational structures associated with modern technology—there is a subtle side effect that results. In order to participate in the benefits of the complex system, and sometimes even in spite of a conscious desire to avoid the system, we must accept the confines and dictates of the system—we must play by the rules. In this way, the system itself begins to exert control over those who created and use it. For example, air travel requires an enormous infrastructure of schedules, baggage handling, people movers, and systems for ticketing and planning. Individuals who wish to travel by air have to conform to specific ways of acting and moving in order to take advantage of the system, even when this conformity is inconvenient, unhelpful, or unpleasant.

With regard to the second point—the reach of modern technology—there is an important, related issue. The reach of technology can extend in two kinds of ways. One way has to do with the power of an individual technology; the nuclear bomb, for example, is a single artifact whose reach when detonated can potentially harm millions of people and destroy entire ecosystems. The second way the reach of technology can extend is a function of population. If one person dumps sewage into the river its effect will be minimal; if a city of a million people does the same, the effects can be catastrophic.

Perspectives on Technology

Various writers over the years have described what can be termed prevailing views of technology. For example, Emmanuel Mesthene, director of the Harvard Program on Technology and Society in the late 1960s, identified what he called "three unhelpful views" of technology.[5] One view holds that technology is a source of advancement, prosperity, and improvement, and that technological progress, by definition, is good. Individuals who adhere to this viewpoint are variously called technocrats, technophiles, and technological optimists. The second view holds that technology is often a curse, leading to environmental destruction, individual powerlessness, and social breakdown. People who subscribe to this world view are sometimes referred to as Luddites, Cynics,[6] and technological pessimists. The third view is not so much a perspective as it is a lack of one: it essentially holds that technology is not worthy of notice. We are reminded of a magazine ad placed by a major corporation some years ago, which showed an attractive young woman in hiking boots sitting atop a mountain with her cell phone, with the caption "I don't care how technology works, I just want it to be there when I need it."

The perspectives as presented here are somewhat distorted by this simplistic description; on the other hand, it's likely that as you read this you can identify more with one of the three views than the others. Recognizing which of these three perspectives resonates most strongly with your beliefs can provide a clue as to how you might evaluate a technology and whether you would be more likely to adopt or reject new technologies. For example, there are some who believe that any tinkering with the human genetic code, no matter how well-intentioned, is dangerous and should be avoided; others believe that genetic manipulation is a potentially powerful tool at our disposal for improving the human condition. Certainly, there is a third group of people who do not know and do not care one way or the other (or at least until they are directly faced with a situation that demands their attention). Additionally, recognizing the existence of these perspectives can provide a clue as to how others might view a technology, and therefore can pave the way for productive debate.

And it may be, as we move further into the 21st Century, that we can adopt more reasoned approaches to technology. There are surely few who would profess that technological progress is always for the best; we know too much about unintended side-effects like pollution, depletion, and inequitable distribution of resources to blindly accept that viewpoint. It is equally naïve to think that a return to a completely natural (i.e., pre-technological) state is possible or even desirable. From our perspective, the third view—not caring or paying attention—is simply not an option. Any new approach will require applying our ingenuity in ways that, to the best of our abilities, take account of the implications and likely outcomes of the technologies we seek to create. The full measure of a technology will consider not just what the technology *does* or enables, but what its social, cultural, environmental, economic, and political ramifications are.

This is not a new idea. In fact, Merritt Roe Smith[7] and others have described the progressive ideals espoused by politicians such as Thomas Jefferson and Benjamin Franklin in the early days of this country. Both of these individuals were gifted technologists and inventors in their own right and saw the potential for expansion of technological might. For this reason, they emphasized the importance of using technology as a means for betterment of the human condition, and cautioned about the potentially corrupting effects of technological progress. This progressive ideal has resurfaced in various movements over the years, including in the Appropriate Technology movement popularized in the 1960s and 1970s and still in evidence today. The key tenet of this movement is that the technology must match the user, the location, and the need in terms of its cost, complexity, and scale; the movement further advocates for energy efficiency, environmental sustainability, and local control.[8] In recent years, the increasing attention being paid to so-called "green" technologies shows that public sentiment is coalescing around the need for technological solutions that allow us to waste less and to minimize the impact of human activity on the environment. The added benefit is that these solutions often lead to more local employment and more local control.

Practical Ethics for a Technological World

The readings included in this section are excerpted from the book *Practical Ethics for a Technological World*. In these excerpts, author Paul Alcorn provides a definition of technology ("everything that we use that is not as it comes to us in nature") that is as broad as his definition of ethics ("knowing the difference between right and wrong"). Each of these definitions might be considered overly general; nevertheless, in the case of the first definition such a simple view is at least inclusive and not subject to conflicting interpretations. By examining the nexus between technology and ethics, Alcorn focuses on a central component of the society/technology discussion: technological choice, and the factors that go into making those choices.

Choice, in Alcorn's view, is the primary characteristic that distinguishes human activity from that of other animals. Through our unique ability to devise complex artificial systems for survival we have done something that other species cannot: "we have effectively externalized the process of evolutionary development," thus circumventing our physical shortcomings. Yet, as we create ever more powerful artifacts and systems, the reach and impacts of our technological development also expand over space and time. To the extent that any of us cares about the effects of our actions on the environment and on other humans, including our offspring, we are thus faced with the ethical imperative to select those technologies that are most beneficial and least harmful, and therein lies the responsibility of choice.

Alcorn also suggests that technologies themselves are neither good nor bad; that it is the ways technologies are used that create ethical problems. This is a common, but not universally held, belief. In his influential book *Autonomous Technology*, political theorist and author Langdon Winner systematically dismantles the basis for claims of neutrality.[9] In his view, the rules that govern the way technologies work and must be used, and the purposes for which technologies are designed, provide inherent obstacles to the notion of neutrality. This is particularly true of complex technologies and systems. As you read this and other excerpts in this book, consider the question: is it possible to separate the artifact or the system from its effects?

Alcorn is a professor at the DeVry Institute of Technology and the author of two books focusing on social issues in technology.

The Relationship between Ethics and Technology

By Paul A. Alcorn

Definition of Technology

Essentially, technology is that whole collection of methodology and artificial constructs created by human beings to increase their probability of survival by increasing their control over the environment in which they operate. Technology includes and is essentially a means of manipu-lating natural laws to our benefit by constructing objects and methodology that increase our efficiency and reduce waste in our lives. The objects we create are artifacts, literally artificial constructs, that have been manufactured for specific uses and purposes. Everything that we use that is not as it comes to us in nature falls under the heading of technology. This is a very

Alcorn, Paul A., *Practical Ethics for a Technological World, First Edition,* © 2001, Pgs. 17–27. Reprinted by permission of Pearson Education, Inc., Upper Saddle River, NJ.

broad definition. All of the physical objects of our lives that were in any way altered from the way they appeared in nature represent technology. A sharpened stick is technology, as is a dollar bill or a caterpillar tractor; they merely have different functions and have been produced through a different series of steps, usually through the use of other technology.

It may be noted that human beings are not the only animals that create artifacts, and for that reason, the mere creation of artifacts does not in and of itself constitute technology. Birds build nests, chimpanzees use sticks as tools to gather food, and bees build elaborate hives. What is missing in these artifacts that separates them from what we mean by technology is the matter of choice. A bee contributes to the development of a hive because of genetic encoding. It is a process that is "hard wired," as an electrical engineer would say. It has no choice about what it is doing. The same is true of a bird building a nest or an otter using a rock to open a clam by resting the clam on its stomach as it floats and hammering it with a stone. Such behavior is instinctual. But not all methodology used by living creatures other than humans is instinctual. Some higher primates, chimpanzees, for example, are capable of reasoning through problems and using objects to create methodology for solving those problems. They have been observed experimentally under controlled conditions learning to attach telescoping rods together to gather food that is otherwise out of reach. Yet they have very limited capacity in this regard and do not pass this information on to others in a cultural way. What truly separates humans from the other members of the animal kingdom in this regard is our incredible power of choice.

Technology and Choice

With humans, the technology we choose to build and the manner in which we use it is totally a matter of choice. We have an infinite capacity to produce technological goodies, within the boundaries of natural law, and we can accept or reject an idea as we choose. Thus, at one point in time, we may choose to develop the use of fire for cooking and at another decide to develop the art or science of architecture for the purpose of providing ourselves with shelter. Additionally, at one point we may decide to use dome-shaped hovels as shelter and at another time and place opt for alabaster palaces or multistory office buildings. The choice is all ours. It is in that choice of what artifacts to produce and the range of artifacts that we are capable of producing that we find the true nature of technology. And, as nearly as we can tell, that choice seems to be the sole province of human activity.

Technology and Evolution

In *Social Issues in Technology: A Format for Investigation,* I offered a detailed explanation of technology and the technological process. In this book I offer a general understanding of technology and why it exists in our lives. Technology is a vital part of what it is to be human; in order to understand our world, it is necessary to understand the purpose, the source, and the processes of our technological world.

For a human being, doing technology is a natural process. It represents one of the chief capacities with which nature has provided us for our survival. As with any other creature, Homo sapiens has certain characteristics that allow the species to perpetuate itself and successfully compete with other species for a niche in the natural world. Ecologically, we are an integral part of a much larger system that is designed to grow, develop, and maintain itself as an extensive living structure.

Every element in that system has the capacity to survive based on certain characteristics. For human beings, those *survival traits,* as these characteristics are called, include our capacity to create and use technology. There are specific and overwhelming advantages to this ability. Because we use artificial structures for our survival rather than develop the necessary characteristics through genetic alteration to our being, we are able to develop and adapt at a much higher rate than other animals or plants. We have effectively externalized the process of evolutionary development.

As an example, consider the characteristics of other animals versus those of a human being. Other animals have the advantage of speed, or claws, or special poisons that they can inject into their prey. Herbivores have specially designed digestive systems that allow them to consume large amounts of cellulose, a very difficult substance to break down, and turn it into useful energy. Some animals fly, others are very fleet of foot, others have incredible capacities to blend into the environment, and still others design complex living environments (e.g., hanging basket nests or colonized networks of tunnels). Each species has specific characteristics that offer it an advantage.

Now compare this with a human being. We do not have armored bodies covered with scales or shells. We cannot run particularly fast (though genetically we do have incredible stamina compared to most animals, a characteristic that allowed our hunter ancestors to follow game for days until the game was exhausted). Nor can we take to the air, with wings on our backs, or glide on membranes built into our bodies as bats or flying squirrels do. Yet we are capable of moving at a rate of speed far beyond that of a cheetah or other fleet-footed animal.

We are able to fly across the face of the planet and into the outer reaches of our world and beyond. We can live underwater in craft that outperform the largest fish and exist in environments in which the extremes of temperature or altitude would kill most other creatures. We do it all in spite of the fact that we have at our disposal not a single physical trait that allows us to do so.

That is because the nature of our evolution has been external to our bodies. Instead of developing the eyes of a hawk, we develop binoculars and telescopes. Instead of becoming fleet of foot, we build automobiles and locomotives and airplanes. Instead of wings on our back, we have the wings of air transports and helicopters and the lifting power of balloons and dirigibles. Our characteristics are external to our physical being. It is in this ability to artificially create what we need for survival that we find our chief advantage. Like other animals, we use the laws of nature to aid us in our survival, but whereas other species do this through genetic alteration, a process that takes thousands if not millions of years, we manufacture the alterations quickly and efficiently. We find ourselves at last at a point at which we do not adapt to nature, we adapt nature to us! Such capacity is unparalleled in nature.

But with this capacity comes a problem. Nature is an experimenter. Nature will try numerous variations on a theme to find the combination of characteristics that allow a given organism to survive in a competitive world. If one alteration does not work, such as growing extra wings or limiting the number of eyes of a species to one, then that version fails and does not survive long enough to create progeny, or pass on the undesirable trait. If a variation offers superior opportunities for survival, many more of that version survive to pass on the characteristics to offspring, and eventually, that version predominates. Thus, through evolutionary mutation and survival of the fittest, we arrive at a creature that is perfectly adapted to its environment.

This is also true of humans, but with one exception. Since we are producing change through the creation of technology rather than trial-and-error mutation, we can very quickly generalize a new "trait" over the entire population in a relatively short period of time. In a matter of generations rather than millennia, a new technological device such as the bow and arrow or the chariot can come into general use by everyone who sees it. If it offers a very great advantage to those who have it, everyone either perishes or soon learns to use the new technology. There is little time for experimentation and testing here.

This has been seen often in the past with sometimes devastating results. The practice of agriculture is an excellent example if we look at the relationship between climatic change and the extensive use of agriculture in a region. Some of the most arid regions of the globe were once great forests or grasslands that were cleared for agriculture. Unfortunately, with the deforestation came a host of environmental changes that led to everything from soil erosion to changes in weather patterns. This is just a single example of the problems that can arise from moving too quickly to embrace a technology. Other examples include the virtual lack of forests in Lebanon today, where once stood vast woodlands of cedar, a prized wood traded all over the Mediterranean, from North Africa to Egypt to ancient Israel, and the cliff dwellers of the southwestern United States, who flourished toward the end of the first millennium and then abandoned their cities when they could not adjust to climactic changes in growing cycles.

What if the governments of the world in the last half of the twentieth century had decided that since nuclear weapons were the ultimate in destructive power, they would embrace that technology as is and abandon other means of war? We would have been left with no alternative but to create a nuclear holocaust in case of threat or attack. We are perhaps now in a similar predicament with biological and chemical weapons of mass destruction; they are cheap, effective, and easily produced and delivered. A single strain of a deadly bacterium or virus could cause a reduction of population around the world that would bring civilization as we know it to an end. And the tragic event would be the result of industrial and technological processes at work.

Technology and Resistance to Change

Because of this danger to our well-being, these seeds of destruction within our success, nature has also equipped us with another trait. That other trait is a resistance to changes in our culture. *Homeostasis,* as it is known, represents a fear of the unknown that extends to any technological device that may come along. Any new idea or new technology is initially suspect to most of the population because it is untested, unfamiliar, and therefore considered a potential threat. This is as much a survival mechanism as the capacity to create that technology in the first place. Because of homeostasis, time is a necessary ingredient for a given advance in technology to be generalized over the whole society. It is first embraced by a small section of the population eager to try new things and ideas, but the rest of society either initially ignores it or cautiously watches to see where it will lead. Should the new idea not be a particularly good one, that is, should it not increase the probability of individual and group survival, it tends to go by the wayside without much further ado. On the other hand, if it is actually a valuable idea, the new technology will continue to exist long enough for people to get used to it or to lose their initial fear of it, and then they are more willing to try this new gizmo. This is particularly true if those who first accept it have illustrated its value. Eventually, the acceptance and use of the new technology spreads throughout the culture.

This process can be easily seen in the case of the computer. Less than a century old, this device, once a curiosity used for certain esoperic operations by scientists and government, has become one of the primary tools of a modern technological society. It has been viewed as an oddity, feared, mystically couched in arcane terminology and given unrealistic assumptions of power by the uninitiated, seen as the subject of hobbyists and gadgeteers, embraced by big business, then small business, and finally accepted as an unavoidable way of life. The process took time while the population figured out how to use the new technology and how to configure it so that it was useful for their needs. It took time to gain acceptance and overcome the natural tendency of human beings to do things in the "same old way." It grew in popularity and use as a solution to a range of problems over the life of its development. All of that time was a gestation period for society to absorb and gain benefit from the new technology. Every invention goes through the same process, affected by a number of factors such as complexity, range of application, expense, and the degree of societal resistance.

The point to remember is that that resistance is necessary and natural, a safety net built into us by nature that allows us to take time to differentiate between new ideas that are truly beneficial and those that are potentially or truly dangerous to our survival. It is all part of the same natural process of creation and use of technology.

Human beings cannot help being creative. It is an element of our makeup that cannot be changed. Creativity and technological expertise require nurturance, but the tendency to learn the laws of nature and apply them to creating artificial constructs to enhance our lives comes as natural to us as breathing.

Technology and Ethics

Given that creating technology is natural and that within the limits of our understanding as to the nature of the universe, we can choose what technology to use and how to use it, where do the ethics of the process arise? If you remember back to our working definition, ethics is the process of doing what works. Apparently, from the history of the human race, using technology tends to work. This is evidenced, if in no other way, by the predominance and domination of our species over the face of the earth. We are incredibly successful as a species, reflecting incredibly successful natural traits, and that includes technology and its use. Apparently, technology works for us, or we would not include the capacity to create it in our repertoire of survival traits in the first place. By definition, then, in and of itself, it must be ethical.

That's a nice idea, and it would certainly be a blessing for all of us if that were true. Unfortunately, it is not as simple as that. Technology, as it turns out, is neither ethical nor unethical; it is merely a tool to be used or misused as we choose. Thus, we are back to the choice of action again, the one control we have in our lives.

Each technology and each application of technology raises ethical issues with which we must deal. Each new device or application of what we know requires some consideration of whether the use of that device will work for us or not. To further muddy the issue, we often cannot even say with certainty whether a technology will benefit us or not. In fact, in most cases, technology turns out to be a double-edged sword, with both costs and benefits in its use, and this in turn requires us to determine whether or not the benefits are worth the costs. And that's assuming we can even actually determine the costs accurately in the first place.

Also, we need to consider the idea that the use of technology may benefit some while costing others. This is not an uncommon occurrence, particularly where one technology replaces another, as in the case of the automobile replacing the horse-drawn buggy or the word processor replacing the "steno pool."

As you can see, this cost-benefit situation creates quite a dilemma. Just knowing that the ethical thing to do is to do what works is not very useful as a guide to behavior if we do not know what works in the first place. This is not a new idea. It is a problem that we as a species have been wrestling with off and on for ten thousand years or more, particularly when new technologies and new ways of manipulating the world present themselves. A few examples will clarify this point nicely.

When the automobile was first introduced, it was hailed not only as a solution to transportation problems within cities but also as a defense against growing pollution. That may seem quite confusing from our perspective as citizens of the world at the beginning of the twenty-first century, but a century ago, the pollution problems faced by industrial urban dwellers was decidedly different. At that time, at the birth of the automobile age, the chief means of transportation was the horse. Anyone who wasn't walking or traveling by train within an urban environment was traveling on foot or by horse. Carriages, drays (freight wagons), and specialized coaches were all horse drawn. With the horses came horse dung, and it was everywhere. The streets were pocked with piles of dung to be cleaned up, dung that ran into the sewers and that produced a prodigious number of flies. And with the flies came disease. We do not think of horses and horse dung as being a major health hazard in our lives today, but a hundred years

ago, it was a major problem. Thus, the "horseless carriage" was hailed as the eliminator of the "hay burner" technology of equestrian transportation.

Yet today, we view the automobile as a chief air pollution source; it dumps tons of carbon monoxide and other pollutants into the atmosphere, promoting global warming and creating smog in any city of size. Hence the solution becomes the issue. At the present time, there is a movement toward nonpolluting electric cars. California has gone so far as to mandate a 10 percent noncombustion engine vehicle quota for the state. Electric cars are the obvious noncombustion engine choice, and as the number of electric vehicles rises, replacing gasoline engine automobiles, it is believed substantial improvement in the environment will result. And so another solution has been found.

This being the case, should we not expect these electric vehicles to create other dilemmas? At the present time, nearly all electric automobiles are powered by heavy lead-acid batteries, deep charged and able to deliver power at sufficient rates for a reasonable amount of time. And much research is being done to develop better and more powerful batteries that will charge more quickly and deliver more power for even longer periods of time. Thus it appears, at least for the foreseeable future, that a dependence on lead-acid batteries will be dominant. But a new problem arises: What will we do with the spent batteries? Batteries are already seen as a pollution problem, with only one per car. What will happen when the number of batteries per vehicle rises to twelve or twenty? Could we be exchanging one form of pollution for another? It is not just lead-acid batteries that present this type of dilemma as we progress and change technology.

With any technological change and any acceptance of a new technology as standard, there is always a cost. There is never a free lunch, though payment can be deferred for some length of time. Yet in the end, someone has to pay, and I'm sure it comes as no surprise that delaying payment until our children or grandchildren are making the rules is not a very efficient way to operate. Intuitively it is unethical to use this approach, though economically or politically it may be expedient.

To what extent should we consider the future payment for our exploitation of technology and technological possibility? Though we do not always know (indeed, seldom do we know) the true cost of a technological development, there are certainly some issues that we do know will need to be handled. History offers numerous examples of what to expect from technological change. How far does our responsibility go? One school of thought says not to worry about the future consequences because we have always been able to deal with what comes along. Still newer technology will solve the problem. New ideas and alternative ways of handling the issues will arise naturally out of necessity. We need only utilize what is available to us now, and let the future generations worry about how to handle the problems that arise. These are the attitudes that led to the destruction of environments in the ancient world. As agriculture and population exploded beginning some ten thousand years ago, whole civilizations were destroyed by resultant drought and crop failure. Whole ecosystems were altered, turning fertile plains into deserts and lush forests into arid wasteland. Solutions were found, but what was the cost? The people of these transitional periods endured starvation and being uprooted as their productivity collapsed.

On the other hand, consider the approach of the Five Nations of the Iroquois Confederation. These Native Americans of the northeastern United States banded together in a peaceful structure that allied independent nations, building a greater confederation. The Cuyahoga, Seneca, Onondaga, Mohican, and Oneida nations agreed to work together for the betterment of all and for their mutual defense against their unfriendly neighbors, chiefly the Algonquin. This amazing group of people elected fifty men from among their number to collectively make the decisions for the whole group. (Interestingly, it was the women of the tribe who actually chose the fifty men to head the joint council.) They always considered the future consequences of those decisions, *for seven generations hence!* No decision that was merely expedient was acceptable. Compare this approach with the political process present in most industrialized countries today. How many decisions are made on the basis of how the people will be affected a century and a half in the future? It appears we could learn a great deal from these Native American tribes. (Incidentally, it would not be a wise idea to embrace the wisdom of the Native Americans without exception. The Iroquois, for example, are noted for their horrific treatment of prisoners of war, whom they first honored and then tortured for as long as possible without killing them, then ritually ate them, not for the food value, but to absorb some of their bravery and strength. It was considered a pity if the prisoner could not be kept alive in a state of agony for at least twenty-four hours before he or she died.)

Numerous other examples can be cited describing the failure of humans to include negative future circumstances in their deliberations. Again and again we see in the industrialized world the adoption of a technology that results in future problems. This is not to paint a dark portrait of technology or to suggest that we should abandon our technological ways. Our whole history as a nation has been one of progress and growth. It is merely a reminder that every new opportunity brings with it an obligation to consider the consequences of our actions, and this we seem rather reluctant to do.

Counterpoint and Application

If technologizing, that is, creating and using technology, is so natural to being human, then it would appear that it is always an ethical process, as it always works. It is not very useful for any species to go against its nature in the quest for survival, except as a part of the evolutionary process, and natural selection would seem to be quite adequate to this end. Why all the fuss about the ethical nature of technology? It is neutral. It is what it is. Talking about the ethical nature of technology is like talking about the ethical nature of a stick. Isn't that true?

Of course, that is not true at all. It must be remembered that the drive to create technology and thus evolve externally to our bodies is indeed a natural process, yet it still entails free will, or choice, on our part. An almost infinite array of technological possibilities is available to us, depending on how we choose to apply the basic principles that constitute our understanding of the physical universe (physical laws). It is because of that choice that we must consider ethical content.

Surely, the homeostatic tendencies of the species goes a long way toward allowing us to adjust if we make mistakes in our choices in technological design and creation. But considering the speed at which the world changes and the far-reaching effects of even the seemingly most insignificant changes in methodology, it becomes critical to consider the usefulness of technological change in the broadest of terms, and that is a matter of what is the ethical thing to do. Technology has ethical content by virtue of the free will with which we create it. What do we choose to do and not do? We make those choices in a desire to improve our position in life, either individually, collectively, or both. Do we know that our choices are sound ones, and do they truly work to achieve the goals that they are designed to achieve? Therein lies the ethical issue.

When looking at technology and creating technological change through the modification, production, or application of technology, it is wise to think in a broader context. It is best to consider why exactly we are doing whatever it is we are doing, what our goals are, and whether the process undertaken actually achieves those goals. Additionally, we must consider what other goals or conditions are affected by the new creation or application and how that affects our overall goals in life. In other words, what would happen if we all behaved like the Native American confederacy mentioned earlier and considered the consequences of our actions for the next seven generations, or 150 years. How would we behave differently?

The Ethics of Rational Technology

By Paul A. Alcorn

Technology is a tool of society. It is a cultural element as much as family, political structure, economics, or religion. It is an integral part of the fabric of what it is to be human and live in a human community, a necessary element without which who and what we are would be far different. The issue is not whether technology is ethical or unethical; to approach the question in that manner is fruitless. The question that needs to be answered is, How do we develop and use technology in an ethical manner, in a manner that works for us? This is a very different issue altogether.

This theme of how to develop and use technology in an ethical manner is by no means a new issue. Each time a major technological shift has occurred it has caused disruption to our lifestyle and culture. This is natural. We must remember that part of the process of culture is to transform who and what we are, and technology is certainly a large part of that process. It must also be remembered, however, that the purpose of culture is also to reproduce itself, passing on the successful methodology and social interactions that lend themselves to our survival as a group and as individuals. We are a system, and we operate within that system according to rules that tend toward maximizing efficiency and success. It is in this reproductive process that we find the ethical issues. It is part of the homeostatic tendency toward resistance to change that we find the roots of the reluctance to take on new ways.

When faced with new technology, particularly technology that is obviously and rapidly changing our way of life, the cry of those afraid of the change will be heard. New ideas may be seen as the "work of the devil" or as a sign of our doom. They may be seen as a method of creating misery and unemployment for many. This is resistance to the new in the face of unknown effects. Caution is wise with sweeping technology, and our natural tendency toward caution keeps us from moving too quickly. However, it also tends to create technophobia among the most conservative members of the society. Hence we find survivalists involved in bunker mentality and preparing for the end of civilization or the breakdown of social order. In truth, this is a possibility with sweeping changes in technology. Periods of great change in society are often accompanied by social unrest and violent upheaval, as was experienced in Europe as it emerged to a more rational philosophy in the sixteenth and seventeenth centuries. Chaos occurs at the point of shift, where the old gives way to the new. It is not surprising to find people resisting those changes that will so thoroughly disrupt their ordered, structured lives, based on a lifetime of tradition. Whether it is the invention of the printing press or the emergence into the industrial age with its steam engines and great factories, violent reaction to rapid change is not unusual. Every such change will have its Luddites, destroying the new to preserve the old. Fear is a great motivator.

As part of this resistance, the ethics of the technology involved in the change is often scrutinized. "If God had meant us to fly, He would have given us wings!" is a prime example of this.

Alcorn, Paul A., *Practical Ethics for a Technological World, First Edition,* © 2001, Pgs. 153–157. Reprinted by permission of Pearson Education, Inc., Upper Saddle River, NJ.

At various times, the printing press, the steam engine, the automobile, the airplane, television, and computers have all been viewed by some as the work of the devil, and they have been vehemently fought against by those afraid of change. Yet it must be reiterated that it is not the technology that is at fault; the manner in which it is used creates the ethical problems. Rational technology means conceiving of technology rationally, designing it rationally, choosing technology rationally, and implementing it rationally.

The people of any society are the clients of engineers and technologists. They have an implied contract with those who develop technology in that the society supports the efforts of the engineers and gives them the freedom to produce technology in return for value and support of the population's well-being. Additionally, there is an agreement implied that the engineers will produce items that are useful, efficient, and appropriate. It is also implied that they will create new and different technologies that explore the possibilities of creation to be evaluated by the members of society, usually in the marketplace. This is an extremely effective way of handling technological development in a competitive market. When any part of that process goes awry, problems develop.

We normally use the market as a mechanism for evaluating the usefulness of technology. In the marketplace, the technology can be tested; if it is found valuable, it is allowed to exist by virtue of people being willing to buy it, use it, and continue using it. If it is not found to be useful or desirable, it is excluded by dollar votes being devoted to other items rather than the technology in question.

In theory, this is fine, but in practice, it is much more complicated. As with the rest of society, our economic system is highly complex, convoluted in its actions, and slow to adjust on its own to changes in need. There are very large economic units in all facets of commerce that tend to dominate, whether the field is computers, automobile production, or banking. There is good reason for these dominant players, mainly that we look to bigness for efficiency and low costs. Being able to muster vast economic resources means the ability to invest in the necessary experimentation and development that bring about much of the new technology we experience. In return, the dominant producers and marketers receive control and high profits. The trouble is that they too will be homeostatic in nature, at once seeking new product ideas and new technologies to continue their profits and simultaneously resisting shifts to revolutionary methodology that they do not control. To do otherwise would seem to be a poor economic decision. No firm or industry wishes to support its own competition.

In addition, government that understandably dictates how the money will be spent supplies much of the research funds available. Its desires and views may be quite different from those of the engineers and research personnel seeking to create new and useful technology, and this can be stifling. Government tends to limit creativity by only funding projects it finds in its best interest to produce. Yet, is not the government representative of the people? Is it not the collective manifestation of our consciousness and desires? And as such, is it not appropriate for government to guide the development of technology in accordance with those desires?

The issue here is not whether or not the government of the United States truly reflects the desires of the population. That is a topic for a far different discussion. The issue here is how an engineer or other technologist is to react to a world in which the practitioner's personal beliefs are in opposition to his or her agreements, duties and job requirements. If I am making weaponry, is it to defend my country or is it to conquer and control others? If I am producing nuclear power, do the benefits derived from relatively cheap electricity override the potential calamity of a nuclear accident? If I am experimenting on animals in order to produce lifesaving methodology for hospitals and doctors, does that justify the suffering of the animals? How do you make the decisions necessary in the face of such dilemmas? That is the central issue.

Be aware that the decision is an individual one, and must be an individual one, depending on the consciousness and understanding of the person who has to do the deciding. As much as we would like to have someone tell us what to do, we must face reality. All our decisions are our own. We alone are responsible for our decisions. We alone are the ones who must live with the consequences of those decisions. And we alone must decide how we will choose to interact with this world.

Earlier I pointed out that the members of society are the clients of technologists. That creates an obligation on the part of the technologist to act in the best interest of those clients or to cease being a part of the agreement. It is a matter of reciprocity and a matter of realizing the connection among us all whereby each contributes to the well-being or pain of the rest. We cannot separate ourselves from those whom we affect, and that includes everyone. We cannot blithely deny the connections between our work and our actions and the lives of those around us. If we are to be responsible human beings (and remember that this means being able to respond), then we must understand that there is a contract among us all and that the way we carry out that contract—the way we fulfill our agreements with humanity—will determine the quality of life for all.

This does not mean that we must subordinate our own desires and needs to those of others. It means, rather, that we need to see the connection between our own well-being and that of others. It means it would behoove us to work for the mutual benefit of all by creating opportunities for freedom, wealth, health, peace of mind, and self-expression without demanding it, imposing it, or judging the choices others make regarding their own behavior. It is not our place to judge. It is not our place to say what others should or should not do. It is only our place to contribute to the process that which is positive, uplifting, and supportive of success. Such an example seldom goes unnoticed and always creates an opportunity for others to find a better way.

Choosing the word *client* rather than *customer* when referring to the contract between technologists and the people of the society was purposive. When you have customers, you are there to fulfill their desires and see to it that they get what they want. It is a matter of making things available to the public; they choose what they wish to have. With clients, on the other hand, the relationship is quite different. You are seen as the supplier of knowledge and tools. You are the expert, the one to whom the clients come to find what needs to be done, needs to be used, and needs to be instigated. You are not there to give them what they want. Quite the contrary, you are there to give them what they need, and they trust you to do just that. They do not always like what they hear and are not always happy with what you present to them, but they are there to find out what they do not already know and benefit from your expertise and creative ability. They may think that they will be happier by involving themselves in destructive processes. That may be what they want, but it is definitely not what they need if they are about the business of supporting their freedom, health, wealth, peace of mind, and self-expression.

How do you deal with these clients? What do you supply them? Do you create technology that slowly kills them or technology that improves their experience of life? What is your purpose in doing what you do, and how is all of this altered by the fact that we are usually serving multiple clients simultaneously? This is a reciprocal process as well, and whatever energy you put into your work, whether it be greed or anger or love or joy, it will be reflected in the product of your efforts. What do you offer your clients, and what do we as a culture offer those with whom we interact?

We are all engineers and technologists, in a sense; we all create the fabric of this world by thought, word, and deed. What goods do we demand? What concepts and directions in future technology do we support? What kind of world are we creating with our interaction with the earth, the environment, and our fellow human beings? The system acts and reacts, and we all contribute to that dynamism. When people look back on your life, what will they see and say about your contribution to the whole? How will they view your decisions and your successes and failures? What will they remember? Much more importantly, what will you say and remember?

Discussion Questions

1. What is technological literacy? Why is it important?
2. Alcorn notes that we have "an infinite capacity" to create new technologies. What factors constrain this capacity, if any?
3. The introduction to Section One describes three prevailing views of technology, and suggests a fourth path, which might be called the progressive path. With which of these perspectives do you most strongly align, and why?
4. Alcorn states that members of a society can evaluate new technologies through the choices they make in the marketplace, and that this is "an extremely effective way of handling technological development in a competitive marketplace." Do you agree or disagree with this statement? Provide at least two examples from the text that illustrate why this does not always hold true.
5. This author (and many others) has noted that technology's effects can vary from one person or group to the next: a technology can benefit some while harming others. Give an example from your own experience to illustrate this point. Propose a strategy that could be used by policy makers to resolve this dilemma.

 Supporting Activities

Note that the supporting activities included in this section are designed to be adapted for use with any section in the book.

1. Talk to five friends or family members to find out how they define *technology*. If you can, determine what their dominant perspective about technological progress is. Are they technological optimists? Pessimists? Progressives? Or are they largely unconcerned or uninterested in technology? Contrast this with your response to Question 3 above.
2. Generate a list of popular movies (recent or older; there are a lot!) that explore themes associated with the impacts of technology (titles might include *Apollo 13, Gattica, Fat Man and Little Boy,* and *The Island)*. Watch the movie, and then write a review of the movie that provides a synopsis of the plot and a discussion of how the movie addresses class discussions.
3. Find and report on a current event that in your view illustrates some aspect of the relationship between society and technology. Describe why you selected the event and why you think it's interesting and/or important.
4. Identify technology policy issues that are currently being discussed at the local, national, or international level and conduct a classroom debate. Examples of topics include labeling on genetically modified food products, increasing federal support for public transit systems, use of national identity cards, and installation of utility-scale wind farms. Divide into opposing pairs or teams, research the facts and opinions on both sides of the argument, and conduct an oral debate in class. An excellent resource for this activity is the International Debate Education Association Web site: http://www.idebate.org/.

Additional Resources

1. A series of lectures on science, technology, and society developed by professor John Dwyer at York University, Toronto: http://opencopy.org/library/lectures/science-technology-and-society/.

2. The International Technology Education Association's *Standards for Technological Literacy*, published in 2000, outline the knowledge and skills necessary for technological literacy. They can be viewed online at: http://www.iteaconnect.org/TAA/Publications/TAA_Publications.html.

3. The Society for the History of Technology (SHOT) has published the quarterly journal *Technology and Culture* for over fifty years. An index to all volumes, and electronic access to all articles published since 1998, can be found at: http://etc.technologyandculture.net/about/.

4. There are a number of scholarly and popular journals that regularly publish articles dealing with technology and society. Notable titles include *Technology Review, Wired, National Geographic*, and *Scientific American*.

5. The Office of Technology Assessment (OTA) archive, housed at Princeton University, provides a brief history of the OTA and an electronic repository to all reports created during the OTA's 23-year history (over 500 assessment reports): http://www.princeton.edu/~ota/.

 Endnotes

1. Ellul, Jacques. 1964. *The Technological Society.* New York: Alfred A. Knopf, Inc.

2. National Academy of Engineering and National Research Council, Committee on Technological Literacy. (2002). *Technically Speaking: Why all Americans Need to Know More about Technology.* Washington, DC: National Academies Press.

3. Dimitri, Carolyn; Effland, Anne; and Conklin, Neilson. 2005. *The 20th Century Transformation of U.S. Agriculture and Farm Policy.* United States Department of Agriculture Economic Research Service. Available: http://www.ers.usda.gov/publications/EIB3/eib3.pdf.

4. DeVore, Paul. 1980. *Technology: An Introduction.* Worcester, MA: Davis Publications, Inc.

5. Mesthene, Emmanuel G. 1970. *Technological Change: Its Impact on Man and Society.* Cambridge, MA: Harvard University Press.

6. Greenfield, Susan. 2003. *Tomorrow's People.* London: Penguin Books. (Also see Section Ten of this text.)

7. Roe Smith, Merritt. (1994). Technological determinism in American culture. In Leo Marx and Merritt Roe Smith (Eds.), *Does Technology Drive History? The Dilemma of Technological Determinism.* Cambridge, MA: The MIT Press.

8. See, for example: Hazeltine, Barrett and Bull, Christopher. 1999. *Appropriate Technology: Tools, Choices, and Implications.* San Diego, CA: Academic Press.

9. Winner, Langdon. 1977. *Autonomous Technology: Technics-out-of-Control as a Theme in Political Thought.* Cambridge, MA: The MIT Press.

Technological Decision Making

A major argument made in the National Academies publication *Technically Speaking: Why All Americans Need to Know More About Technology* (2002) is that technological literacy is necessary so that all citizens can be active participants in establishing technology policy, in addition to making personal decisions about which technologies to adopt.[1] As a society we need to make decisions about which technologies should be promoted or supported, what criteria we want to apply to the design and development of those technologies, and whether they need to be regulated in some way. Governments play a tremendous role in all of these stages.

How do policy makers reach decisions about technologies? There are at least three primary sources for input. The federal government and many state governments have in place science and technology advisory boards. For example, between the years 1972 and 1995, the Office of Technology Assessment, which served the members of the U.S. Congress, conducted bipartisan analyses of emerging technological trends at the behest of congressmen and women. During the 23-year existence of this Office, over 700 comprehensive reports and case studies were prepared.[2] The executive branch is advised by the Office of Science and Technology Policy (OSTP), which was established by Congress in 1976 with the mandate to advise the President

and others about the effects of science and technology on domestic and international affairs.[3] The OSTP has counterparts in many governors' offices nationwide. These sometimes take a decidedly pro-development stance, such as the North Carolina Board of Science and Technology, whose mission statement reads: "As a State-authorized advisory board administered by the North Carolina Department of Commerce, the North Carolina Board of Science and Technology encourages, promotes, and supports scientific, engineering, and industrial research applications in North Carolina."[4] Generally speaking, much of the science and technology policy effort at the state level is focused on innovation and economic development.[5]

A variation on the practice of maintaining a technology policy board is to establish independent (but often government-supported) boards that are charged with investigating a single issue of broad importance. The Intergovernmental Panel on Climate Change (IPCC) is an excellent example. The IPCC is a large-scale body set up by the United Nations Environment Programme (UNEP) and the World Meteorological Organization (WMO) and is open to membership from all member countries of the WMO and UNEP. It was established not to perform research or monitor climate data, but rather to conduct objective and comprehensive assessments of the existing scientific, technical, and socioeconomic research being conducted world-wide regarding climate change, and to make those assessments widely available. Its series of climate change reports is considered by many to be the authoritative source for current information on climate change.[6]

Another avenue for input on technology policy is through expert testimony. Numerous non-governmental think tanks such as the Brookings Institution have as one of their primary activities the role of providing expert testimony on topics related to the core missions of the organizations,[7] and this is routine practice during policy debates in Congress as well as during legal debates within the judicial branch.[8] Expert testimony is an important and useful source of information, but it can also be fraught with bias and balanced representation of the issues is not assured.

A third important source of input is public comment, both formal and informal. This can occur through forums set up by government agencies expressly for the purpose of public input, or can happen through individual or group mail, phone, or email campaigns on particular issues.

The challenges of establishing responsible science and technology policy are many. As we see from the excerpt by William Evan and Mark Manion, even systematic tools that attempt to gather objective data for decision making have significant flaws. This is primarily due to the fact that technological systems must not only satisfy the immediate challenges of *technical* functionality, they are also inextricably linked to the sociocultural, political, environmental, and economic contexts in which they are created and used. Technologies, by definition, are systems created to serve humankind; challenges can arise in determining exactly who is to be served, how, and at what cost. The dilemma of competing priorities is further compounded by

the fact that the data do not always provide clear-cut solution pathways. As we see from the article by Mark Hertsgaard, problems that will require massive shifts in infrastructure to address (such as climate change) confront considerable resistance from those who have a vested interest in the status quo, and it's understandable that many policy makers are loathe to act when uncertainties exist.

Another important challenge with regard to technology policy is that as technological systems become ever more complex they become harder to understand. Thus, fewer and fewer people (including policy makers) have the capability to engage in debate about technologies at more than a superficial level, if at all. Complex systems are also subject to what has been termed *normal accidents*, defined as malfunctions that will inevitably occur due simply to the fact of the system's complexity. In short, these accidents are "normal" because they are unavoidable in our current mode of risk analysis and response.[9] Therefore, even careful attempts to anticipate and manage risks associated with technology can fall short of desired goals.

Finally, it's clear that neither governmental policy nor individual decisions about technologies are always based on sound judgment, or even on accurate interpretations of data. As we see from the article by Malcolm Gladwell, human decision makers can sometimes revert to a more primal logic when perceptions and emotions gain the upper hand. Thus, even with the most powerful modeling and data collection tools, there is no guarantee that we will make the "right" choices.

From a policy standpoint, once a decision *is* made, for better or worse, there are a variety of mechanisms for shaping human behavior relative to a technology. One method is to mandate or *legislate* that behavior. For example, most states now have seat belt laws that require all persons riding in automobiles to use seat belts. Another method is to provide *incentives* to encourage a particular action. For example, many states have offered tax breaks to individuals and businesses that install renewable energy systems in their homes or buildings. A third method is to put in place *disincentives* that will have the effect of deterring a course of action. Charging higher rates for water users who exceed an established limit is an example of a disincentive. Yet another mechanism for shaping behavior is to *educate* about more attractive or desirable alternatives. A fifth mechanism, which is somewhat less direct than the other four mentioned, is to make available reasonable alternatives. For example, although many individuals might have wished to reduce the amount of gasoline they used, until affordable alternatives in the form of low-maintenance hybrid or diesel cars became widely available, their options were relatively limited.

Not mentioned yet is the one decision-making approach that is perhaps the most widely used of all: the decision to do nothing. In the face of uncertainties it's certainly much easier to let technological development proceed unchecked, following the whims and wishes of individual developers or according to its own imperatives. We become passive users or bystanders, potentially affected in both direct and indirect ways, but without the benefit of analysis or a chance for input. As should be clear from Section One and the sections that follow, we advocate instead for informed participation, and argue that the responsibility for technological literacy lies with all of us.

Assessing the Risks of Technology

What might at first seem like a strictly technical examination of two analytical tools—probabilistic risk assessment and risk-cost-benefit analysis—is at its core a cogent argument for a technology assessment strategy that looks broadly at social impacts and policy implications. Evan and Manion reinforce this point by describing in detail the shortcomings of more conventional analytical approaches that focus on quantitative measures.

The analytical tools described by these authors are part of an overall approach to assessing systems that can be broadly categorized as risk management. These tools are designed to try to predict either system failure or the likelihood of negative outcomes such as damage or loss of life or property. Tools like probabilistic risk assessment have most commonly been applied to hazardous undertakings such as nuclear power plants or oil rigs. They provide information that can help system designers anticipate, and manage, risks associated with these systems. In spite of their usefulness, these and similar methodologies have significant shortcomings that reduce their utility as decision-making tools. Nevertheless, they are an important part of our decision-making arsenal and over time they can be refined to better overcome these shortcomings.

William M. Evan is Professor Emeritus of Sociology and Management at the University of Pennsylvania, where he taught from 1966–1993. He is the author of over 100 articles for various professional journals and of 14 books, including *Nuclear Proliferation and the Legality of Nuclear Weapons* (1995), *War and Peace in an Age of Terrorism* (2005), and *Knowledge and Power in a Global Society* (1981). Mark Manion is a faculty member in the Department of English and Philosophy at Drexel University, where he teaches courses in business and organizational ethics and in the philosophy of technology. He is also a consultant to corporations on issues of crisis management and corporate social responsibility.

Assessing the Risks of Technology

By William M. Evan and Mark Manion

"In all traditional cultures . . . human beings worried about the risks coming from external nature . . . very recently . . . we started worrying less about what nature can do to us, and more about what we have done to nature. This marks the transition from the predominance of external risk to that of manufactured risk."—ANTHONY GIDDENS

The prevalence of technological disasters points to deficiencies in the way technology is assessed—the way technologies are determined to be or not to be risky. In this chapter we focus on two prominent methods for assessing risk: probabilistic risk assessment (PRA) and risk-cost-benefit analysis (RCBA). If we find the standard methods deficient, then it should not be surprising that we have more disasters than we can expect. The overall lesson is that, if we want to reduce the number and magnitude of technological disasters, we must reform our methods of evaluating the potential impacts of technology—PRA and RCBA—and develop more effective methods.

From *Minding the Machines: Preventing Technological Disasters* by William Evan and Mark Manion. Copyright © 2002 by William Evan & Mark Manion. Reprinted by permission of the author.

Experts attempt to separate risk assessment techniques into two independent procedures—the risk identification or risk estimation level, which is supposedly factual, scientific, objective, and value-neutral, and the risk assessment or risk management level—which is supposedly normative, political, subjective, and value-laden (Humphreys, 1987). This rigid demarcation into the "factual" or scientific measurement of risks vs. the "normative" management of the social acceptability of risks is thought to secure for risk assessors a level of scientific objectivity and value neutrality.

We will argue, however, that the factual/normative split is no longer adequate for the proper identification, assessment, and management of technological risk. Consequently, the so-called objective activities of risk identification or risk estimation need to be integrated with the normative and evaluative aspects of risk evaluation and risk management.

Probabilistic Risk Assessment

Probabilistic risk assessment (PRA), or quantitative risk assessment (QRA), attempts to provide a model of the causal interactions of the technological system under study. The goal of PRA is to supply a mathematical technique for estimating the probability of events that cause physical damage or loss of life (Thompson, 1982; 114). A comprehensive probabilistic risk assessment involves three steps: (1) the identification of events that lead to, or initiate, unwanted consequences; (2) the modeling of identified event sequences with respect to probabilities and consequences; and (3) the determination of the magnitude of risks and harms involved (Bier, 1997).

PRA has become one of the standard methods used by engineers for determining the likelihood of an industrial accident or a technological disaster. This method makes use of technical procedures called *fault-tree analysis* and *event-tree analysis*. Fault-trees and event-trees generate diagrams that trace out the possible ways a malfunction can occur in complex technological systems. They enable design engineers to analyze in a systematic fashion the various failure modes associated with a potential engineering design (Henley and Kumamoto, 1981: 24–28). Failure modes are the ways in which a structure, mechanism, or process can malfunction.

In an event-tree analysis one begins with an initial event—such as a loss of electrical power to a nuclear power plant—and, using inductive logic, reasons *forward,* trying to determine the state of the system to which the event can lead (Henley and Kumamoto, 1981, 24–28). Figure 1 illustrates an event-tree analysis of the probability of radiation release from a standard nuclear power plant. The diagram is based on the authoritative reactor safety study, WASH 1400, the so-called "Rasmussen Report," commissioned by the U.S. government in 1975 (*Reactor Safety Study,* 1975).

The Reactor Safety Study was performed to determine the public risks associated with existing and planned nuclear power plants. The simplified event tree begins with a definite accident-initiating event and tries to identify all the safety systems that can be called upon to mitigate the consequences. The study determined that the failure of the reactor cooling system is the most critical component that could lead to a radiation release. The analysis therefore begins with the initiating event that a (coolant) pipe might break. If the pipe breaks, without any other system failing at the same time, then the probability that there would be a radiation release is P_A, a very small release, as shown in Figure 1. Possible failures are next defined for each system; and accident sequences are constructed, consisting of the initiating event with specific systems failing and specific systems succeeding.

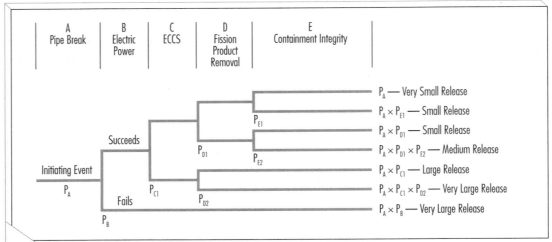

Figure 1. Event-tree analysis of a possible fission product release from a nuclear power plant.

Source: Henley, Ernest and Kumamoto, Hiromitsu (1981). *Reliability engineering and risk assessment*. Englewood Cliffs, NJ: Prentice Hall: 25.

For example, the probability of both a pipe breaking and a corresponding loss of electrical power to the plant ($P_A \times P_B$), would lead to a very large release of radiation. Keep in mind that a probability of 1 means that an event is certain to happen. Therefore, the probability that P_A occurs is less than one. In fact, all of the assigned probabilities will be less than 1, and, as the probabilities are multiplied, the total probability will diminish. For example, if the probability of P_A occurring is 0.01 and the probability of P_B occurring is 0.001, then the overall probability that a pipe will break per day and the electrical power will fail is 0.01×0.001, which equals 0.00001 or one in 100,000 events. Even though the probability of a pipe breaking at the same time as the electrical system failing is rather low, the potential consequences are very high.

If electric power does not fail during the pipe break, the analysis moves to determining the relationship between the breaking pipe and the emergency core coolant system (ECCS). The ECCS could either succeed or fail. The probability that ECCS fails at the same time that a

pipe breaks would lead to a large release, namely, ($P_A \times P_{C1}$). If the ECCS succeeds, then the probability that the fission product removal is inhibited and that a pipe breaks would lead to a small release, namely, ($P_A \times P_{D1}$). Likewise, the probability of a pipe breaking and a failure of the ECCS as well as the fission product removal being inhibited would lead to a very large release, namely, ($P_A \times P_{C2} \times P_{D2}$). In the end, each possible system state (failure or success) is connected through a branching logic to give all the specific accident sequences that can arise. The event tree is particularly useful when many individual systems and subsystems interact.

In a fault-tree study, the analyst begins with a hypothetical undesirable event, then, using deductive logic, reasons *backwards* to determine what might have led to the event. Fault-trees follow a cause-and-effect model and can be used whenever hypothetical events can be resolved into more basic, discrete units for which failure data exist or for which failure probabilities are generally easily calculable. Figure 2 illustrates a fault tree for analyzing the possible causes of why a car would not start. For example, a good mechanic would, more than likely, already be aware of all of the possible reasons of why a car will not start. The mechanic would then construct a fault tree as illustrated in Figure 2, checking each subsystem as a possible cause of why the car will not start. An insufficient battery charge is the most likely cause of a car not starting, so the mechanic would begin there and proceed to check whether there was a faulty ground connection, the battery terminals were loose or corroded, or the battery charge was weak, etc. If, for example, it is determined that the terminals are not loose or corroded or the battery charge was not weak, then the mechanic would check to see if there was rust on the ground connections, the connections were corroded or otherwise dirty, or the ground connections were loose. If the battery checks out,

the mechanic would move to an analysis of the starter system, checking each related subsystem. If this checks out, then the mechanic would move to the fuel system and each of the other related subsystems. The mechanic reasons step-by-step through the fault tree until the cause of the car not starting is identified.

Since the first comprehensive application of probabilistic risk assessment in 1975—the U.S. Reactor Safety Study—more than 15 large-scale PRAs have been carried out for nuclear power plants in the United States. In addition, large-scale PRAs have been carried out in Sweden and West Germany and have also been used in determining levels of safety in such varied industries as chemical production, liquid gas transport and storage, oil-drilling rigs, transport of toxic chemicals, and the aerospace and nuclear in-

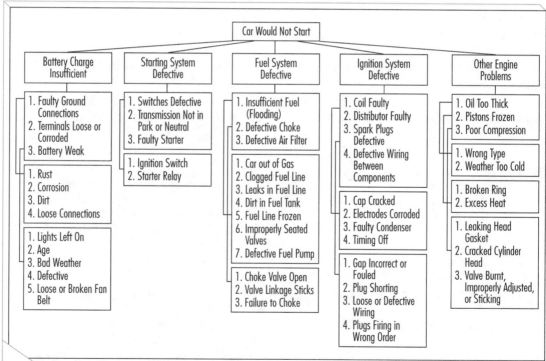

Figure 2. Fault-tree analysis of the failure of an automobile to start.

Source: Fischoff, B., Slovick, P., & Lichtenstein, S.A. (1978). Fault trees: Sensitivity and estimated failure problem representation. *Journal of Experimental Psychology: Human Perception and Performance, 4.* Reprinted with permission.

dustries (Linnerooth-Bayer and Wahlstrom, 1991: 240). Even though PRA has been used extensively, there are substantial methodological problems, some of which we will now consider.

The first set of methodological problems in PRA arises when experts attempt to determine which factors to include and which to exclude. The second set of problems arises when scientific uncertainties appear in the modeling process (Rowe, 1994). Thirdly, there are reservations about the adequacy of the method due to uncertainties that arise in attempting to trace out unknown cause-and-effect relationships. A fourth deficiency of the method is its inability to account for uncertainties that inevitably arise due to operator error and other human factors. Fifth, the very complexity of many large-scale technologies renders the PRA method inadequate as the sole source of assessing risks and adequate safety levels. Table 1 lists the five problems pertaining to PRA and the associated issues that arise with each problem.

Given the methodological deficiencies of PRA discussed above, it is safe to assume that technical methods alone, no matter how sophisticated, cannot be the only way to assess the benefits and burdens of technology. Moreover, exclusive focus on probabilities leads analysts to ignore *low-probability but high-consequence events*. In other words, PRA often ignores the category of "catastrophe," because catastrophes entail low-probability, high-consequence events. Ignoring low-probability, high-consequence events is unwise, given the immense complexity of many technologies, especially large-scale sociotechnical systems. No matter how detailed a fault-tree or an event-tree analysis may be, the methodology simply cannot begin to capture all of the common mode failure events that are possible. The inadequacy of PRA in treating low-probability, high-consequence events is glaringly evident in the Three Mile Island, Chernobyl, Challenger, and Bhopal cases. As Lanthrop puts it, "deciding that, say, a nuclear power plant is safe because it is only expected to fail once in every 10,000 successful usages does not rule out that a catastrophe may happen tomorrow, or next year, or the next" (Lanthrop, 1982: 171). This is exactly the kind of assessment failure that happened in the Three Mile Island case.

Even if PRA were an effective method for determining the risks of technology, which it is

Table 1. Problems and Issues with Probabilistic Risk Assessment

Problems	Issues
1. Problems of identifying all potential risk factors	1. Uncertainties arise when experts attempt to anticipate all of the mechanical, physical, electrical, and/or chemical factors to be included in a fault-tree or an event-tree analysis.
2. Problems with uncertainties in the modeling of systems	2. Uncertainties arise from the failure to incorporate in the model important characteristics of the process under investigation.
3. Problems associated with determining cause-and-effect relationships	3. Direct cause-and-effect relationships between potential hazards and consequent harms are often not demonstrable.
4. Uncertainties due to human factors	4. Potential errors are associated with human operators, which often cannot be "modeled" and hence are rarely anticipatable.
5. Problems of complexity and coupling	5. Tight coupling and interactive complexity between system components disallow any complete modeling of potential system failures.

not, it would not be enough in any event. As we have seen in numerous cases discussed previously, beyond technical factors, human, organizational, and socio-cultural factors are often at the root of technological disasters.

Risk-Cost-Benefit Analysis

Along with PRA, cost-benefit analysis (CBA) and risk-cost-benefit analysis (RCBA) arose as the preeminent methods of assessing the risks of technology during the late 1960s and early 1970s, as Congress began to enact legislation on the regulation and monitoring of technology and its social and environmental impacts. RCBA is a variant of CBA in which human health and welfare are brought into the equations, along with the material costs and benefits of a proposed technology.

Comprehensive statutes such as the National Environmental Policy Act of 1970 (NEPA), the Federal Water Pollution Control Act Amendments of 1972, the Consumer Protection Act, and the Clean Air and Clean Water Acts require a government agency to consider technical and economic feasibility characteristics and health and environmental effects when contemplating a technological intervention. In order to accomplish these goals, organizations turned, and continue to turn, to CBA and RCBA in an effort to comply with statutory and judicial requirements (Baram, 1977). The National Aeronautics and Space Administration (NASA) uses RCBA in its feasibility and safety studies. The Nuclear Regulatory Commission (NRC) has followed NASA's lead in employing RCBA almost exclusively in setting "acceptable" radiation standards and in decisions concerning the licensing of nuclear facility construction and operation (Kneese, Ben-David, and Schultze, 1983: 60–61).

RCBA has also been the leading method used by experts as a basis for policy choices concerning controversial problems surrounding the storage and disposal of nuclear waste (Grossman and Cassedy, 1985). In addition, RCBA is utilized frequently in medical economics for assessments of medical interventions and other health-care contexts (Gewirth, 1990: 222). RCBA is also used widely in analysis of and policy making concerning environmental toxins (Baram, 1976). Finally, RCBA is used frequently in large-scale water and waste management technologies.

In order to set up a risk-cost-benefit analysis, one begins by trying to enumerate all adverse consequences that might arise from the implementation of a given technology. Next, one attempts to estimate the probability that each of these adverse consequences will occur. The third step is to estimate the cost or loss to social and individual health and well-being should any or all of the projected adverse consequences come to pass. Fourth, one tries to calculate the expected loss from each possible consequence. Finally, one attempts to compute the total expected losses from the proposed project by summing the expected losses for each of the various possible consequences. One follows a similar procedure to calculate the benefits. In the end, one subtracts the overall costs from the overall benefits. If the benefits outweigh the costs, the project is generally described as feasible.

However, there are significant methodological deficiencies in the RCBA method, especially those that raise ethical problems. Our analysis has identified five methodological deficiencies. They are: (1) problems of identification, (2) the value-of-life problem, (3) the commensurability problem, (4) problems associated with values and market mechanisms, and (5) problems of social and ecological justice. These problems and associated issues are listed in Table 2.

The first methodological problem associated with RCBA is the unquestioned assumption

Table 2. Problems and Issues with Risk-Cost-Benefit Analysis

Problems	Issues
1. Problems of identification	1. It is almost impossible to arrive at a complete enumeration of *all* risks and benefits because one can never know all of the variables that need be assigned diagnostic values, let alone be able to calculate all the costs and benefits.
2. The value-of-life problem	2. A fundamental moral problem arises in assigning a monetary value to human life, a necessary requirement of RCBA.
3. The commensurability problem	3. The erroneous assumption that disparate costs and benefits are quantifiable according to an identical metric leads analysts to believe that all values are commensurable with one another.
4. Human values and market mechanisms	4. Utility maximizations fail to provide satisfaction for all crucial human needs and values.
5. Problems of social and ecological justice	5. RCBA fails to take into account issues of fairness in the distribution of risks and harms across social groups, between different generations, and throughout the natural environment.

that *all* significant consequences can be enumerated in advance. The assumption is that all of the costs and benefits of a particular implementation of a new technology or extension of a "known" technology can be clearly identified and catalogued, that meaningful probability, cost, and benefit values can be obtained and assigned to them, and that often disparate costs and benefits can somehow be made comparable to one another. Such judgments are grounded in unrealistic assumptions about the availability of the data needed to complete the analysis.

As with probabilistic risk assessment, not all of the crucial questions regarding the nature, estimation, or acceptability of the risks, costs, and benefits can be answered with quantitative analysis alone. Conscious normative judgments arise in determining what will be included and what will be excluded. In other words, at least as far as the "problems of identification" are concerned, the same problems associated with PRA also arise with RCBA (or CBA). As Martin (1982) points out:

> PRA and CBA are different techniques, but they have important similarities. Both attempt to translate seemingly incomparable sorts of considerations into a quantifiable common denominator of some sort (whether dollars or mathematical formulae), then tallying up the results for various options, and finally presenting this information in a form that can be readily digested by decision makers . . . [However] . . . cost-benefit analyses, as well as probabilistic risk assessment are value-laden, both in what they count out (usually, for example, considerations of rights and justice) and in what they count in (for example, assumptions about what sorts of things constitute costs and benefits, whose costs and benefits are to be weighed, and how relative values are to be assigned to them). (p. 147)

Uncertainties as to how one should define "harm" or "risk" of a particular action force analysts to make judgments that are value-laden. For example, one contested assumption of both PRA and RCBA is that mortality rates—ignoring morbidity rates—are usually chosen as the focus of analysis.

The second methodological problem with RCBA is a hotly debated issue: the assignment of a monetary value to human life, a necessary requirement of a robust risk-cost-benefit analysis (Byrne, 1988; Kahn, 1986; MacKinnon, 1986; Rescher, 1987). As MacKinnon puts it, "of all the difficulties that surround the attempt to calculate the economic 'value of a life' one of the thorniest is a moral one, namely whether it is morally permissible to place any 'price' on a human life" (MacKinnon, 1986: 29).

Of course, certain practices are used by insurance companies, economists, and risk assessors that demonstrate that society does place some implicit monetary value on human lives (VOL). As one philosopher argues, "If it is permissible to forego life-saving treatment due to its cost, life has a monetary price" (Bayless, 1978: 29). On the other hand, there is a long and venerable tradition in our philosophical attitudes toward the VOL problem, perhaps best articulated by the Enlightenment philosopher Immanuel Kant (1785), when he wrote:

> In the realm of ends everything has either a price or a dignity. Whatever has a price can be replaced by something else as its equivalent; on the other hand, whatever is above all price, and therefore admits of no equivalent, has a dignity.

Of course for Kant, human persons are such creatures who exhibit "dignity." As Rescher puts it "How much is it worth to prevent the death of a person? . . . the question has no answer . . . it assumes that 'life' and 'risk to life' is some measurable quantity that actually exists in a stable and determinable way" (Rescher, 1987: 226). But, since this is false, Rescher concludes: "The question of value of life pushes beyond the proper limits of cost-benefit analysis in its insistence on quantifying something that is inherently unquantifiable" (Rescher, 1987: 226).

Byrne's analysis reveals three general methods to assess the value of life that are used in RCBAs: insurance-based, earnings-related, and willingness-to-pay (WTP) strategies (Byrne, 1988). Unsurprisingly, each one of these methods has serious limitations and deficiencies.

Rescher (1987) points out the limitations of the earnings-related method. As he puts it:

> One study that examined salary as a function of occupational risk concluded that a premium of about $200 per year (1986) was sufficient to induce workers in risky occupations to accept an increase of 0.001 in their annual probability of accidental death, a finding that was interpreted to indicate a life-valuation of around $200,000. . . . The linearity assumption involved in such calculations is questionable—the man who accepts a 1% chance of death for $10,000 may well balk at accepting $1,000,000 for certain death. (p. 227)

In other words, the supposedly higher or lower wages people accept for different types of hazardous jobs are interpreted as a valid measure of the cash value people are thought to place on their own lives. All too frequently, however, when lives are valued based on such criteria as economic worth or expected earnings, this turns into "life is cheap" in poorer neighborhoods or less developed nations. This issue is clearly illustrated in the Bhopal case. Life in Bhopal was implicitly valued less than life in the United States. Therefore, the safety equipment and emergency preparedness at the Bhopal plant in India were far less adequate than those at a similar plant operated by Union Carbide in Institute, West Virginia.

Barbour (1980) states the consequences of following the valuation of life principle to its logical conclusion:

> If applied consistently, the method would require that the lives of the elderly would be valueless. If future earnings are discounted, a child's life would be worth much less than an adult's. . . . I would maintain that there are distinctive characteristics of human life that should make us hesitant to treat it as if it were a commodity on the market. Life cannot be transferred and its loss to a person is irreversible and irreplaceable. (p. 73)

The third methodological problem of RCBA is how to deduce the value attribution of all the identified risks, costs, and benefits. Analysts automatically assume that often disparate costs and benefits can somehow be compared with another—that is, that all values are commensurable and can be fully quantified to reasonably determine whether the benefits of the proposed technological intervention or policy do, in fact, outweigh the risks and costs. Such calculations are necessary for RCBA so that disparate values can be compared and traded off, one against the other. Money becomes the common metric so that "goods" and "bads" can be compared with one another, and price becomes the medium through which all alternatives are evaluated, even those that are not normally perceived to have a market value (Kelman, 1981). This is evident in the "willingness-to-pay" criterion of a free-market economy: what a willing buyer will pay a willing seller. Take, for example, our aesthetic relationship to nature. How much is a beautiful view worth in monetary terms? How much is a landscape worth? A sunset? How much would someone be willing to pay to avoid having a toxic waste dump, a power plant, or an oil refinery built in his or her community?

The fourth methodological deficiency of RCBA becomes visible when one begins to probe the unquestioned assumption that market values provide the best opportunities for human beings to advance their life goals (Kelman, 1981). In other words, an RCBA methodology makes the assumption that the decisions people make in the marketplace are rational with regard to price, needs, and wants. However, it must be admitted that even in the open market the notion of utility maximization does not fully satisfy the variety of human needs and purposes. Notions such as freedom, equality, justice, and aesthetics also matter (Hausman and McPhearson, 1996: 77). In other words, one cannot always trust the market to satisfy all of our prefer-

ences and sustain all of our values. This became all too evident in the case of the Ford Pinto. The public was outraged when they were informed, perhaps for the first time, as to how decisions like this are made. In the end, the problem is that:

> *By regarding human happiness, human well-being, human life, and non-human life as mere commodities, cost-benefit analysis ignores the non-market value of these things and the central role they should play in public policy.* (Anderson, 1993: 190)

These sentiments are reflected in a sign that Albert Einstein is reported to have had hanging in his office. The sign read: "Not everything that counts can be counted, and not everything that can be counted, counts" (Diwan, 2000). After everything is said, Einstein's aphorism perhaps best sums up the problems that beset using risk-cost-benefit analysis as the preeminent method for assessing the risks of technology. The aphorism also points to why risk-cost-benefit analysis fails as the sole method of determining the appropriate and equitable level of acceptability of those risks. This is no more evident than in RCBA's neglect of social values that contribute to our idea of justice, qualities that one can be sure Einstein would consider among those things that "count, but cannot be counted."

The fifth set of problems that beset the RCBA method are the well-known criticisms that RCBA fails to address adequately issues of fairness associated with the equitable distributions of risks and harms. For one thing, RCBA places exclusive focus on aggregate benefits and cannot address the ways in which those benefits are distributed. It is *not* designed to pay attention to the ethically crucial question: "Who pays the costs, and who gets the benefits?" Typically, such analysis reaches its "bottom line" by aggregating all costs, all risks, and all benefits. Its goal is to determine, within its limited definition of the goods and harms involved, the *net* good, or harm that a technological intervention will produce. In other words, risk-benefit analysis is concerned only with the amounts of "goods" and "bads" in society, not with their fair or equitable distribution. For example, if the oil refinery in a neighborhood can be calculated to allow millions of distant persons to benefit from the gasoline and other products of that refinery, this can be multiplied into a major benefit. On the other hand, if the refinery results in higher cancer rates, greater medical costs, and residential property devaluation in the immediate neighborhood, this can also be calculated as part of the net costs, or harms, and subtracted from the "greater good." Although the net benefit may greatly outweigh the overall costs, the distribution of goods and harms may not be fair, because as Ferre (1995) puts it: "the principle of beneficence, to create greater good, is satisfied, but the principle of justice has been overlooked" (p. 83).

Justice across geographical, economic, and social space is one crucial set of values that RCBA leaves out of its calculations and equations. In addition, justice across time is almost totally neglected. Since RCBA is geared toward favoring short-range exploitation of opportunities and resources, it tends to ignore what Barbour (1980) calls "intergenerational justice" (p. 173). In other words, RCBA fails to address questions about the duties, obligations, and responsibilities one generation has to the next. Given recent concern over questions of ecological sustainability, resource depletion, and harm to future generations, this constitutes a major ethical flaw in the RCBA method of risk assessment.

In addition to overlooking questions about our duties and obligations to future generations, economists and policy makers seem to either ignore or deny that the market process

in general, and cost- and risk-benefit analysis in particular, systematically undervalue irreplaceable natural assets. RCBA tends to ignore considerations of what Ferre (1995) calls "ecological justice" (p. 84). The scarcity of nonrenewable resources, the irreversibility of habitat and land destruction, the extinction of endangered species, the depletion of the ozone layer, global warming, etc., are all pressing concerns that RCBA fails to address.

Technology Assessment

PRA and RCBA are not the only ways to assess the risks and harms of technology. Another approach is called *technology assessment* (TA). As originally conceived, TA was sensitive to the problems and issues previously discussed. Take, for example, the definition of TA given by one early theorist:

> *Technology assessment is the process of taking a purposeful look at the consequences of technological change. It includes the primary cost-benefit balance of short-term localized market-place economics, but particularly goes beyond these to identify affected parties and unanticipated impacts in as broad and long-range fashion as is possible . . . both 'good' and 'bad' side-effects are investigated since a missed opportunity for benefit may be detrimental to society just as an unexpected hazard. (Coates, 1976: 141)*

This definition introduces two ideas: the first points to a feasibility analysis performed so as to determine whether a proposed technology would maximize public utility. The second idea calls for mechanisms that focus on second- and higher-order (noneconomic) consequences, which are to be balanced against first-order (economic) benefits. Only with the aid of such an analysis is it possible to take account of unanticipated impacts of technology and also identify how they affect different stakeholders or constituencies. These two different but complementary concerns give voice to two general models, a "narrow" and a "broad" definition of technology assessment.

The narrow definition tends to restrict the meaning of TA to basically an operational analysis of particular technologies defined as concretely as possible (as in PRA):

> *Technology assessment is viewed as a systematic planning and forecasting process which encompasses an analysis of a given production method or a line of products . . . it may be considered as a natural follow-up to systems engineering . . . (Coates, 1976: 142)*

The broad definition, on the other hand, tends to consider technology assessment as a framework for societal analysis. This requires a systematic and interdisciplinary analysis of the impacts of technological innovation on the social, political, ethical, and medical aspects of life.

Conclusion

To enhance our capacity to prevent technological disasters, a broad concept of technology assessment is in order, the features of which are as follows:

1. *Social impacts.* TA should be concerned with second-, third-, and higher-order impacts such as impacts on human health, society, and the environment, as distinguished from economic utility of exclusively first-order concerns.
2. *Multi-disciplinary analysis.* TA should require that all pertinent aspects—economic, social, ethical, cultural, environmental, and political—be taken into account. Diverse methodologies and inputs from all disciplines are to be employed.

3. *Multi-constituency impacts.* TA should consider the widest range of stakeholders that may be affected by the proposed technology. Comprehensive TAs should require the informed consent of all affected stakeholders, inviting their active participation in the decision-making process.
4. *Policy-making tool.* TA should not be concerned with just technical expertise but, more essentially, with the socio-political problems associated with the impacts and consequences of a proposed technological innovation.

Such principles for a broad technology assessment can only be realized if risk assessment becomes a democratic process rather than one that is dominated by a technocratic and power elite. This critical issue will be the subject of our final chapter.

Author Citations

Anderson, Elizabeth. (1993). *Value in ethics and economics.* Cambridge, MA: Harvard University Press.

Baram, Michael. (1976). "Regulation of environmental carcinogens: Why cost-benefit analysis may be harmful to your health," *Technology Review,* July/August; 78: 40–42.

Baram, Michael. (1977). "An assessment of the use of cost-benefit analysis." In Joel Tarr (Ed.), *Retrospective technology assessment.* San Francisco, CA: San Francisco Press: 15–30.

Barbour, Ian. (1980). *Technology, environment, and human values.* New York: Praeger.

Bayless, Michael. (1978). "The price of life," *Ethics* 89 (1): 28–39.

Bier, Vicki. (1997). "An overview of probabilistic risk analysis for complex engineered systems." In Vlasta Molak (Ed.), *Fundamentals of risk analysis and risk management.* Boston, MA: Lewis Publishers: 67–85.

Bougumil, R.J. (1986). "Limitations of probabilistic assessment," *IEEE Technology and Society Magazine* 24 (8): 24–27.

Byrne, L.J. (1988). "The value of life: The state of the art." In Larry Martin (Ed.), *Risk assessment and management: Emergency planning perspectives*. Waterloo, Canada: University of Waterloo Press: 79–101.

Coates, Joseph. (1976). "The role of formal models in technology assessment," *Technological Forecasting and Social Change* 9: 140–146.

Diwan, Romesh. (2000). "Relational wealth and the quality of life," *The Journal of Social Economics* 29 (4): 305–322.

Ferre, Frederick. (1995). *Philosophy of technology*. Athens, GA: University of Georgia Press.

Gewirth, Alan. (1990). "Two types of cost-benefit analysis." In Donald Scherer (Ed.), *Upstream/downstream: Issues in environmental ethics*. Philadelphia: Temple University Press: 205–232.

Greenberg, Michael, and Goldberg, Laura. (1994). "Ethical challenges to risk scientist exploratory analysis of survey data," *Science, Technology, and Human Values* 19 (2): 223–241.

Grossman, P.Z., and Cassedy, E.S. (1985). "Cost-benefit analysis of nuclear waste disposal: Accounting for safeguards," *Science, Technology, and Human Values* 10 (4): 47–54.

Haimes, Yacov. (1998). *Risk modeling, assessment, and management*. New York: John Wiley & Sons.

Harris, Charles E., Pritchard, Michael S., and Rabins, Michael J. (2000). *Engineering ethics: Concepts and cases*. Belmont, CA: Wadsworth.

Hausman, Daniel, and McPhearson, Michael. (1996). *Economic analysis and moral philosophy*. London: Cambridge University Press.

Henley, Ernest, and Kumamoto, Hiromitsu. (1981). *Reliability engineering and risk assessment*. Englewood Cliffs, NJ: Prentice Hall.

Humphreys, Paul. (1987). "Philosophical issues in the scientific basis of quantitative risk analyses." In James Humber and Robert Almeder (Eds.), *Quantitative risk assessment: Biomedical ethics reviews*. Clifton, NJ: Humana Press: 205–223.

Kahn, Shulamit. (1986). "Economic estimates of the value of life," *IEEE Technology and Society Magazine*, June: 24–29.

Kant, Immanuel. (1785). *Groundwork for the metaphysics of morals*. Translated by James W. Ellington. (1981). Indianapolis, IN: Hackett Publishing Company.

Kelman, Stephen. (1981). "Cost benefit analysis: An ethical critique." Reprinted in Thomas Donaldson and Patricia Werhane (Eds.), *Ethical issues in business* (5th ed.). Upper Saddle River, NJ: Prentice Hall.

Kneese, Allen, Ben-David, Shaul, and Schultze, William. (1983). "The ethical foundations of cost-benefit analysis." In Douglas MacLean and Peter Brown (Eds.), *Energy and the future*. Totowa, NJ: Rowman and Littlefield: 59–74.

Lanthrop, John. (1982). "Evaluating technological risk: Prescriptive and descriptive perspectives." In Howard Kunreuther and Eryl Levy (Eds.), *The risk analysis controversy: An institutional perspective*. Heidelberg, Germany: Springer-Verlag: 165–180.

Linnerooth-Bayer, Joanne, and Wahlstrom, Bjorn. (1991). "Applications of probabilistic risk assessments: The selection of appropriate tools," *Risk Analysis* 11 (2): 239–248.

MacKinnon, Barbara. (1986). "Pricing human life," *Science, Technology, and Human Values* 11 (2): 29–39.

Martin, Mike. (1982). "Comments on Levy and Copp and Thompson." In Vivian Weil (Ed.), *Beyond whistleblowing: Defining engineers' responsibilities*. Chicago: Center for the Study of Ethics in the Profession, Illinois Institute of Technology: 146–152.

Reactor safety study—An assessment of accident risks in U.S. commercial nuclear power plants. WASH-1400, NUREG-75/014, October 1975. Washington, DC: U.S. Nuclear Regulatory Commission, 1974.

Rescher, Nicholas. (1987). "Risk and the social value of a life." In James Humber and Robert Almeder (Eds.), *Quantitative risk assessment: Biomedical ethics reviews*. Clifton, NJ: Humana Press: 225–237.

Rowe, William. (1994). "Understanding uncertainty," *Risk Analysis* 14 (5): 743–750.

Thompson, Paul. (1982). "Ethics and probabilistic risk assessment." In Vivian Weil (Ed.), *Beyond whistleblowing: Defining engineers' responsibilities*. Chicago: Center for the Study of Ethics in the Profession, Illinois Institute of Technology: 114–126.

Discussion Questions

1. What are the basic features of probabilistic risk assessment? What are the problems or short-comings of probabilistic risk assessment as enumerated by Evan and Manion?

2. The authors identify and describe five methodological deficiencies of risk-cost-benefit analysis (RCBA). What are they? Give an example to illustrate each of these deficiencies.

3. Why is it difficult for tools such as probabilistic risk assessment to adequately assess low-probability, high-consequence events such as Chernobyl?

4. One of the reasons why intangible goals such as environmental health and social equity are often not factored into cost-benefit analyses is that they are extremely difficult to quantify. If they are considered, how are such intangibles factored in? What are the shortcomings of attempts to quantify such factors?

 Supporting Activities

1. Evan and Manion note that "in order to set up a risk-cost-benefit analysis, one begins by trying to enumerate all the adverse consequences that might arise from the implementation of a given technology." Select a technological development that you have recently read about, or one that is under discussion in your community or state, and try to brainstorm all of the potential consequences that might emerge. Try to identify primary, secondary, and even tertiary impacts. It can sometimes be helpful to create a web diagram that shows primary outcomes and the secondary and tertiary outcomes that stem from them.

2. Learn more about the concept of intergenerational equity and discuss it from an economic, environmental, and social standpoint. Should intergenerational equity be addressed in decision making? If so, how should this be accomplished? What principles should apply?

3. Carry out a modified cost-benefit analysis as a small group or class project. One good site to help structure the process is provided by the California Department of Transportation: http://www.dot.ca.gov/hq/tpp/offices/ote/benefit_cost/.

 Additional Resources

1. Review the Endnotes listed in this section for more information about the Office of Science and Technology Policy and the Office of Technology Assessment.

2. To view a case study of risk management strategies in the area of information technologies, see: Stoneburner, Gary; Goguen, Alice; and Feringa, Alexis. 2002. *Risk management guide for information technology systems: Recommendations of the National Institute of Standards and Technology*. Gaithersburg, MD: National Institute of Standards and Technology. Available: http://csrc.nist.gov/publications/nistpubs/800-30/sp800-30.pdf.

Big and Bad

If you're an SUV owner you might feel a sense of annoyance or even anger at some of the claims made in this article. Gladwell relates information that systematically refutes the notion that sport utility vehicles are safer than passenger cars. If you *are* inclined toward anger, hold off for a minute. A main function of this article is not to insult SUV owners, but rather to call into question the reasoning that we sometimes use with relation to safety and management of risk.

The popularity of SUVs, in spite of the accumulated data about their safety relative to passenger vehicles, provides clear evidence of two things: one, that the "reptilian" response is often stronger than more rational responses,[10] and two, that consumers of a technology are not necessarily well informed about its details. Of all the reasons why an individual might choose to own an SUV, safety should not be at the top of the list. (Although one might try, it's difficult to argue with the laws of physics.) The case of the SUV illustrates that we sometimes make decisions based purely on perception, superstition, or emotion; but if we're serious about reducing the risks associated with technology, we should probably rely on more objective data.

Malcolm Gladwell has been a staff writer at *The New Yorker* magazine since 1996 and is the author of the bestselling books *The Tipping Point: How Little Things Make a Big Difference* (2000), *Blink: The Power of Thinking Without Thinking* (2005), and *Outliers: The Story of Success* (2008). Gladwell also served as a reporter for the *Washington Post* for nine years, where he reported on business and science. In 2005, he was named one of *Time* magazine's 100 Most Influential People.

Big and Bad
How the S.U.V. Ran Over Automotive Safety

By Malcolm Gladwell

In the summer of 1996, the Ford Motor Company began building the Expedition, its new, full-sized S.U.V., at the Michigan Truck Plant, in the Detroit suburb of Wayne. The Expedition was essentially the F-150 pickup truck with an extra set of doors and two more rows of seats—and the fact that it was a truck was critical. Cars have to meet stringent fuel-efficiency regulations. Trucks don't. The handling and suspension and braking of cars have to be built to the demanding standards of drivers and passengers. Trucks only have to handle like, well, trucks. Cars are built with what is called unit-body construction. To be light enough to meet fuel standards and safe enough to meet safety standards, they have expensive and elaborately engineered steel skeletons, with built-in crumple zones to absorb the impact of a crash. Making a truck is a lot more rudimentary. You build a rectangular steel frame. The engine gets bolted to the front. The seats get bolted to the middle. The body gets lowered over the top. The result is heavy and rigid and not particularly safe. But it's an awfully inexpensive way to build an automobile. Ford had planned to sell the Expedition for thirty-six thousand dollars, and its best estimate

From *The New Yorker, 79(42), January 5, 2004* by Malcolm Gladwell. Copyright © by Malcolm Gladwell. Reprinted by permission of the author.

was that it could build one for twenty-four thousand—which, in the automotive industry, is a terrifically high profit margin. Sales, the company predicted, weren't going to be huge. After all, how many Americans could reasonably be expected to pay a twelve-thousand-dollar premium for what was essentially a dressed-up truck? But Ford executives decided that the Expedition would be a highly profitable niche product. They were half right. The "highly profitable" part turned out to be true. Yet, almost from the moment Ford's big new S.U.V.s rolled off the assembly line in Wayne, there was nothing "niche" about the Expedition.

Ford had intended to split the assembly line at the Michigan Truck Plant between the Expedition and the Ford F-150 pickup. But, when the first flood of orders started coming in for the Expedition, the factory was entirely given over to S.U.V.s. The orders kept mounting. Assembly-line workers were put on sixty- and seventy-hour weeks. Another night shift was added. The plant was now running twenty-four hours a day, six days a week. Ford executives decided to build a luxury version of the Expedition, the Lincoln Navigator. They bolted a new grille on the Expedition, changed a few body panels, added some sound insulation, took a deep breath, and charged forty-five thousand dollars—and soon Navigators were flying out the door nearly as fast as Expeditions. Before long, the Michigan Truck Plant was the most profitable of Ford's fifty-three assembly plants. By the late nineteen-nineties, it had become the most profitable factory of any industry in the world. In 1998, the Michigan Truck Plant grossed eleven billion dollars, almost as much as McDonald's made that year. Profits were $3.7 billion. Some factory workers, with overtime, were making two hundred thousand dollars a year. The demand for Expeditions and Navigators was so insatiable that even when a blizzard hit the Detroit region in January of 1999—

burying the city in snow, paralyzing the airport, and stranding hundreds of cars on the freeway—Ford officials got on their radios and commandeered parts bound for other factories so that the Michigan Truck Plant assembly line wouldn't slow for a moment. The factory that had begun as just another assembly plant had become the company's crown jewel.

In the history of the automotive industry, few things have been quite as unexpected as the rise of the S.U.V. Detroit is a town of engineers, and engineers like to believe that there is some connection between the success of a vehicle and its technical merits. But the S.U.V. boom was like Apple's bringing back the Macintosh, dressing it up in colorful plastic, and suddenly creating a new market. It made no sense to them. Consumers said they liked four-wheel drive. But the overwhelming majority of consumers don't need four-wheel drive. S.U.V. buyers said they liked the elevated driving position. But when, in focus groups, industry marketers probed further, they heard things that left them rolling their eyes. As Keith Bradsher writes in "High and Mighty"—perhaps the most important book about Detroit since Ralph Nader's "Unsafe at Any Speed"—what consumers said was "If the vehicle is up high, it's easier to see if something is hiding underneath or lurking behind it." Bradsher brilliantly captures the mixture of bafflement and contempt that many auto executives feel toward the customers who buy their S.U.V.s. Fred J. Schaafsma, a top engineer for General Motors, says, "Sport-utility owners tend to be more like 'I wonder how people view me,' and are more willing to trade off flexibility or functionality to get that." According to Bradsher, internal industry market research concluded that S.U.V.s tend to be bought by people who are insecure, vain, self-centered, and self-absorbed, who are frequently nervous about their marriages, and who lack confidence in their driving skills. Ford's S.U.V. designers took their cues from seeing "fashionably dressed women wearing hiking boots or even work boots while walking through expensive malls." Toyota's top marketing executive in the United States, Bradsher writes, loves to tell the story of how at a focus group in Los Angeles "an elegant woman in the group said that she needed her full-sized Lexus LX 470 to drive up over the curb and onto lawns to park at large parties in Beverly Hills." One of Ford's senior marketing executives was even blunter: "The only time those S.U.V.s are going to be off-road is when they miss the driveway at 3 a.m."

The truth, underneath all the rationalizations, seemed to be that S.U.V. buyers thought of big, heavy vehicles as safe: they found comfort in being surrounded by so much rubber and steel. To the engineers, of course, that didn't make any sense, either: if consumers really wanted something that was big and heavy and comforting, they ought to buy minivans, since minivans, with their unit-body construction, do much better in accidents than S.U.V.s. (In a thirty-five m.p.h. crash test, for instance, the driver of a Cadillac Escalade—the G.M. counterpart to the Lincoln Navigator—has a sixteen-per-cent chance of a life-threatening head injury, a twenty percent chance of a life-threatening chest injury, and a thirty-five-per-cent chance of a leg injury. The same numbers in a Ford Windstar minivan—a vehicle engineered from the ground up, as opposed to simply being bolted onto a pickup-truck frame—are, respectively, two percent, four percent, and one percent.) But this desire for safety wasn't a rational calculation. It was a *feeling*. Over the past decade, a number of major automakers in America have relied on the services of a French-born cultural anthropologist, G. Clotaire Rapaille, whose speciality is getting beyond the rational—what he calls "cortex"—impressions of consumers and tapping into their deeper, "reptilian" responses. And what Rapaille concluded

from countless, intensive sessions with car buyers was that when S.U.V. buyers thought about safety they were thinking about something that reached into their deepest unconscious. "The No. 1 feeling is that everything surrounding you should be round and soft, and should give," Rapaille told me. "There should be air bags everywhere. Then there's this notion that you need to be up high. That's a contradiction, because the people who buy these S.U.V.s know at the cortex level that if you are high there is more chance of a rollover. But at the reptilian level they think that if I am bigger and taller I'm safer. You feel secure because you are higher and dominate and look down. That you can look down is psychologically a very powerful notion. And what was the key element of safety when you were a child? It was that your mother fed you, and there was warm liquid. That's why cupholders are absolutely crucial for safety. If there is a car that has no cupholder, it is not safe. If I can put my coffee there, if I can have my food, if everything is round, if it's soft, and if I'm high, then I feel safe. It's amazing that intelligent, educated women will look at a car and the first thing they will look at is how many cupholders it has." During the design of Chrysler's PT Cruiser, one of the things Rapaille learned was that car buyers felt unsafe when they thought that an outsider could easily see inside their vehicles. So Chrysler made the back window of the PT Cruiser smaller. Of course, making windows smaller—and thereby reducing visibility—makes driving *more* dangerous, not less so. But that's the puzzle of what has happened to the automobile world: feeling safe has become more important than actually being safe.

One day this fall, I visited the automobile-testing center of Consumers Union, the organization that publishes *Consumer Reports*. It is tucked away in the woods, in south-central Connecticut, on the site of the old Connecticut

Speedway. The facility has two skid pads to measure cornering, a long straightaway for braking tests, a meandering "handling" course that winds around the back side of the track, and an accident-avoidance obstacle course made out of a row of orange cones. It is headed by a trim, white-haired Englishman named David Champion, who previously worked as an engineer with Land Rover and with Nissan. On the day of my visit, Champion set aside two vehicles: a silver 2003 Chevrolet TrailBlazer—an enormous five-thousand-pound S.U.V.—and a shiny blue two-seater Porsche Boxster convertible.

We started with the TrailBlazer. Champion warmed up the Chevrolet with a few quick circuits of the track, and then drove it hard through the twists and turns of the handling course. He sat in the bucket seat with his back straight and his arms almost fully extended, and drove with practiced grace: every movement smooth and relaxed and unhurried. Champion, as an engineer, did not much like the TrailBlazer. "Cheap interior, cheap plastic," he said, batting the dashboard with his hand. "It's a little bit heavy, cumbersome. Quiet. Bit wallowy, side to side. Doesn't feel that secure. Accelerates heavily. Once it gets going, it's got decent power. Brakes feel a bit spongy." He turned onto the straightaway and stopped a few hundred yards from the obstacle course.

Measuring accident avoidance is a key part of the Consumers Union evaluation. It's a simple setup. The driver has to navigate his vehicle through two rows of cones eight feet wide and sixty feet long. Then he has to steer hard to the left, guiding the vehicle through a gate set off to the side, and immediately swerve hard back to the right, and enter a second sixty-foot corridor of cones that are parallel to the first set. The idea is to see how fast you can drive through the course without knocking over any cones. "It's like you're driving down a road in suburbia," Champion said. "Suddenly, a kid on a bicycle

veers out in front of you. You have to do whatever it takes to avoid the kid. But there's a tractor-trailer coming toward you in the other lane, so you've got to swing back into your own lane as quickly as possible. That's the scenario."

Champion and I put on helmets. He accelerated toward the entrance to the obstacle course. "We do the test without brakes or throttle, so we can just look at handling," Champion said. "I actually take my foot right off the pedals." The car was now moving at forty m.p.h. At that speed, on the smooth tarmac of the raceway, the TrailBlazer was very quiet, and we were seated so high that the road seemed somehow remote. Champion entered the first row of cones. His arms tensed. He jerked the car to the left. The TrailBlazer's tires squealed. I was thrown toward the passenger-side door as the truck's body rolled, then thrown toward Champion as he jerked the TrailBlazer back to the right. My tape recorder went skittering across the cabin. The whole maneuver had taken no more than a few seconds, but it felt as if we had been sailing into a squall. Champion brought the car to a stop. We both looked back: the TrailBlazer had hit the cone at the gate. The kid on the bicycle was probably dead. Champion shook his head. "It's very rubbery. It slides a lot. I'm not getting much communication back from the steering wheel. It feels really ponderous, clumsy. I felt a little bit of tail swing."

I drove the obstacle course next. I started at the conservative speed of thirty-five m.p.h. I got through cleanly. I tried again, this time at thirty-eight m.p.h., and that small increment of speed made a dramatic difference. I made the first left, avoiding the kid on the bicycle. But, when it came time to swerve back to avoid the hypothetical oncoming eighteen-wheeler, I found that I was wrestling with the car. The protests of the tires were jarring. I stopped, shaken. "It wasn't going where you wanted it to go, was it?" Champion said. "Did you feel the weight pulling you sideways? That's what the extra weight that S.U.V.s have tends to do. It pulls you in the wrong direction." Behind us was a string of toppled cones. Getting the TrailBlazer to travel in a straight line, after that sudden diversion, hadn't been easy. "I think you took out a few pedestrians," Champion said with a faint smile.

Next up was the Boxster. The top was down. The sun was warm on my forehead. The car was low to the ground; I had the sense that if I dangled my arm out the window my knuckles would scrape on the tarmac. Standing still, the Boxster didn't feel safe: I could have been sitting in a go-cart. But when I ran it through the handling course I felt that I was in perfect control. On the straightaway, I steadied the Boxster at forty-five m.p.h., and ran it through the obstacle course. I could have balanced a teacup on my knee. At fifty m.p.h., I navigated the left and right turns with what seemed like a twitch of the steering wheel. The tires didn't squeal. The car stayed level. I pushed the Porsche up into the mid-fifties. Every cone was untouched. "Walk in the park!" Champion exclaimed as we pulled to a stop.

Most of us think that S.U.V.s are much safer than sports cars. If you asked the young parents of America whether they would rather strap their infant child in the back seat of the TrailBlazer or the passenger seat of the Boxster, they would choose the TrailBlazer. We feel that way because in the TrailBlazer our chances of surviving a collision with a hypothetical tractor-trailer in the other lane are greater than they are in the Porsche. What we forget, though, is that in the TrailBlazer you're also much more likely to hit the tractor-trailer because you can't get out of the way in time. In the parlance of the automobile world, the TrailBlazer is better at "passive safety." The Boxster is better when it comes to "active safety," which is every bit as important.

Consider the set of safety statistics compiled by Tom Wenzel, a scientist at Lawrence Berkeley National Laboratory, in California, and Marc Ross, a physicist at the University of Michigan. The numbers are expressed in fatalities per million cars, both for drivers of particular models and for the drivers of the cars they hit. (For example, in the first case, for every million Toyota Avalons on the road, forty Avalon drivers die in car accidents every year, and twenty people die in accidents involving Toyota Avalons.) The numbers below have been rounded:

Make/Model	Type	Driver Deaths	Other Deaths	Total
Toyota Avalon	large	40	20	60
Chrysler Town & Country	minivan	31	36	67
Toyota Camry	mid-size	41	29	70
Volkswagen Jetta	subcompact	47	23	70
Ford Windstar	minivan	37	35	72
Nissan Maxima	mid-size	53	26	79
Honda Accord	mid-size	54	27	82
Chevrolet Venture	minivan	51	34	85
Buick Century	mid-size	70	23	93
Subaru Legacy/Outback	compact	74	24	98
Mazda 626	compact	70	29	99
Chevrolet Malibu	mid-size	71	34	105
Chevrolet Suburban	S.U.V.	46	59	105
Jeep Grand Cherokee	S.U.V.	61	44	106
Honda Civic	subcompact	84	25	109
Toyota Corolla	subcompact	81	29	110
Ford Expedition	S.U.V.	55	57	112
GMC Jimmy	S.U.V.	76	39	114
Ford Taurus	mid-size	78	39	117
Nissan Altima	compact	72	49	121
Mercury Marquis	large	80	43	123
Nissan Sentra	subcompact	95	34	129
Toyota 4Runner	S.U.V.	94	43	137
Chevrolet Tahoe	S.U.V.	68	74	141
Dodge Stratus	mid-size	103	40	143
Lincoln Town Car	large	100	47	147

(continued)

Ford Explorer	S.U.V.	88	60	148
Pontiac Grand Am	compact	118	39	157
Toyota Tacoma	pickup	111	59	171
Chevrolet Cavalier	subcompact	146	41	186
Dodge Neon	subcompact	161	39	199
Pontiac Sunfire	subcompact	158	44	202
Ford F-Series	pickup	110	128	238

Are the best performers the biggest and heaviest vehicles on the road? Not at all. Among the safest cars are the midsize imports, like the Toyota Camry and the Honda Accord. Or consider the extraordinary performance of some subcompacts, like the Volkswagen Jetta. Drivers of the tiny Jetta die at a rate of just forty-seven per million, which is in the same range as drivers of the five-thousand-pound Chevrolet Suburban and almost half that of popular S.U.V. models like the Ford Explorer or the GMC Jimmy. In a head-on crash, an Explorer or a Suburban would crush a Jetta or a Camry. But, clearly, the drivers of Camrys and Jettas are finding a way to avoid head-on crashes with Explorers and Suburbans. The benefits of being nimble—of being in an automobile that's capable of staying out of trouble—are in many cases greater than the benefits of being big.

I had another lesson in active safety at the test track when I got in the TrailBlazer with another Consumers Union engineer, and we did three emergency-stopping tests, taking the Chevrolet up to sixty m.p.h. and then slamming on the brakes. It was not a pleasant exercise. Bringing five thousand pounds of rubber and steel to a sudden stop involves lots of lurching, screeching, and protesting. The first time, the TrailBlazer took 146.2 feet to come to a halt, the second time 151.6 feet, and the third time 153.4 feet. The Boxster can come to a complete stop from sixty m.p.h. in about 124 feet. That's a difference of about two car lengths, and it isn't hard to imagine any number of scenarios where

two car lengths could mean the difference between life and death.

The S.U.V. boom represents, then, a shift in how we conceive of safety—from active to passive. It's what happens when a larger number of drivers conclude, consciously or otherwise, that the extra thirty feet that the TrailBlazer takes to come to a stop don't really matter, that the tractor-trailer will hit them anyway, and that they are better off treating accidents as inevitable rather than avoidable. "The metric that people use is size," says Stephen Popiel, a vice-president of Millward Brown Goldfarb, in Toronto, one of the leading automotive market-research firms. "The bigger something is, the safer it is. In the consumer's mind, the basic equation is, If I were to take this vehicle and drive it into this brick wall, the more metal there is in front of me the better off I'll be."

This is a new idea, and one largely confined to North America. In Europe and Japan, people think of a safe car as a nimble car. That's why they build cars like the Jetta and the Camry, which are designed to carry out the driver's wishes as directly and efficiently as possible. In the Jetta, the engine is clearly audible. The steering is light and precise. The brakes are crisp. The wheelbase is short enough that the car picks up the undulations of the road. The car is so small and close to the ground, and so dwarfed by other cars on the road, that an intelligent driver is constantly reminded of the necessity of driving safely and defensively. An S.U.V. embodies the opposite logic. The driver is seated as high and far from the road as possible. The vehicle is designed to overcome its environment, not to respond to it. Even four-wheel drive, seemingly the most beneficial feature of the S.U.V., serves to reinforce this isolation. Having the engine provide power to all four wheels, safety experts point out, does nothing to improve braking, although many S.U.V.

owners erroneously believe this to be the case. Nor does the feature necessarily make it safer to turn across a slippery surface: that is largely a function of how much friction is generated by the vehicle's tires. All it really does is improve what engineers call tracking—that is, the ability to accelerate without slipping in perilous conditions or in deep snow or mud. Champion says that one of the occasions when he came closest to death was a snowy day, many years ago, just after he had bought a new Range Rover. "Everyone around me was slipping, and I was thinking, *Yeahhh*. And I came to a stop sign on a major road, and I was driving probably twice as fast as I should have been, because I could. I had traction. But I also weighed probably twice as much as most cars. And I still had only four brakes and four tires on the road. I slid right across a four-lane road." Four-wheel drive robs the driver of feedback. "The car driver whose wheels spin once or twice while backing out of the driveway knows that the road is slippery," Bradsher writes. "The SUV driver who navigates the driveway and street without difficulty until she tries to brake may not find out that the road is slippery until it is too late." Jettas are safe because they make their drivers feel unsafe. S.U.V.s are unsafe because they make their drivers feel safe. That feeling of safety isn't the solution; it's the problem.

Perhaps the most troublesome aspect of S.U.V. culture is its attitude toward risk. "Safety, for most automotive consumers, has to do with the notion that they aren't in complete control," Popiel says. "There are unexpected events that at any moment in time can come out and impact them—an oil patch up ahead, an eighteen-wheeler turning over, something falling down. People feel that the elements of the world out of their control are the ones that are going to cause them distress."

Of course, those things really aren't outside a driver's control: an alert driver, in the right kind of vehicle, can navigate the oil patch, avoid the truck, and swerve around the thing that's falling down. Traffic-fatality rates vary strongly with driver behavior. Drunks are 7.6 times more likely to die in accidents than non-drinkers. People who wear their seat belts are almost half as likely to die as those who don't buckle up. Forty-year-olds are ten times less likely to get into accidents than sixteen-year-olds. Drivers of minivans, Wenzel and Ross's statistics tell us, die at a fraction of the rate of drivers of pickup trucks. That's clearly because minivans are family cars, and parents with children in the back seat are less likely to get into accidents. Frank McKenna, a safety expert at the University of Reading, in England, has done experiments where he shows drivers a series of videotaped scenarios—a child running out the front door of his house and onto the street, for example, or a car approaching an intersection at too great a speed to stop at the red light—and asks people to press a button the minute they become aware of the potential for an accident. Experienced drivers press the button between half a second and a second faster than new drivers, which, given that car accidents are events measured in milliseconds, is a significant difference. McKenna's work shows that, with experience, we all learn how to exert some degree of control over what might otherwise appear to be uncontrollable events. Any conception of safety that revolves entirely around the vehicle, then, is incomplete. Is the Boxster safer than the TrailBlazer? It depends on who's behind the wheel. In the hands of, say, my very respectable and prudent middle-aged mother, the Boxster is by far the safer car. In my hands, it probably isn't. On the open road, my reaction to the Porsche's extraordinary road manners and the sweet, irresistible wail of its engine would be to drive much faster than I should. (At the end of my day at Consumers Union, I parked the Boxster, and immediately got into my own car to drive home. In my mind, I was still at the wheel of the Boxster. Within twenty minutes, I had a two-hundred-and-seventy-one-dollar speeding ticket.) The trouble with the S.U.V. ascendancy is that it excludes the really critical component of safety: the driver.

In psychology, there is a concept called learned helplessness, which arose from a series of animal experiments in the nineteen-sixties at the University of Pennsylvania. Dogs were restrained by a harness, so that they couldn't move, and then repeatedly subjected to a series of electrical shocks. Then the same dogs were shocked again, only this time they could easily escape by jumping over a low hurdle. But most of them didn't; they just huddled in the corner, no longer believing that there was anything they could do to influence their own fate. Learned helplessness is now thought to play a role in such phenomena as depression and the failure of battered women to leave their husbands, but one could easily apply it more widely. We live in an age, after all, that is strangely fixated on the idea of helplessness: we're fascinated by hurricanes and terrorist acts and epidemics like SARS—situations in which we feel powerless to affect our own destiny. In fact, the risks posed to life and limb by forces outside our control are dwarfed by the factors we can control. Our fixation with helplessness distorts our perceptions of risk. "When you feel safe, you can be passive," Rapaille says of the fundamental appeal of the S.U.V. "Safe means I can sleep. I can give up control. I can relax. I can take off my shoes. I can listen to music." For years, we've all made fun of the middle-aged man who suddenly trades in his sedate family sedan for a shiny red sports car. That's called a midlife crisis. But at least it involves some degree of engagement with the act of driving. The man who gives up his sedate family sedan for an S.U.V. is saying something far more troubling—that he finds the demands of the road to be overwhelming. Is acting out really worse than giving up?

On August 9, 2000, the Bridgestone Firestone tire company announced one of the largest product recalls in American history. Because of mounting concerns about safety, the company said, it was replacing some fourteen million tires that had been used primarily on the Ford Explorer S.U.V. The cost of the recall—and of a follow-up replacement program initiated by Ford a year later—ran into billions of dollars. Millions more were spent by both companies on fighting and settling lawsuits from Explorer owners, who alleged that their tires had come apart and caused their S.U.V.s to roll over. In the fall of that year, senior executives from both companies were called to Capitol Hill, where they were publicly berated. It was the biggest scandal to hit the automobile industry in years. It was also one of the strangest. According to federal records, the number of fatalities resulting from the failure of a Firestone tire on a Ford Explorer S.U.V., as of September, 2001, was two hundred and seventy-one. That sounds like a lot, until you remember that the total number of tires supplied by Firestone to the Explorer from the moment the S.U.V. was introduced by Ford, in 1990, was fourteen million, and that the average life span of a tire is forty-five thousand miles. The allegation against Firestone amounts to the claim that its tires failed, with fatal results, two hundred and seventy-one times in the course of six hundred and thirty billion vehicle miles. Manufacturers usually win prizes for failure rates that low. It's also worth remembering that during that same ten-year span almost half a million Americans died in traffic accidents. In other words, during the nineteen-nineties hundreds of thousands of people were killed on the roads because they drove too fast or ran red lights or drank too much. And, of those, a fair proportion involved people in S.U.V.s who were lulled by their four-wheel drive into driving recklessly on slick roads, who drove aggressively because they felt invulnerable, who disproportionately killed those they hit because they chose to drive trucks with inflexible steel-frame architecture, and who crashed because they couldn't bring their five-thousand-pound vehicles to a halt in time. Yet, out of all those fatalities, regulators, the legal profession, Congress, and the media chose to highlight the .0005 percent that could be linked to an alleged defect in the vehicle.

But should that come as a surprise? In the age of the S.U.V., this is what people worry about when they worry about safety—not risks, however commonplace, involving their own behavior but risks, however rare, involving some unexpected event. The Explorer was big and imposing. It was high above the ground. You could look down on other drivers. You could see if someone was lurking behind or beneath it. You could drive it up on someone's lawn with impunity. Didn't it seem like the safest vehicle in the world?

Discussion Questions

1. Why were auto manufacturers in the U.S. surprised by the success of the SUV? From a marketing standpoint, why are SUVs appealing to manufacturers? To consumers?
2. Based on the statistics provided, can you draw any conclusions about safety and the size of a vehicle? What factors appear to make the biggest difference in automotive safety?
3. Gladwell states that with regard to driving safety we have shifted from an active to a passive conception of safety, and that we worry more about external elements that we perceive to be beyond our control. What does he mean by these statements? Do you agree with these ideas?

 Supporting Activities

1. Visit the Web site of Clotaire Rapaille, whose motto is "the reptilian always wins," to learn more about his approach to marketing psychology (http://www.rapailleinstitute.com/).
2. If you carry automobile or other forms of insurance, you have been impacted by the work of an actuary. Actuaries are people who calculate the financial impacts of risk and uncertainty. For one of the best overviews of what actuaries do, visit Wikipedia: http://en.wikipedia.org/wiki/Actuary.
3. Read the full text of the report by Ross and Wenzel (mentioned in the article): Ross, Marc; & Wenzel, Tom. (March 2002). *An Analysis of Traffic Deaths by Vehicle Type and Model, Report Number T021*. Washington, DC: American Council for an Energy-Efficient Economy. Available: http://www.aceee.org/pubs/t021full.pdf.
4. Research the safety ratings for the car you drive.

 Additional Resources

1. Visit Malcolm Gladwell's Web site (http://www.gladwell.com), where you can view the full text of his recent articles in *The New Yorker*, including his January 22, 1996 article about risk theory and normal accidents, "Blowup."
2. The book *The Struggle for Auto Safety* (1990) by Jerry Mashaw and David Harfst (Cambridge, MA: Harvard University Press) describes the history of legislation and efforts to regulate automotive safety in the U.S.

Shaping the Future

Echoing the concerns raised by other authors about the shortcomings of our decision-making tools, Lempert, Popper, and Bankes propose some strategies for improving these tools. The first step is acknowledging that the future is always uncertain; even the best predictions prove to be flawed. Yet from these authors' standpoint, uncertainty about the future does not mean that we should ignore long-term threats or only focus on the aspects of technological systems that we understand more completely.

The key is to generate a series of "what-if scenarios" for likely events or developments, and then to examine each of those scenarios using computer models. This approach blends the more intuitive and diverse thinking of the human mind with the capacity of computers to thoroughly analyze data associated with each scenario. In the end, we may pick the options that are the most robust for multiple potential outcomes, even in the face of uncertainties. These scenarios can be used to anticipate what the effects of various policy options would be: so-called business-as-usual or "stay the course" options; "golden carrot" or growth approaches; and so on. The authors' suggestion to establish built-in safety valves to adapt to changing future conditions, whereby a particular course of action (or policy) could be discontinued if it doesn't meet expectations, provides a flexibility that is appealing in situations where there are competing points of view about an issue.

Robert Lempert is a senior scientist at RAND Corporation, where he has led studies on climate change policy, long-term policy analysis, and science and technology investment strategies for clients such as the White House Office of Science and Technology Policy and the U.S. Department of Energy. Lempert is a member of the Council on Foreign Relations and a professor of policy analysis in the RAND Graduate School. Steven W. Popper is a senior economist at RAND and professor of science and technology policy in the RAND Graduate School. Popper has served as associate director of RAND's Science and Technology Policy Institute and has served as advisor to foreign governments and international organizations on issues relating to science and technology policy. Steven C. Bankes is a senior computer scientist at RAND. He is the originator of the computational research methodologies known as "exploratory modeling," which provide a basis for studying complex systems. Bankes is a professor at the RAND Graduate School and a member of the board of directors for the Center for Computational Social Science at UCLA. Popper, Lempert, and Bankes co-authored, among other publications, the book *Shaping the Next One Hundred Years: New Methods for Quantitative, Long-Term Policy Analysis* (2003), which can be read in its entirety on the Rand Corporation Web site.

Shaping the Future

By Steven W. Popper, Robert J. Lempert, and Steven C. Bankes

Last year a high-profile panel of experts known as the Copenhagen Consensus ranked the world's most pressing environmental, health and social problems in a prioritized list. Assembled by the Danish Environmental Assessment Institute under its then director, Bjørn Lomborg, the panel used cost-benefit analysis to evaluate where a limited amount of money would do the most good. It concluded that the highest priority should go to immediate concerns with relatively well understood cures, such as control of malaria. Long-term chal-

Reprinted by permission. Copyright © 2005 by Scientific American, Inc. All rights reserved.

lenges such as climate change, where the path forward and even the scope of the threat remain unclear, ranked lower.

Usually each of these problems is treated in isolation, as though humanity had the luxury of dealing with its problems one by one. The Copenhagen Consensus used state-of-the-art techniques to try to bring a broader perspective. In so doing, however, it revealed how the state of the art fails to grapple with a simple fact: the future is uncertain. Attempts to predict it have a checkered history—from declarations that humans would never fly, to the doom-and-gloom economic and environmental forecasts of the 1970s, to claims that the "New Economy" would do away with economic ups and downs. Not surprisingly, those who make decisions tend to stay focused on the next fiscal quarter, the next year, the next election. Feeling unsure of their compass, they hug the familiar shore.

This understandable response to an uncertain future means, however, that the nation's and the world's long-term threats often get ignored altogether or are even made worse by shortsighted decisions. In everyday life, responsible people look out for the long term despite the needs of the here and now: we do homework, we save for retirement, we take out insurance. The same principles should surely apply to society as a whole. But how can leaders weigh the present against the future? How can they avoid being paralyzed by scientific uncertainty?

In well-understood situations, science can reliably predict the implications of alternative policy choices. These predictions, combined with formal methods of decision analysis that use mathematical models and statistical methods to determine optimal courses of action, can specify the trade-offs that society must inevitably make. Corporate executives and elected officials may not always heed this advice, but they do so more often than a cynic might suppose. Analysis has done much to improve the quality

of lawmaking, regulation and investment. National economic policy is one example. Concepts introduced by analysts in the 1930s and 1940s—unemployment rate, current-account deficit and gross national product—are now commonplace. For the most part, governments have learned to avoid the radical boom-and-bust cycles that were common in the 19th and early 20th centuries.

The trouble now is that the world faces a number of challenges, both long- and short-term, that are far from well understood: how to preserve the environment, ensure the future of Social Security, guard against terrorism and manage the effects of novel technology. These problems are simply too complex and contingent for scientists to make definitive predictions. In the presence of such deep uncertainty, the machinery of prediction and decision making seizes up. Traditional analytical approaches gravitate to the well-understood parts of the challenge and shy away from the rest. Hence, even sophisticated analyses such as the one by the Copenhagen Consensus have trouble assessing the value of near-term steps that might shape our long-term future.

The three of us—an economist, a physicist and a computer scientist all working in RAND's Pardee Center—have been fundamentally rethinking the role of analysis. We have constructed rigorous, systematic methods for dealing with deep uncertainty. The basic idea is to liberate ourselves from the need for precise prediction by using the computer to help frame strategies that work well over a very wide range of plausible futures. Rather than seeking to eliminate uncertainty, we highlight it and then find ways to manage it. Already companies such as Volvo have used our techniques to plan corporate strategy.

The methods offer a way to break the ideological logjam that too often arises in Washington, D.C. By allowing decision makers to explore a rich variety of what-if scenarios, the new approach reframes the age-old but unanswerable question—What will the long-term future bring?—to one better reflecting our real concern: What actions today will best shape the future to our liking?

The Perils of Prediction

Striking a balance between the economy and the environment is one leading example of the difficulty in using science to inform long-term decisions. In his 2002 book *The Future of Life*, Edward O. Wilson described the debate between economists and environmental scientists [see "The Bottleneck," by Edward O. Wilson; *Scientific American*, February 2002]. The former group frequently argues that present policies will guide society successfully through the coming century. Technological innovation will reduce pollution and improve energy efficiency, and changes in commodity prices will ensure timely switching from scarce to more plentiful resources. The latter group argues that society's present course will prove unsustainable. By the time the signs of environmental stress become unambiguous, society may have passed the point of easy recovery. Better to apply the brakes now rather than jam them on later when it may be too late.

No matter how compelling their arguments, both sides' detailed predictions are surely wrong. Decisions made today will affect the world 50 to 100 years hence, but no one can credibly predict what life will be like then, regardless of the quality of the science. Interested parties view the same incomplete data, apply different values and assumptions, and arrive at different conclusions. The result can be static and acrimonious debate: "Tree hugger!" "Eco-criminal!"

The (in)famous report *The Limits to Growth* from the early 1970s is the perfect ex-ample of how the standard tools of analysis often fail to mediate such debates. A group of scientists and opinion leaders called the Club of Rome predicted that the world would soon exhaust its natural resources unless it took immediate action to slow their use. This conclusion flowed from a then state-of-the-art computer model of the dynamics of resource use. The report met with great skepticism. Since the days of Thomas Malthus, impending resource shortages have melted away as new technologies have made production more efficient and provided alternatives to dwindling resources.

But the model was not wrong; it was just used incorrectly. Any computer model is, by definition, a simplified mirror of the real world, its predictions vulnerable to some neglected factor. The model developed for *The Limits to Growth* revealed some important aspects of the challenges faced by society. In presenting the analysis as a forecast, the authors stretched the model beyond its limits and reduced the credibility of their entire research program.

Grappling with the Future

Conscious of this failing, analysts have turned to techniques such as scenario planning that involve exploring different possible futures rather than gambling on a single prediction. As an example, in 1995 the Global Scenario Group, convened by the Stockholm Environment Institutes, developed three scenario families. The "Conventional Worlds" family described a future in which technological innovation, driven by markets and lightly steered by government policy, produces economic growth without undermining environmental quality. In the "Barbarization" set of scenarios, the same factors—innovation, markets and policy—prove inadequate to the challenge, leading to social collapse and the spread of violence and misery. The third set, "Great Transitions," portrayed the widespread adoption of eco-friendly social values. The Global Scenario Group argued that the Conventional Worlds scenarios are plausible but not guaranteed; to avoid the risk of Barbarization, society should follow the Great Transitions paths.

Although scenario analysis avoids making definite predictions, it has its own shortcomings. It addresses no more than a handful of the many plausible futures, so skeptics can always question the choice of the highlighted few. More fundamentally, scenario families do not translate easily into plans for action. How should decision makers use the scenarios? Should they focus on the most threatening case or the one regarded by experts as most likely? Each approach has faults.

The European Union often favors the "precautionary principle"—in essence, basing policy on the most hazardous plausible scenarios. The Kyoto treaty on climate change, for example, requires reductions of greenhouse gas emissions even though their long-term effects are far from understood. On one level, the precautionary principle makes perfect sense. It is better to be safe than sorry. The long-term future will always be cloudy; some dangers may become certain only when it is too late to prevent them. Yet the principle is an imperfect guide. The future presents many potential harms. Should we worry about them all equally? Few choices are risk-free, and the precautionary principle can lead to contradictory conclusions. For instance, both the harm from greenhouse gas emissions and the cost of reducing them are uncertain. To safeguard the environment, we should reduce the emissions now. To safeguard the economy, we should postpone reductions. So what do we do?

In contrast, many in the U.S. favor cost-benefit analysis, which balances the benefits of eliminating each potential harm against the costs of doing so. When outcomes are uncertain, cost-benefit analysis weights them with odds. We should be willing to pay up to $500 to eliminate a $1,000 harm whose chance of occurring is 50–50. Cost-benefit analysis provides unambiguous answers in many instances. Lead in gasoline enters the environment and affects the developing brains of children. Even though scientists do not know precisely how many children are affected, the benefit of removing lead from gasoline far exceeds the cost. But the long-term future rarely offers such clear choices. Often both the costs and benefits are sufficiently unclear that small disagreements over assigning odds can make a huge difference in the recommended policy.

Making Policies Robust

Traditional tools such as cost-benefit analysis rely on a "predict then act" paradigm. They require a prediction of the future before they can determine the policy that will work best under the expected circumstances. Because these analyses demand that everyone agree on the models and assumptions, they cannot resolve many of the most crucial debates that our society faces. They force people to select one among many plausible, competing views of the future. Whichever choice emerges is vulnerable to blunders and surprises.

Our approach is to look not for optimal strategies but for robust ones. A robust strategy performs well when compared with the alternatives across a wide range of plausible futures. It need not be the optimal strategy in any future; it will, however, yield satisfactory outcomes in both easy-to-envision futures and hard-to-anticipate contingencies.

This approach replicates the way people often reason about complicated and uncertain decisions in everyday life. The late Herbert A. Simon, a cognitive scientist and Nobel laureate who pioneered in the 1950s the study of how people make real-world decisions, observed that they seldom optimize. Rather they seek strategies that will work well enough, that include hedges against various potential outcomes and that are adaptive. Tomorrow will bring information unavailable today; therefore, people plan on revising their plans.

Incorporating robustness and adaptability into formal decision analysis used to be impossible because of the complexity and vast number of required calculations. Technology has overcome these hurdles. Confronting deep uncertainty requires more than raw computational power, though. The computers have to be used differently. Traditional predict-then-act methods treat the computer as a glorified calculator. Analysts select the model and specify the assumptions; the computer then calculates the optimal strategy implied by these inputs.

In contrast, for robust decision making the computer is integral to the reasoning process. It stress-tests candidate strategies, searching for plausible scenarios that could defeat them. Robust decision making interactively combines the complementary abilities of humans and machines. People excel at seeking patterns, drawing inferences and framing new questions. But they can fail to recognize inconvenient facts and can lose track of how long chains of causes relate to effects. The machine ensures that all claims about strategies are consistent with the data and can reveal scenarios that challenge people's cherished assumptions. No strategy is completely immune to uncertainty, but the computer helps decision makers exploit whatever information they do have to make choices that can endure a wide range of trends and surprises.

BALANCING THE ECONOMY AND THE ENVIRONMENT

How can we clean the planet over the coming century without breaking the bank? The answer depends on how fast the economy will grow and how much existing trends and regulations will cut pollution—and nobody knows either of those things. Many proposed approaches (*left* and *center*) would strike a good balance for some growth rates but not for others, whereas a flexible strategy (*right*) could handle a wide range of scenarios. In the graphs below, shaded boxes correspond to particular future rates of growth and "decoupling" (the pace at which existing trends cut pollution). The shades represent how the strategy compares with the theoretically optimal strategy for each scenario: perfectly (■); acceptably (■); poorly (■); or very poorly (■). Dots represent historical rates, which may provide some clue for what is to come.

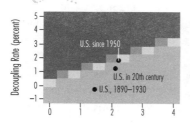

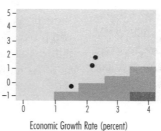

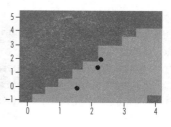

Stay the course adds no new environmental policies. It is a good approach if the decoupling rate is high; otherwise, a poor one.

Crash program is an all-out effort to clean up. It justifies itself only if the decoupling rate turns out to be naturally very low.

Safety valve sets a goal for cutting pollution but relaxes the deadline if the cost runs too high. It works in almost every plausible case.

Sustainable Development

To see how this approach works in practice, return to the dilemma of sustainable development. The first step is to figure out what exactly the computer should calculate. Robust decision making requires the machine to generate multiple paths into the future, spanning the full diversity of those that might occur. We may not know the exact future that will transpire, but any strategy that performs well across a sufficiently diverse set of computer-generated scenarios is likely to meet the challenges presented by what actually comes to pass.

In our analysis of sustainable development, we used a revised version of the Wonderland model originally created by economist Warren C. Sanderson of Stony Brook University and the International Institute for Applied Systems Analysis in Laxenburg, Austria. The Wonderland simulation incorporates, in a very simple manner, scientific understanding of the dynamics of the global economy, demographics and environment. Growing population and wealth will increase pollution, whereas technological innovation may reduce it. The pollution, in turn, hurts the economy when it taxes the environment beyond its absorptive capacity.

Our version of Wonderland is similar to—but with only 41 uncertain parameters, much simpler than—the simulation used for *The Limits to Growth*. This simplicity can be a virtue: experience demonstrates that additional detail alone does not make predictions more accurate if the model's structure or inputs remain uncertain. For robust planning, models should be used not to predict but to produce a diversity of scenarios, all consistent with the knowledge we do possess.

Running models within special "exploratory modeling" software, analysts can test various strategies and see how they perform. The human user suggests a strategy; for each scenario in the ensemble, the computer compares this approach to the optimal strategy (the one that would have been chosen with perfect predictive foresight) according to such measures as income or life expectancy. A systematic process reveals futures in which the proposed strategies could perform poorly. It also highlights ways each strategy could be adjusted to handle those stressful futures better.

In the sustainability example, we run the model through the year 2100. Two key uncertainties are the average global economic growth rate during this period and the business-as-usual "decoupling rate" (that is, the reduction in pollution per unit of economic output that would occur in the absence of new environmental policies). The decoupling rate will be positive if existing regulations, productivity increases and the shift to a service economy lessen pollution without lessening growth. It can go negative if growth requires an increase in pollution.

Depending on the values of these quantities, different strategies perform differently. One strategy, "Stay the Course," simply continues present policy. It performs well in futures where the decoupling rate exceeds the growth rate, but if the reverse is true, pollution eventually becomes so serious that policymakers are forced to abandon the strategy and try to reverse the damage. During the 20th century, the growth and decoupling rates were nearly equal. If the same proves to be true for the 21st, the world will totter on a knife-edge between success and failure (*see box on the previous page*).

The more aggressive "Crash Program" pours money into technological development and environmental regulations that speed decoupling beyond its business-as-usual rate. Although this strategy eliminates the risk of catastrophe, it can impose unnecessarily high costs, inhibiting economic growth.

Becoming Flexible

Both these strategies involve policies that are fixed in advance. An adaptive strategy bests them both. Inspired by the complementary strengths and weaknesses of "Stay the Course" and "Crash Program," we considered a flexible alternative that imposes rigorous emissions limits but relaxes them if they cost too much. Such a strategy can be robust. If the technological optimists are right (the decoupling rate turns out to be high), the cost threshold is never breached and industry meets the aggressive environmental goals. If technological pessimists prove correct (the decoupling rate is low), then tight pollution restrictions will exceed the agreed-on cost limits, in which case the strategy gives industry more time to meet the goals.

Such strategies can help cut through contentious debates by providing plans of action that all can agree will play out no matter whose view of the future proves correct. Our adaptive strategy is similar to the "safety valve" strategies that some economists have proposed as alternatives to the immutable emissions targets in the Kyoto treaty. Our new analytical machinery enables decision makers both to design such strategies and to demonstrate their effectiveness to the various interest groups involved.

Of course, even adaptive strategies have their Achilles' heel. In the case of the safety valve, the combination of environmental goals and cost constraints that works best in most futures performs poorly when technological innovation proves to be extremely expensive. To get around this problem, the user can repeat the analysis to come up with a variety of robust strategies, each of which breaks down under different conditions. One strategy may work well when another fails, and vice versa, so the choice between them involves an unavoidable trade-off. The computer calculates how likely each set of circumstances would have to be to justify picking one strategy over the other. Our method thus reduces a complex problem to a small number of simple choices. Decision makers make the final call. Instead of fruitlessly debating models and other assumptions, they can focus on the fundamental trade-offs, fully aware of the surprises that the future may bring.

Clearly, this approach is applicable not only to sustainable development but also to a wide range of other challenges: bringing new products to market, managing the nation's entitlement programs, even defeating terrorism. Science and technology cannot change the future's fundamental unpredictability. Instead they offer an answer to a different question: Which actions today can best usher in a desirable future? Humans and computers search for plausible futures in which a proposed strategy could fail and then identify means to avoid these potential adverse outcomes.

Past failures of prediction should humble anyone who claims to see a clear course into the decades ahead. Paradoxically, though, our greatest possible influence in shaping the future may extend precisely over those timescales where our gaze becomes most dim. We often have little effect on a predictable, near-term future subject to well-understood forces. Where the future is ill defined, unpredictable and hardest to see, our actions today may well have their most profound effects. New tools can help us chart the right course.

Discussion Questions

1. What are some of the shortcomings of scenario analysis as a decision making tool?
2. These authors recommend that we seek out "robust" strategies rather than optimal strategies when establishing policy to address long-term problems. What do they mean by this?
3. In the sustainability example provided by the authors, they describe a "stay the course" and a "crash program" strategy. To what does each of these refer? Think of a modern example to illustrate each of these policy approaches.

Supporting Activities

1. Find a set of predictions about society and technology that were made 20, 50, or 100 years ago and identify those that proved to be correct; those that came to pass but that evolved in different ways than predicted; and those that have never transpired. One place to start is the Club of Rome "Limits to Growth" report mentioned in this article.
2. Review an example of a scenario analysis that identifies various policy options and then makes projections for the future for each scenario. For one example, read the Summary section of *Building Energy Efficiency* (May 1992), U.S. Congress Office of Technology Assessment, which can be found at: http://www.fas.org/ota/reports/9204.pdf.

Additional Resources

1. For a technical description of the Wonderland simulation model, see: Herbert, Ric; & Leeves, Gareth. (1998). "Troubles in Wonderland." Complexity International, Volume 6. Available: http://www.complexity.org.au/ci/vol06/herbert/herbert.html.
2. Read a RAND Corporation scenario analysis by Richard Silberglitt and Anders Hove focused on the future of energy: http://www.rand.org/scitech/stpi/Evision/Supplement/scenario.pdf.
3. Read a Powerpoint slide show that provides a user-friendly overview of probabilistic scenario analysis by David Oryang (2002), available at: http://www.nappo.org/PRA-Symposium/PDF-Final/Oryang.pdf.

While Washington Slept

Predictions about global climate change are widespread and varied. In most cases, they anticipate what the effects of one, two, and three degree or higher increases in average global temperatures might mean on weather patterns, melting ice caps, water levels, and so on. Although the scientific evidence is compelling, the lack of absolute certainty about causes and effects has hampered global responses to the problem. Thus, in spite of international efforts like the Kyoto Protocol, first adopted in December 1997 and since ratified by 184 parties, human-generated greenhouse gas emissions continue to rise.

In this article, Mark Hertsgaard provides background information on climate change and the responses to this issue within the U.S., particularly as contrasted with those adopted by other countries. His reporting provides an interesting case study on the circuitous route that policy discussions can take, as well as information about what the ramifications of global climate change might be.

Mark Hertsgaard is an independent journalist based in San Francisco and the author of five books, including *Earth Odyssey: Around the World in Search of our Environmental Future* (1998), *Nuclear, Inc.: The Men and the Money Behind Nuclear Energy* (1983), and the forthcoming *Living Through the Storm: Our Future Under Global Warming*. He has written hundreds of articles for a variety of magazines and newspapers worldwide.

While Washington Slept

By Mark Hertsgaard

Ten months before Hurricane Katrina left much of New Orleans underwater, Queen Elizabeth II had a private conversation with Prime Minister Tony Blair about George W. Bush. The Queen's tradition of meeting once a week with Britain's elected head of government to discuss matters of state—usually on Tuesday evenings in Buckingham Palace and always alone, to ensure maximum confidentiality—goes back to 1952, the year she ascended the throne. In all that time, the contents of those chats rarely if ever leaked.

So it was extraordinary when London's *Observer* reported, on October 31, 2004, that the Queen had "made a rare intervention in world politics" by telling Blair of "her grave concerns over the White House's stance on global warming." *The Observer* did not name its sources, but one of them subsequently spoke to *Vanity Fair*.

"The Queen first of all made it clear that Buckingham Palace would be happy to help raise awareness about the climate problem," says the source, a high-level environmental expert who was briefed about the conversation. "[She was] definitely concerned about the American position and hoped the prime minister could help change [it]."

Press aides for both the Queen and the prime minister declined to comment on the meeting, as is their habit. But days after the *Observer* story appeared, the Queen indeed raised awareness by presiding over the opening of a British-German conference on climate change, in Berlin. "I might just point out, that's a pretty unusual thing for her to do," says Sir David King, Britain's chief scientific adviser. "She doesn't take part in anything that would be

From *Vanity Fair, May 2006* by Mark Hertsgaard. Copyright © 2006 by Mark Hertsgaard. Reprinted by permission.

overtly political." King, who has briefed the Queen on climate change, would not comment on the *Observer* report except to say, "If it were true, it wouldn't surprise me."

With spring arriving in England three weeks earlier than it did 50 years ago, the Queen could now see signs of climate change with her own eyes. Sandringham, her country estate north of London, overlooks Britain's premier bird-watching spot: the vast North Sea wetlands known as the Wash. A lifelong outdoorswoman, the Queen had doubtless observed the V-shaped flocks of pink-footed geese that descend on the Wash every winter. But in recent years, says Mark Avery, conservation director of the Royal Society for the Protection of Birds, she also would have seen a species new to the area: little egrets. These shiny white birds are native to Southern Europe, Avery says, "but in the last 5 to 10 years they have spread very rapidly to Northern Europe. We can't prove this is because of rising temperatures, but it sure looks like it."

Temperatures are rising, the Queen learned from King and other scientists, because greenhouse gases are trapping heat in the atmosphere. Carbon dioxide, the most prevalent of such gases, is released whenever fossil fuels are burned or forests catch fire. Global warming, the scientists explained, threatens to raise sea levels as much as three feet by the end of the 21st century, thanks to melting glaciers and swollen oceans. (Water expands when heated.)

This would leave much of eastern England, including areas near Sandringham, underwater. Global warming would also bring more heat waves like the one in the summer of 2003 that killed 31,000 people across Europe. It might even shut down the Gulf Stream, the flow of warm water from the Gulf of Mexico that gives Europe its mild climate. If the Gulf Stream were to halt—and it has already slowed 30 percent since 1992—Europe's temperatures would

plunge, agriculture would collapse, London would no longer feel like New York but like Anchorage.

The Queen, says King, "got it" on climate change, and she wasn't alone. "Everyone in this country, from the political parties to the scientific establishment, to the Archbishop of Canterbury, to our oil companies and the larger business community, has come to a popular consensus about climate change—a sense of alarm and a conviction that action is needed now, not in the future," says Tony Juniper, executive director of the British arm of the environmental group Friends of the Earth.

At the time of his meeting with the Queen, Blair was being attacked on climate change from all ideological sides, with even the Conservatives charging that he was not doing enough. Yet Blair's statements on the issue went far beyond those of most world leaders. He had called the Kyoto Protocol, which has been ratified by 162 countries and requires industrial nations to reduce greenhouse-gas emissions 5 percent below 1990 levels, "not radical enough." The world's climate scientists, Blair pointed out, had estimated that 60 percent cuts in emissions were needed, and he committed Britain to reaching that goal by 2050.

But it wouldn't matter how much Britain cut its greenhouse-gas emissions if other nations didn't do the same. The U.S. was key, not only because it was the world's largest emitter but because its refusal to reduce emissions led China, India, Brazil, and other large developing countries to ask why they should do so. All this Blair had also said publicly. In 2001 he criticized the Bush administration for withdrawing from the Kyoto Protocol. In 2004 he said it was essential to bring the U.S. into the global effort against climate change, despite its opposition to Kyoto.

It was no secret that Bush opposed mandatory emissions limits, but Blair, who had risked his political future to back the deeply unpopular war in Iraq, was uniquely positioned to lobby the president. Bush owed him one. At the same time, Blair needed to show his domestic audience that he could stand up to Bush, that he wasn't the presidential "poodle" his critics claimed.

To compel Bush to engage the issue, Blair made climate change a lead agenda item at the July 2005 meeting of the Group of 8, the alliance of the world's eight richest nations. A month before the meeting, which was held at Gleneagles, in Scotland, Blair flew to Washington to see Bush face-to-face. That same day, the national academies of science of all the G-8 nations, as well as those of China, India, and Brazil, released a joint statement declaring that climate change was a grave problem that required immediate action.

On the morning of July 7, the summit was interrupted by the shocking news that four suicide bombers had set off explosions in London, killing 56 people. Blair rushed to the scene, but he returned that night, still determined to secure an agreement.

In the end, however, Bush held firm. Washington vetoed all references to mandatory emissions cuts or timelines, and the climate-change issue was overshadowed by African debt relief, which had been publicized by Bob Geldof's Live 8 concerts.

"There were no tough targets at Gleneagles because we would not have got all signatures on the document," says King, who adds, "We might well have" gotten seven—that is, every nation but the U.S. The farthest the G-8 leaders went—and even this required a battle, says King—was to include a sentence that read, in part, "While uncertainties remain in our understanding of climate science, we know enough to act now."

But seven weeks later, nature acted first, and it was the United States she hit.

No one can say for sure whether global warming caused Hurricane Katrina, which slammed into the Gulf Coast on August 29, 2005. But it certainly fit the pattern. The scientific rule of thumb is that one can never blame any one weather event on any single cause. The earth's weather system is too complex for that. Most scientists agree, however, that global warming makes extra-strong hurricanes such as Katrina more likely because it encourages hot oceans, a precondition of hurricane formation.

"It's a bit like saying, 'My grandmother died of lung cancer, and she smoked for the last 20 years of her life—smoking killed her,'" explains Kerry Emanuel, a professor at the Massachusetts Institute of Technology who has studied hurricanes for 20 years. "Well, the problem is, there are an awful lot of people who die of lung cancer who never smoked. There are a lot of people who smoked all their lives and die of something else. So all you can say, even [though] the evidence statistically is clear connecting lung cancer to smoking, is that [the grandmother] upped her probability."

Just weeks before Katrina struck, Emanuel published a paper in the scientific journal *Nature* demonstrating that hurricanes had grown more powerful as global temperatures rose in the 20th century. Now, he says, by adding more greenhouse gases to the earth's atmosphere, humans are "loading the climatic dice in favor of more powerful hurricanes in the future."

But most Americans heard nothing about Hurricane Katrina's association with global warming. Media coverage instead reflected the views of the Bush administration—specifically, the National Oceanic and Atmospheric Administration, which declared that the hurricane was the result of natural factors. An outcry from

N.O.A.A.'s scientists led the agency to backtrack from that statement in February 2006, but by then conventional wisdom was set in place. Post-Katrina New Orleans may eventually be remembered as the first major U.S. casualty of global warming, yet most Americans still don't know what hit us.

Sad to say, Katrina was the perfect preview of what global warming might look like in the 21st century. First, Katrina struck a city that was already below sea level—which is where rising waters could put many coastal dwellers in the years ahead. In 2001, the U.N.-sponsored Intergovernmental Panel on Climate Change (I.P.C.C.), a peer-reviewed, international collaboration among thousands of scientists that is the world's leading authority on climate change, predicted that sea levels could rise as much as three feet by 2100. By coincidence, three feet is about how much New Orleans sank during the 20th century. That was because levees built to keep the Mississippi River from flooding also kept the river from depositing silt that would have replenished the underlying land mass, explains Mike Tidwell, the author of *Bayou Farewell: The Rich Life and Tragic Death of Louisiana's Cajun Coast*. "You could say that in New Orleans we brought the ocean to the people," Tidwell adds, "which is pretty much what global warming will do to other cities in the future."

What's more, Katrina was a Category 5 hurricane, the strongest there is. Such extreme weather events will likely become more frequent as global warming intensifies, says the I.P.C.C. Yes, Katrina's winds had slowed to high-Category 3 levels by the time it made landfall, but it was the hurricane's storm surge that killed people—a surge that formed in the Gulf of Mexico when the storm was still Category 5. Thus, Katrina unleashed 10 to 15 feet of water on a city that was already significantly below sea level.

To envision global warming's future impacts, the illustrations found within the May 2006 issue of *Vanity Fair* reflect this and other scenarios. The three large-scale illustrations are an artist's interpretations of projections generated for *Vanity Fair* by Applied Science Associates Inc. (appsci.com), a marine-science consulting firm based in Rhode Island. The projections do not account for small-scale features such as coastal-protection structures.

The effects of a three-foot sea-level rise compounded by a storm surge from a Category 3 hurricane are shown in the image of the Hamptons, which would suffer severe flooding. The image of Washington, D.C., shows the effects of a 20-foot sea-level rise, which is what scientists expect if the entire Greenland ice sheet melts. The ice sheet has shrunk 50 cubic miles in the past year alone, and is now melting twice as fast as previously believed.

Finally, the image of New York City shows the effects of an 80-foot rise in sea levels. That's what would happen if not only the Greenland ice sheet but its counterpart in the Antarctic were to melt, says James Hansen, the director of NASA's Goddard Institute for Space Studies. Hansen, who put climate change on the media map in 1988 by saying that man-made global warming had already begun, made headlines again earlier this year when he complained that White House political appointees were trying to block him from speaking freely about the need for rapid reductions in greenhouse-gas emissions. Hansen warns that, if global emissions continue on their current trajectory, the ice sheets will not survive, because global temperatures will increase by 2 to 3 degrees Celsius by the end of this century. "The last time the earth was that warm, sea levels were 80 feet higher than today," he says. It will likely take hundreds of years for sea levels to rise the full 80 feet, but the process would be irreversible, and the rises would not be gradual. "You're going to be continually faced with a changing coastline, which will force coastal dwellers to constantly relocate," he says.

This article's smaller, aerial-view illustrations are based on simulations by the National Environmental Trust, a nonprofit group in Washington, D.C. N.E.T. relied on data from the I.P.C.C., the U.S. Geological Survey, and the N.O.A.A. Additional N.E.T. simulations are available at net.org. Philip Clapp, N.E.T.'s president, says, "The U.S. government has never released its own simulations. The Bush administration doesn't want these pictures in front of the American people because they show that a three-foot sea-level rise plus storm flooding would have catastrophic consequences."

In New York, it would leave much of Lower Manhattan, including the Ground Zero memorial and the entire financial district, underwater. La Guardia and John F. Kennedy airports would meet the same fate. In Washington, D.C., the Potomac River would swell dramatically, stretching all the way to the Capitol lawn and to within two blocks of the White House.

Since roughly half the world's 6.5 billion people live near coastlines, a three-foot sea-level rise would be even more punishing overseas. Amsterdam, Venice, Cairo, Shanghai, Manila, and Calcutta are some of the cities most threatened. In many places the people and governments are too poor to erect adequate barriers—think of low-lying Bangladesh, where an estimated 18 million people are at risk—so experts fear that they will migrate to neighboring lands, raising the prospect of armed conflict. A Pentagon-commissioned study warned in 2003 that climate change could bring megadroughts, mass starvation, and even nuclear war as countries such as China, India, and Pakistan battle over scarce food and water.

These are just some of the reasons why David King wrote in *Science* in 2004, "Climate change is the most severe problem that we are facing today—more serious even than the threat of terrorism." King's comment raised hackles in Washington and led a top press aide to Tony Blair to try to muzzle him. But the science adviser tells me he "absolutely" stands by his statement. By no means does King underestimate terrorism; advising the British government on that threat, he says, "is a very important part of my job." But the hazards presented by climate change are so severe and far-reaching that, in his view, they overshadow not only every other environmental threat but every other threat, period.

"Take India," King says. "Their monsoon is a fact of life that they have developed their agricultural economy around. If the monsoon is down by 10 percent one year, they have massive losses of crops. If it's 10 percent over, they have massive flood problems. [If climate change ends up] switching off the monsoon in India, or even changing it outside those limits, it would lead to massive global economic de-stabilization. The kind of situation we need to avoid creating is one where populations are so de-stabilized—Bangladesh being flooded, India no food—that they're all seeking alternative habitats. These, in our globalized economy, would be very difficult for all of us to manage."

The worst scenarios of global warming might still be avoided, scientists say, if humanity reduces its greenhouse-gas emissions dramatically, and very soon. The I.P.C.C. has estimated that emissions must fall to 60 percent below 1990 levels before 2050, over a period when global population is expected to increase by 37 percent and per-capita energy consumption will surely rise as billions of people in Asia, Africa, and South America strive to ascend from poverty.

Yet even if such a reduction were achieved, a significant rise in sea levels may be unavoidable. "It's getting harder and harder to say we'll avoid a three-foot sea-level rise, though it won't necessarily happen in this century," says Michael Oppenheimer, a professor of geosciences and international affairs at Princeton. Oppenheimer's pessimism is rooted in the lag effects of the climate system: oceans store heat for a century or longer before releasing it; carbon dioxide remains in the atmosphere for decades or longer before dissipating.

According to King, even if humanity were to stop emitting carbon dioxide today, "temperatures will keep rising and all the impacts will keep changing for about 25 years."

The upshot is that it has become too late to prevent climate change; we can only adapt to it. This unhappy fact is not well understood by the general public; advocates downplay it, perhaps for fear of fostering a paralyzing despair. But there is no getting around it: because humanity waited so long to take decisive action, we are now stuck with a certain amount of global warming and the climate changes it will bring—rising seas, fiercer heat, deeper droughts, stronger storms. The World Health Organization estimates that climate change is already helping to kill 150,000 people a year, mainly in Africa and Asia. That number is bound to rise as global warming intensifies in the years ahead.

The inevitability of global warming does not mean we should not act, King emphasizes: "The first message to our political leaders is, action is required. Whether or not we get global agreement to reduce emissions, we all need to adapt to the impacts that are in the pipeline." That means doing all the things that were not done in New Orleans: building sound levees and seawalls, restoring coastal wetlands (which act like speed bumps to weaken hurricanes' storm surges), strengthening emergency-preparedness networks and health-care systems, and much more.

Beyond this crucial first step—which most governments worldwide have yet to consider—humanity can cushion the severity of future global warming by limiting greenhouse-gas emissions. Hansen says we must stabilize emissions—which currently are rising 2 percent a year—by 2015, and then reduce them. *Avoiding Dangerous Climate Change*, a book based on a scientific conference convened by Tony Blair before the G-8 summit, estimates that we may have until 2025 to peak and reduce.

The goal is to stop global warming before it crosses tipping points and attains unstoppable momentum from "positive feedbacks." For example, should the Greenland ice sheet melt, white ice—which reflects sunlight back into space—would be replaced by dark water, which absorbs sunlight and drives further warming.

Positive feedbacks can trigger the kind of abrupt, irreversible climate changes that scientists call "nonlinear." Once again, Hurricane Katrina provides a sobering preview of what that means. "Hurricanes are the mother of all nonlinear events, because small changes in initial conditions can lead to enormous changes in outcomes," says Hans Joachim Schellnhuber, the director of the Potsdam Institute for Climate Impact Research and the former chief environmental adviser to the German government. "A few percent increase in a hurricane's wind speed can double its destructiveness under certain circumstances."

Although scientists apply the neutral term "climate change" to all of these phenomena, "climate chaos" better conveys the abrupt, interconnected, wide-ranging consequences that lie in store. "It's a very appropriate term for the layperson," says Schellnhuber, a physicist who specializes in chaos theory. "I keep telling politicians that I'm not so concerned about a gradual climate change that may force farmers in Great Britain to plant different crops. I'm worried about triggering positive feedbacks that, in the worst case, could kick off some type of runaway greenhouse dynamics."

Among the reasons climate change is a bigger problem than terrorism, David King tells me, is that the problem is rooted in humanity's burning of oil, coal, and natural gas, "and people don't want to let that go." Which is understandable. These carbon-based fuels have powered civilization since the dawn of the industrial era, delivering enormous wealth, convenience, and well-being even as they overheated the atmosphere. Luckily, the idea that reducing greenhouse-gas emissions will wreck our economy, as President Bush said in 2005 when defending his opposition to the Kyoto Protocol, is disproved by experience. "In Britain," King told the environmental Web site Grist, "our economy since 1990 has grown by about 40 percent, and our emissions have decreased by 14 percent."

Ultimately, society must shift onto a new energy foundation based on alternative fuels, not only because of global warming but also because oil "will get harder and costlier to find" in the years ahead, says Ronald Oxburgh, the former chairman of the British arm of Royal Dutch Shell oil. "The group around President Bush have been saying that, even if climate change is real, it would be terribly costly to shift away from carbon-based fuels," Oxburgh continues. "Of course it would, if you try to make the change overnight. But that's not how you do it. If governments make the decision to shift our society to a new energy foundation, and they make it clear to everyone this is what we're doing by laying out clear requirements and incentives, corporations will respond and get the job done."

The opening move in this transition is to invest massively in energy efficiency. Amory Lovins, co-founder of the Rocky Mountain Institute, a think tank that consults for corporations and governments around the world, has demon-strated that measures such as insulating buildings and driving more fuel-efficient vehicles could reduce humanity's consumption of energy and natural resources by a factor of four. And efficiency investments have a demonstrated record of creating jobs and boosting profits, suggesting that emissions can be reduced without crippling economies.

One of the first moves Angela Merkel announced as the new chancellor of Germany last fall was the extension of a Green Party initiative to upgrade energy efficiency in the nation's pre-1978 housing stock. Most of that housing is in the former East Germany, where unemployment approaches 20 percent. Replacing old furnaces and installing efficient windows and lights will produce thousands of well-paying laborers' jobs that by their nature cannot be outsourced.

Corporations, too, have discovered that energy efficiency can be profitable. Over a three-year period beginning in 1999, BP invested $20 million to reduce the emissions from its internal operations and saved $650 million—32 times the original investment.

Individuals can cash in as well. Although buying a super-efficient car or refrigerator may cost more up front, over time it saves the consumer money through lower energy bills.

Efficiency is no silver bullet, nor can it forever neutralize the effects of billions of people consuming more and more all the time. It can, however, buy humanity time to further develop and deploy alternative-energy technologies. Solar and wind power have made enormous strides in recent years, but the technology to watch is carbon sequestration, a method of capturing and then safely storing the carbon dioxide produced by the combustion of fossil fuels. In theory, sequestration would allow nations to continue burning coal—the most abundant fuel in the world, and the foundation of the Chinese and Indian economies—without worsening the climate problem. "If carbon capture is not feasible, our choices are much less good, and the cost of climate change is going to be much higher," says Jeffrey D. Sachs, the director of the Earth Institute at Columbia University and a special adviser to the United Nations.

No one pretends that phasing out carbon-based fuels will be easy. The momentum of the climate system means that "a certain amount of pain is inevitable," says Michael Oppenheimer. "But we still have a choice between pain and disaster."

Unfortunately, we are getting a late start, which is something of a puzzle. The threat of global warming has been recognized at the highest levels of government for more than 25 years. Former president Jimmy Carter highlighted it in 1980, and Al Gore championed it in Congress throughout the 1980s. Margaret Thatcher, the arch-conservative prime minister of Britain from 1979 to 1990, delivered some of the hardest-hitting speeches ever given on climate change. But progress stalled in the 1990s, even as Gore was elected vice president and the scientific case grew definitive. It turned out there were powerful pockets of resistance to tackling this problem, and they put up a hell of a fight.

Call him the $45 million man. That's how much money Dr. Frederick Seitz, a former president of the National Academy of Sciences, helped R. J. Reynolds Industries, Inc., give away to fund medical research in the 1970s and 1980s. The research avoided the central health issue facing Reynolds—"They didn't want us looking at the health effects of cigarette smoking," says Seitz, who is now 94—but it nevertheless served the tobacco industry's purposes. Throughout those years, the industry frequently ran ads in newspapers and magazines citing its multi-million-dollar research program as proof of its commitment to science—and arguing that the evidence on the health effects of smoking was mixed.

In the 1990s, Seitz began arguing that the science behind global warming was likewise inconclusive and certainly didn't warrant imposing mandatory limits on greenhouse-gas emissions. He made his case vocally, trashing the integrity of a 1995 I.P.C.C. report on the op-ed page of The Wall Street Journal, signing a letter to the Clinton administration accusing it of misrepresenting the science, and authoring a paper which said that global warming and ozone depletion were exaggerated threats devised by environmentalists and unscrupulous scientists pushing a political agenda. In that same paper, Seitz asserted that secondhand smoke posed no real health risks, an opinion he repeats in our interview. "I just can't believe it's that bad," he says.

Al Gore and others have said, but generally without offering evidence, that the people who deny the dangers of climate change are like the tobacco executives who denied the dangers of smoking. The example of Frederick Seitz, described here in full for the first time, shows that the two camps overlap in ways that are quite literal—and lucrative. Seitz earned approximately $585,000 for his consulting work for R. J. Reynolds, according to company documents unearthed by researchers for the Greenpeace Web site ExxonSecrets.org and confirmed by Seitz. Meanwhile, during the years he consulted for Reynolds, Seitz continued to draw a salary as president emeritus at Rockefeller University, an institution founded in 1901 and subsidized with profits from Standard Oil, the predecessor corporation of ExxonMobil.

Seitz was the highest-ranking scientist among a band of doubters who, beginning in the early 1990s, resolutely disputed suggestions that climate change was a real and present danger. As a former president of the National Academy of Sciences (from 1962 to 1969) and a winner of the National Medal of Science, Seitz gave such objections instant credibility. Richard

Lindzen, a professor of meteorology at M.I.T., was another high-profile scientist who consistently denigrated the case for global warming. But most of the public argument was carried by lesser scientists and, above all, by lobbyists and paid spokesmen for the Global Climate Coalition. Created and funded by the energy and auto industries, the Coalition spent millions of dollars spreading the message that global warming was an uncertain threat. Journalist Ross Gelbspan exposed the corporate campaign in his 1997 book, *The Heat Is On*, which quoted a 1991 strategy memo: the goal was to "reposition global warming as theory rather than fact."

"Not trivial" is how Seitz reckons the influence he and fellow skeptics have had, and their critics agree. The effect on media coverage was striking, according to Bill McKibben, who in 1989 published the first major popular book on global warming, *The End of Nature*. Introducing the 10th-anniversary edition, in 1999, McKibben noted that virtually every week over the past decade studies had appeared in scientific publications painting an ever more alarming picture of the global-warming threat. Most news reports, on the other hand, "seem to be coming from some other planet."

The deniers' arguments were frequently cited in Washington policy debates. Their most important legislative victory was the Senate's 95-to-0 vote in 1997 to oppose U.S. participation in any international agreement—i.e., the Kyoto Protocol—that imposed mandatory greenhouse-gas reductions on the U.S.

The ferocity of this resistance helps explain why the Clinton administration achieved so little on climate change, says Tim Wirth, the first under-secretary of state for global affairs, who served as President Clinton's chief climate negotiator. "The opponents were so strongly organized that the administration got spooked and backed off of things it should have done," says

Wirth. "The Kyoto negotiations got watered down and watered down, and after we signed it the administration didn't try to get it ratified. They didn't even send people up to the Hill to talk to senators about ratifying it."

"I wanted to push for ratification," responds Gore. "A decision was made not to. If our congressional people had said there was even a remote chance of ratifying, I could have convinced Clinton to do it—his heart was in the right place. . . . But I remember a meeting in the White House with some environmental groups where I asked them for the names of 10 senators who would vote to ratify. They came up with one, Paul Wellstone. If your most optimistic supporters can't identify 10 likely gettables, then people in the administration start to ask, 'Are you a fanatic, Al? Is this a suicide mission?'" (Clinton did not respond to e-mailed questions.)

James Hansen, without singling out any individual, accuses global-warming deniers of "acting like lawyers, not scientists, because no matter what new evidence comes in, their conclusion is already decided." Richard Lindzen responds that Hansen has been wrong time and time again and operates "one of the worst climate models around." Lindzen agrees that both global temperature and atmospheric concentration of carbon dioxide have increased over the last century. But temperatures won't rise much further, he says, because humans aren't the main driving force in the climate system. The reason most scientists disagree with him, Lindzen explains, is simple careerism. "Once President Bush the elder began spending $2 billion a year on climate science, scientists developed a self-interest in maintaining this is an urgent problem," he says, adding that the scientific community's fixation on climate change will be remembered as an episode of "mass insanity."

Among many rebuttals to the deniers' arguments, perhaps the most authoritative collection is found on the Web site of Britain's national academy of science, the Royal Society. But such rebuttals have little impact on true believers, says Robert May, the Society's former president. "[Nobel Prize–winning physicist] Max Planck used to say that people don't change their minds [because of evidence]," he adds. "The science simply moves on and those people eventually die off."

But if the deniers appear to have lost the scientific argument, they prolonged the policy battle, delaying actions to reduce emissions when such cuts mattered most. "For 25 years, people have been warning that we had a window of opportunity to take action, and if we waited until the effects were obvious it would be too late to avoid major consequences," says Oppenheimer. "Had some individual countries, especially the United States, begun to act in the early to mid-1990s, we might have made it. But we didn't, and now the impacts are here."

"The goal of the disinformation campaign wasn't to win the debate," says Gelbspan. "The goal was simply to keep the debate going. When the public hears the media report that some scientists believe warming is real but others don't, its reaction is 'Come back and tell us when you're really sure.' So no political action is taken."

Representative Henry Waxman, the California Democrat who chaired the 1994 hearings where tobacco executives unanimously declared under oath that cigarettes were not addictive, watches today's global-warming deniers with a sense of déjà vu. It all reminds him of the confidential slogan a top tobacco flack coined when arguing that the science on smoking remained unsettled: "Doubt is our product." Now, Waxman says, "not only are we seeing the same tactics the tobacco industry used, we're seeing some of the same groups. For example, the Advancement of Sound Science Coalition was created [in 1993] to debunk the dangers of second-hand smoking before it moved on to global warming."

The scientific work Frederick Seitz oversaw for R. J. Reynolds from 1978 to 1987 was "perfectly fine research, but off the point," says Stanton A. Glantz, a professor of medicine at the University of California, San Francisco, and a lead author of The Cigarette Papers (1996), which exposed the inner workings of the Brown & Williamson Tobacco Corporation. "Looking at stress, at genetics, at lifestyle issues let Reynolds claim it was funding real research. But then it could cloud the issue by saying, 'Well, what about this other possible causal factor?' It's like coming up with 57 other reasons for Hurricane Katrina rather than global warming."

For his part, Seitz says he was comfortable taking tobacco money, "as long as it was green. I'm not quite clear about this moralistic issue. We had absolutely free rein to decide how the money was spent." Did the research give the tobacco industry political cover? "I'll leave that to the philosophers and priests," he replies.

Seitz is equally nonplussed by the extraordinary disavowal the National Academy of Sciences issued following his most visible intervention in the global-warming debate. In 1998 he urged fellow scientists to sign an Oregon group's petition saying that global warming was much ado about little. The petition attracted more than 17,000 signatories and received widespread media attention. But posted along with the petition was a paper by four global-warming deniers that was presented in virtually the same layout and typeface used by the National Academy of Sciences in its scholarly journal. The formatting, combined with Seitz's signature, gave the clear impression that the academy endorsed the petition. The academy quickly released a statement disclaiming any connection with the petition or its suggestion that global warming was not real. Scientific American later determined that only 1,400 of the petition's signatories claimed to hold a Ph.D. in a climate-related science, and of these, some either were not even aware of the petition or later changed their minds.

Today, Seitz admits that "it was stupid" for the Oregon activists to copy the academy's format. Still, he doesn't understand why the academy felt compelled to disavow the petition, which he continues to cite as proof that it is "not true" there is a scientific consensus on global warming.

The accumulation of scientific evidence eventually led British Petroleum to resign from the Global Climate Coalition in 1996. Shell, Ford, and other corporations soon left as well, and in 2002 the coalition closed down. But Gelbspan, whose Web site tracks the deniers' activities, notes that key coalition personnel have since taken up positions in the Bush administration, including Harlan Watson, the State Department's chief climate negotiator. (Watson declined to be interviewed.)

ExxonMobil—long the most recalcitrant corporation on global warming—is still spending millions of dollars a year funding an array of organizations that downplay the problem, including the George C. Marshall Institute, where Seitz is chairman emeritus. John Passacantando, executive director of Greenpeace USA, calls the denial campaign "one of the great crimes of our era." Passacantando is "quite confident" that class-action lawsuits will eventually be filed against corporations who denied global warming's dangers. Five years ago, he told executives from one company, "You're going to wish you were the tobacco companies once this stuff hits and people realize you were the ones who blocked [action]."

The public discussion about climate change in the U.S. is years behind that in Britain and the rest of Europe, and the deniers are a big reason why. "In the United States, the Chamber of Commerce and National Association of Manufacturers are deeply skeptical of climate-change science and the need to reduce greenhouse-gas emissions," says Fiona Harvey, the environment correspondent for the *Financial Times*. "In Britain, the equivalent body, the Confederation of British Industry, is absolutely behind the science and agrees on the need to cut emissions. The only differences are over how to do that."

America's media coverage is also well behind the curve, says Harvey. "In the United States you have lots of news stories that, in the name of balance, give equal credence to the skeptics. We don't do that here—not because we're not balanced but because we think it's unbalanced to give equal validity to a fringe few with no science behind them."

Prominent right-wing media outlets in the U.S., especially the editorial page of *The Wall Street Journal*, continue to parrot the claims of climate-change deniers. (Paul A. Gigot, the page's editor, declined to be interviewed.) Few beat reporters are still taken in, but their bosses—the editors and producers who decide which stories run, and how prominently—are another matter. Charles Alexander, the former environmental editor at *Time*, complains that, while coverage has improved recently, media executives continue to regard climate change as just another environmental issue, rather than as the overriding challenge of the 21st century.

"Americans are hearing more about reducing greenhouse emissions from BP ads than from news stories in *Time, The New York Times*, or any other U.S. media outlet," Alexander says. "This will go down as the greatest act of mass denial in history."

In 2002, Alexander went to see Andrew Heyward, then the president of CBS News, after running into him at a Harvard reunion. "I talked to him about climate change and other global environmental threats, and made the case that they were more dangerous than terrorism and CBS should be doing much more coverage of them," Alexander recalls. "He didn't dispute any of my factual points, but he did say the reason CBS didn't do more of that coverage was that 'people don't want to hear all that gloom and doom'—in other words, the environment wasn't a ratings winner. He seemed to think CBS News's job was to tell people what they wanted to hear, not what they need to know, and I think that attitude is increasingly true for the news business in general."

"That's bullshit," responds Heyward, who left CBS in 2005. "I've never been one of those guys who thinks news has to be light and bright. And in talking to Charles, I wasn't stating the policy of CBS News. I was just trying to explain to an old college classmate why there isn't more coverage of the environment on TV. Charles is an advocate, and advocates are never happy with the amount of coverage their cause gets."

American television did, however, give prime-time coverage to the latest, and most famous, global-warming denier: novelist Michael Crichton. ABC's *20/20* broadcast a very friendly interview with Crichton when he published *State of Fear*, a novel arguing that anyone who bought into the phony scientific consensus on global warming was a modern equivalent of the early-20th-century eugenicists who cited scientific "proof" for the superiority of the white race.

When Crichton was invited to testify before the Environment and Public Works Committee, observers in Britain were floored. "This is fairyland," exclaims Michael Meacher, the member of Parliament who served as Tony Blair's environment minister from 1997 to 2003. "You have a science-fiction writer testifying before the United States Senate on global-warming policy?

I mean, you can almost see the little boy off to the side, like in the story of the emperor's clothes, saying, 'But he's a science-*fiction* writer, isn't he?' It's just ludicrous."

The man who invited Crichton, committee chairman James M. Inhofe, a Republican from oil-rich Oklahoma, had already said on the floor of the Senate that global warming was "the greatest hoax ever perpetrated on the American people." In an e-mail interview, Inhofe defended Crichton's appearance, noting that the writer holds a medical degree from Harvard. (Crichton is also a post-doctoral fellow at the Salk Institute for Biological Studies.) The senator added that he stood by his hoax statement as well.

David King responded that Britain's climate-science research is headquartered within the Ministry of Defense, "and you wouldn't find a group of people less likely to perpetrate a hoax than the people in the Ministry of Defense."

King has "extremist views," Inhofe replied. If the I.P.C.C. and the world's leading academies of science echo King's views, he argued, it is because they actively silence dissidents: "Scientists who believe warming trends are naturally occurring, or benign, are almost always excluded from climate-change conferences and meetings because their conclusions do not support the political agendas of the others who host the conferences." (The I.P.C.C. denies this accusation.) The truth, Inhofe continued, is that "there is no consensus on the science of global warming." As proof, he cited—what else? —Frederick Seitz's Oregon petition.

Paul H. O'Neill, who served nearly two years as George W. Bush's secretary of the Treasury, does not buy the common notion that Bush and Vice President Dick Cheney resist taking action on global warming because they are oilmen. "I don't think either one of them is an oilman," insists O'Neill. "You have to have success to be an oilman. It's like saying you're a ballplayer, but you never got on the field."

In 1998, while running the aluminum giant Alcoa, O'Neill was among the first U.S. business leaders to recognize the enormity of climate change. He says Bush asked him, early in the first term, to put together a plan of action, but it was ignored. Like Bush, O'Neill opposed Kyoto, so he proposed other ways to move forward. But instead, he says, the administration "cherry-picked" the science on climate change to justify taking no action, "just like it cherry-picked the intelligence on weapons of mass destruction" to justify the invasion of Iraq.

"The United States is the only entity on this planet turning its back on this problem," says Massachusetts senator John Kerry. "Even as he talks about protecting the security of the nation, the president is willfully choosing not to tackle this problem. History will record it as one of the greatest derelictions of duty ever."

Bush-administration officials counter that they are doing more to fight global warming than anyone else—just with different tools than those favored by supporters of the Kyoto Protocol. James L. Connaughton, the head of the White House Council on Environmental Quality, starts by pointing out that Bush has raised federal mileage standards for S.U.V.'s and light trucks. When I point out that the increase is tiny (a mere 0.3 miles per gallon, says Dan Becker of the Sierra Club), Connaughton maintains that over time further increases will result in substantial energy savings, especially when paired with the administration's new tax credits for efficient vehicles. It's also important, he says, to "keep personal income taxes in check" to encourage people to buy these new cars. What's more, the administration recently provided $10 billion in incentives for alternative-energy development and $40 billion over 10 years to encourage farmers to plant trees and preserve grassland that can soak up carbon dioxide.

The administration opposes the Kyoto Protocol, Connaughton claims, because its mandatory emissions cuts would punish the American economy, costing as many as five million jobs. It would also dry up the capital needed to fund the technological research that will ultimately solve global warming.

"It's important not to get distracted by chasing short-term reductions in greenhouse emissions. The real payoff is in long-term technological breakthroughs," says John H. Marburger III, the president's science adviser. Besides, "there is no question that mitigating the impact of climate change as it takes place will be much less [expensive] than the costs of reducing oil and coal use in the short term."

"The world is now on a trajectory to slow the growth in greenhouse-gas emissions," concludes Connaughton, who as a lawyer represented mining and chemical interests before joining the administration. "I'm highly confident we will stabilize [those emissions]." He says that's exactly what happened over the last 80 years with air pollution. He seems to take pleasure in observing that, under Bush, the U.S. has actually reduced its annual emissions, which, he says, is more than some of its harshest critics overseas have done.

It's a cheerful story, but virtually no one else believes it. Waiting 80 years to eliminate greenhouse-gas emissions would guarantee runaway global warming, says James Hansen. In January, six former chiefs of the Environmental Protection Agency, including five who served Republican presidents, said Bush needed to do much more to fight climate change. In Britain, Peter Ainsworth, the Conservative Party's shadow secretary of state for the environment, says his party is "saddened" by the Bush administration's approach. "We would have preferred the Bush administration to take a leadership position on this problem . . . instead of allowing itself to be seen as foot-dragging."

Outsiders doubt President Bush's desire to confront the issue, pointing out that his right-wing political base agrees with Inhofe that global warming is a liberal hoax. Critics also question the administration's faith in volunteerism. They argue that imposing mandatory timelines and emissions limits would put a price tag on carbon and push corporations and individuals to use less of it. "Long-term research is fine, but to offer that as a substitute for the stark necessity of near-term cuts in emissions is a kind of magical thinking—trusting that something will happen to make everything all right," says Donald Kennedy, the editor in chief of *Science*. In fact, despite Bush's call to end our "addiction" to oil, his 2007 budget actually reduced funding for alternative energy and efficiency.

Nor has the Bush administration cut short-term emissions, says a European diplomat who requested anonymity because he has to work with Bush officials. Citing data from the Energy Information Administration, the diplomat says Connaughton is correct to say that U.S. greenhouse-gas emissions declined, but only in the single year following the 2001 terrorist attacks, owing to the ensuing economic recession. U.S. emissions increased in every other year of Bush's presidency, making it "complete hokum" to claim that Bush's policies are cutting emissions, the diplomat says, adding of Connaughton, "I'm afraid Jim has drunk the Kool-Aid."

As for John Marburger's assertion that it will be cheaper to adapt to climate change than to try to head it off, Michael Oppenheimer says, "It's a sad day when the president is being told by his science adviser that climate change isn't worth avoiding. It may be possible for rich nations and people to adapt, but 90 percent of humanity doesn't have the resources to deal with climate change. It's unethical to condemn them just because the people in power don't want to act."

"I think it is a slam dunk that we are on a path of dangerous anthropogenic interference with the climate, and it is also absolutely clear that what this administration has proposed so far will not get us off that path," says Jeffrey Sachs. "The administration says several things I agree with: technology is extremely important, global warming is a long-term issue, and we can't do it without China and India [because their greenhouse-gas emissions will soon outstrip our own]. But none of this adds up to taking no action. The fact that China and other developing economies have to be involved doesn't mean the United States refuses to commit to specific actions; it means the U.S. should commit itself, in part to help bring the others in.

"I've had discussions with leaders in China and India," adds Sachs. "They are very concerned about climate change because they see the effects it could have on them. We should help to set up prototype carbon-capture-and-sequestration power plants in China and India, and the rich countries should help to finance them. It's hard to ask poor countries to bear the full financial burden of these technologies, especially when it is the rich countries' past burning of carbon fuels that has created most of the problem. But the U.S. takes every opportunity to do virtually nothing to engage in practical steps with the developing countries."

Ask Al Gore how to avoid dangerous climate change and, despite his wonkish reputation, he doesn't begin by talking about hybrid cars or carbon sequestration. No, says Gore, the first imperative is to "punch through the massive denial and resistance" that still exist in the United States.

But the rest of the world is no longer waiting for the Bush administration. At the international climate conference held in Montreal last year, European nations called the administration's bluff when it refused to commit even to the breathtakingly modest step of someday discussing what framework might follow the Kyoto Protocol, which expires in 2012. At past summits, the administration's stubbornness led other nations to back down in hopes of keeping America involved in the process. At Montreal, the world quit waiting for Godot and recognized, as Elliot Morley, Tony Blair's minister of the environment, says, "there are a lot of voices in the United States in addition to the Bush administration, and we will work with all of them to address this problem."

The same thing is happening inside the U.S. "It is very clear that Congress will put mandatory greenhouse-gas-emission reductions in place, immediately after George W. Bush leaves office," says Philip Clapp of N.E.T. "Even the Fortune 500 is positioning itself for the inevitable. There isn't one credible 2008 Republican presidential candidate who hasn't abandoned the president's do-nothing approach. They have all adopted the approach the rest of the world took at the Montreal talks—we're moving forward, you're a lame duck, and we have to deal with it."

Regardless of what happens in Washington, D.C., state and local governments across America are aggressively confronting the problem. Two hundred and eight mayors have committed their cities to meet or exceed the emissions reductions mandated by the Kyoto Protocol, and some have gone further. Governor Arnold Schwarzenegger has committed California to 30 percent cuts by 2020.

California officials have also held talks with their counterparts in Oregon and Washington about launching a so-called carbon-trading system like the one currently in force in Europe. Such a system allows efficient users to profit while wasteful users must pay for burning more fuel. A similar mechanism worked in the 1990s to dramatically reduce emissions of sulfur dioxide—the cause of acid rain—at far less cost than industrialists or environmentalists anticipated.

New York and seven other northeastern states, which together with California amount to the third-biggest economy in the world, are also considering a carbon-trading system. Their collective actions—investing in energy efficiency, installing wind turbines, sequestering carbon—could boost production runs and lower costs to the point where the green technologies needed to fight global warming become affordable for everyone.

At the same time, investors and others worried about global warming are pressuring corporations and Wall Street to take the problem seriously. The Investor Network on Climate Risk, a coalition of pension-fund managers and institutional investors representing $3 trillion in assets, has put corporations on notice that its members will reconsider investing in companies that don't pay enough attention to climate change. In 2005, investment-banking giant Goldman Sachs pledged to embrace carbon trading and invest $1 billion in renewable energy.

"To use a term coined by George W. Bush in the context of the Iraq war, I think this coalition of the willing might be much more successful than the Kyoto process," says Hans Schellnhuber. "I've been to a lot of these international conferences, and it's a pretty frustrating experience that usually produces little more than cheap talk. Whereas a true coalition of the willing can bring together regional governments, enterprises, and individuals and show that it is technologically and economically possible to take meaningful action."

No matter what happens, the global warming that past human activity has already unleashed will make this a different planet in the years ahead. But it could still be a livable, even hospitable, planet, if enough of us get smart in time. If we don't, three feet of water could be just the beginning.

Discussion Questions

1. The issue of global climate change is championed by many and aggressively challenged by others. Why do you think this issue is so divisive? What are the primary arguments on either side of this issue? Whose arguments do you feel are most compelling, and why?
2. Some scientists have warned about human-induced global climate change for many years, and fear that our "window of opportunity" to effectively counteract this effect may have passed. What does this mean? What evidence points to this possibility?
3. Hertsgaard notes that media coverage of climate change by mainstream U.S. news organizations is "behind the curve" of other nations. If true, do you believe this continues to be the case, or has the situation changed? Provide evidence to support your point of view.

 Supporting Activities

1. Read about the latest position adopted by the U.S. EPA relative to greenhouse gas emissions in an article by *Washington Post* reporter Juliet Eilperin (April 18, 2009): http://www.washingtonpost.com/wp-dyn/content/article/2009/04/17/AR2009041701453.html.
2. Watch the video "Earth Focus Episode 14: Obama's Climate Action" on Link TV. Available: http://www.linktv.org/video/3993/earth-focus-episode-14-obamas-climate-action. You can also search Link TV for other titles on environment and climate change.
3. Visit Mark Hertsgaard's Web site (http://www.markhertsgaard.com/) and select and read another of his articles on climate change.
4. Log on to the Office of Science and Technology Policy site and view the short video available on the home page that provides an overview of the OSTP from the new Director, Dr. John Holdren (http://www.ostp.gov/). Log on to the OSTP blog, read the latest posting, and submit a response.

 Additional Resources

1. Read more about Frederick Seitz and other prominent global warming skeptics on the *Frontline* Web site: http://www.pbs.org/wgbh/pages/frontline/hotpolitics/reports/skeptics.html.
2. Watch the movie *An Inconvenient Truth*, for which former Vice-President earned an Academy Award for Best Documentary in 2007. For contrast, read and view some of the many attempts to "debunk" climate change claims made in this film.
3. Learn more about the Kyoto Protocol on the United Nations Framework Convention on Climate Change site at: http://unfccc.int/kyoto_protocol/items/2830.php.

 Endnotes

1. National Academy of Engineering and National Research Council, Committee on Technological Literacy. 2002. *Technically Speaking: Why all Americans Need to Know More About Technology*. Washington, DC: National Academies Press.

2. The Office of Technology Assessment was a casualty of the "Contract with America" spearheaded by then-Congressman Newt Gingrich (R-GA), which led to the discontinuance of a number of programs in an effort to cut government spending. All of the OTA reports, as well as historical information about the OTA, are available through a site maintained at Princeton University (http://www.princeton.edu/~ota/). Since the OTA was disbanded, no similar agency has emerged to perform the functions that were served by that office.
3. Read more about the history and current initiatives of the Office of Science and Technology Policy at: http://www.ostp.gov/.
4. North Carolina Board of Science and Technology Policy. January 9, 2009. *About NCBST*. Available: http://www.ncscitech.com/about.htm.
5. See, for example, the report *State Science and Technology Policy Advice: Issues, Opportunities, and Challenges: Summary of a National Convocation*. 2008. National Academy of Sciences, National Academy of Engineering, and Institute of Medicine. Washington, DC: National Academies Press. Available: http://books.nap.edu/catalog.php?record_id=12160.
6. More information about the IPCC and full text of the IPCC reports are available online at: http://www.ipcc.ch/index.htm.
7. Browse by topic and read the transcripts of expert testimony provided by Brookings Institution experts at: http://www.brookings.edu/media/TestimonyList.aspx?byTopic=true. For another example from among the many organizations that conduct similar work, see the National Council for Science and the Environment site: http://ncseonline.org/06policy/cms.cfm?id=1034.
8. National Research Council. 2002. *The Age of Expert Testimony: Science in the Courtroom*. Washington, DC: National Academies Press. Available: http://books.nap.edu/catalog.php?record_id=10272.
9. Perrow, Charles. 1999. *Normal Accidents: Living With High-Risk Technologies*. Princeton, NJ: Princeton University Press.
10. *Frontline*: "Interview with Clotaire Rapaille." November 9, 2004. Available: http://www.pbs.org/wgbh/pages/frontline/shows/persuaders/interviews/rapaille.html.

Basic Human Needs: Rethinking Food, Water, and Shelter

If we give much thought at all to the impacts of technologies, it's unlikely that the mundane technologies associated with food, water, and sanitation top the list unless the work we do is related to addressing these needs. Such technologies are largely invisible: running underground, tucked out of range of sight and smell, or forgotten as the means that result in the attractive displays of food on grocery store shelves. We forget or don't need to pay attention to the fact that these technologies are fundamental to existence as we know it. Access to clean water, sewage systems, and improved living conditions are generally agreed to have resulted in greater reductions in mortality rates in the early part of the 20th Century than any other single category of technology.[1] Such benefits are nowhere near universal, however; according to UNICEF statistics, over 2.5 billion people worldwide still lack access to improved sanitation facilities, and although safe drinking water is more accessible than ever before in history, there are still over 850 million people worldwide who don't have safe drinking water supplies.[2] The statistics on world hunger levels are just as staggering: the United Nations estimates that over 960 million people worldwide are undernourished, a problem exacerbated by rising food prices in the last two years.[3]

The sheer enormity of the statistics presented in the last paragraph can make the problems of hunger and lack of access to water and sanitation seem too big to contemplate, even more so when we contemplate them from the relative comfort of our living and working conditions in the developed world. It's far easier to put these issues out of mind and get on to the business of our everyday lives. But it may be that the problems being experienced in many parts of the developing world are closer to us than we think; indeed, recent articles in popular publications such as *Scientific American* and *National Geographic* highlight what may represent looming crises in water supplies and food production capacity that could affect developed and developing nations alike.[4]

Population levels play an integral role in the broader problems of pollution and resource depletion, and all of these factors contribute to the increasing uncertainties about water and food supplies. Simply put, the more of us there are, the more pollution and resource use results. Most of us are familiar with the fundamental principles of population growth, which often progresses exponentially, resulting in accelerating increases in population. In 1900, world population was estimated at 1.6 billion; by 1950 it had climbed to 2.5 billion and in the 40-year span to 2009 world population more than doubled, to 6.8 billion.[5] Projections for the future vary, but U.S. Census Bureau data suggest a world population of nine billion by 2040

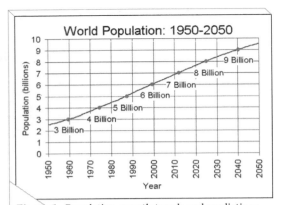

Figure 1. Population growth trends and predictions, 1950–2050.

Source: U.S. Census Bureau, International Data Base. December 2008 Update.

(see Figure 1). In addition, resource consumption per capita is growing—over 40 percent annually in developing countries between 1990 and 2005.[6] This growth means that unprecedented demands are being, and will continue to be, placed on natural resources and on the capacity of the soils, water, and atmosphere to absorb the waste products that are generated.

There are three main reactions to evidence about human and environmental crises linked to technological activity. One reaction is to simply deny that the evidence (and, therefore, the problems) exists.[7] A second reaction is to look for technological solutions that apply human ingenuity to finding ways around constraints or problems.[8] From this vantage point (a technocratic view), humans will always be able to devise strategies, given enough time, money, or attention. The third type of reaction calls for drastic changes that include doing without many of the amenities to which some of us have grown accustomed (a Luddite's view). As described in Section One of this book, the best-reasoned reaction is likely to be one that searches for multi-pronged responses by collecting data and then looking for both social

and technical solutions to the documented problems. For example, the U.S. Geological Survey is currently monitoring water levels throughout the Ogallala High Plains Aquifer, a 174,000 square mile underground reservoir in the middle section of the United States that is used to irrigate large swaths of productive farm land from South Dakota to Texas. It also supplies drinking water to over 80 percent of the people living within that region. Monitoring suggests that this water is being drawn (or *discharged*) at levels far higher than are capable of being recharged, with some estimates showing the reservoir depleted in as little as 25 years. With this knowledge in hand, policies can be adopted to better conserve water use in the region, and new technologies can be developed that enable significant reductions in the amount of water used for irrigation, commercial, and home use.

The technology of shelter is another area in which significant reductions in water, material, and energy use can be realized. Approaches to shelter design and construction vary considerably around the world, from thatched earthen huts to yurts to brick mansions, and everything in between. In the United States, the average size of homes has doubled in the past 50 years, from less than 1,000 square feet in 1950 to 2,400 square feet today.[9] This has occurred even as the average family size has decreased. Although the buildings' *share* (residential and commercial structures combined) of total energy consumption in the U.S. has decreased in the past 30 years, it still represents approximately 40 percent of *total* national energy use, according to Department of Energy statistics.[10] (And one shouldn't be too optimistic about this statistic, anyhow: an increase in transportation energy use is largely responsible!) This share is projected to increase as relative energy consumption in the industrial sector declines.

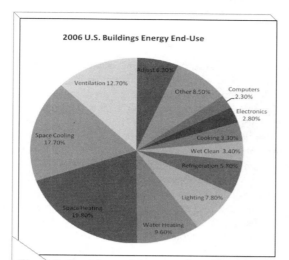

2006 U.S. Buildings Energy End-Use

Adjust 6.30%
Ventilation 12.70%
Other 8.50%
Computers 2.30%
Electronics 2.80%
Space Cooling 17.70%
Cooking 3.30%
Wet Clean 3.40%
Refrigeration 5.80%
Space Heating 19.80%
Lighting 7.80%
Water Heating 9.60%

Figure 2. Breakdown of energy use in residential and commercial structures in the U.S. "Wet clean" includes dishwashers and washing machines; "Adjust" percentage accounts for variation between commercial and residential energy use and other variations.

Source: Adapted from the U.S. Department of Energy.[10]

Space heating, cooling, and ventilation make up approximately half of energy used in buildings (see Figure 2).

A growing list of standards, codes, and guidelines has emerged in the past decade that attempts to identify and promote so-called "green" building strategies. These include the U.S. EPA Energy Star for Homes standards, the Green Building Council's Leadership in Energy Efficient Design (LEED) standards, and efforts to reduce the overall size of homes.[11] An investigation into any of the green building standards reveals that they focus on sustainable use of materials; incorporating water saving measures; landscaping to enhance cooling and to prevent the need for irrigation; as well as measures to reduce energy use such as low-emissivity windows, insulation, and passive solar siting.

The excerpts included in this section will provide a starting point for investigation and discussion about these issues. You are encouraged to do additional reading on these and related topics of interest.

When the Rivers Run Dry

Water use is one of the hidden impacts of globalization. As author Fred Pearce points out in this excerpt, when you purchase a shirt made of cotton grown in Pakistan you are unwittingly influencing the hydrology of the Pakistani region. Water used to grow or manufacture goods in one area that are then exported to another area has been termed "virtual water," because although the water itself is not transferred, its use as embodied in the goods that are exported has the same effect. The U.S. is the biggest "exporter" of virtual water; countries in the Middle East are among the major importers of virtual water.

As knowledge about the importance of better management of our freshwater supplies grows, many individuals have instituted water-saving measures in their homes and communities have enacted water conservation policies. Although helpful and important, conservation in homes and businesses pales in comparison to water use for irrigation; the volume of water needed for the production of crops is staggering, as Pearce points out. To meet the need for water to irrigate and to supply municipalities, local and federal governments pursue new and larger water projects, generally drawn from existing surface water sources such as rivers and lakes. Pearce describes several large-scale projects underway or proposed in China, India, Russia, and Canada.

Large-scale water projects such as these illustrate the "technological hubris" that underlies some of the most extravagant of the technological optimists' utopian solutions. With a selective myopia that is often typical of the technocratic approach, the attention in these projects is focused simply on moving water, without considering the potential ecological impacts of large-scale changes to the natural systems. Beyond the sheer costs and engineering challenges presented by these projects are the unknown effects of, for instance, intermingling sewage supplies across regions or decreasing water levels in existing waterways. Furthermore, with the potential for meteorological changes in the amount of natural precipitation received due to global climate change, the long-term viability of these engineered waterways is uncertain. Lake Powell in the southwestern United States illustrates the plight of a large-scale water system in the face of prolonged drought.[12]

Linked to the issue of water use is the problem of how we handle human organic waste. Incredibly, in many parts of the world we pull water for our domestic use, including drinking water, from the same surface waters into which we then discharge treated and untreated sewage waste. For example, in what it hailed as a "landmark settlement," the USEPA in 2007 reached an agreement with the Allegheny County (PA) Sanitary Authority to reduce the amount of raw sewage that was flowing into surface waterways from Pittsburgh, Pennsylvania and 82 surrounding municipalities. The multi-year plan to upgrade sewage treatment facilities that was part of that settlement was designed to reduce the estimated 22 *billion* gallons of raw sewage discharged annually into Pittsburgh area waterways.[13]

Fred Pearce, who calls water "the defining crisis of the twenty-first century," is a science writer who was born and educated in the U.K. He is the author of several books focused on environmental topics, including *Confessions of an Eco-Sinner: Tracking Down the Sources of My Stuff* (2008) and *With Speed and Violence: Why Scientists Fear Tipping Points in Climate Change* (2007). Pearce writes a biweekly blog for *New Scientist* magazine.

The Human Sponge

By Fred Pearce

Few of us realize how much water it takes to get us through the day. On average, we drink no more than a gallon and a half of the stuff. Including water for washing and for flushing the toilet, we use only about 40 gallons each. In some countries suburban lawn sprinklers, swimming pools, and sundry outdoor uses can double that figure. Typical per capita water use in suburban Australia is about 90 gallons, and in the United States around 100 gallons. There are exceptions, though. One suburban household in Orange County, Florida, was billed for 4.1 million gallons in a single year, or more than 10,400 gallons a day. Nobody knows how they got through that much.

We can all save water in the home. But as laudable as it is to take a shower rather than a bath and turn off the faucet while brushing our teeth, we shouldn't get hold of the idea that regular domestic water use is what is really emptying the world's rivers. Manufacturing the goods that we fill our homes with consumes a certain amount, but that's not the real story either. It is only when we add in the water needed to grow what we eat and drink that the numbers really begin to soar.

Get your head around a few of these numbers, if you can. They are mind-boggling. It takes between 250 and 650 gallons of water to grow a pound of rice. That is more water than many households use in a week. For just a bag of rice. Keep going. It takes 130 gallons to grow a pound of wheat and 65 gallons for a pound of potatoes. And when you start feeding grain to livestock for animal products such as meat and milk, the numbers become yet more startling. It takes 3000 gallons to grow the feed for enough cow to make a quarter-pound hamburger, and between 500 and 1000 gallons for that cow to fill its udders with a quart of milk. Cheese? That takes about 650 gallons for a pound of cheddar or brie or camembert.

And if you think your shopping cart is getting a little bulky at this point, maybe you should leave that 1-pound box of sugar on the shelf. It took up to 400 gallons to produce. And the 1-pound jar of coffee tips the scales at 2650 gallons—or 10 tons—of water. Imagine taking *that* home from the store.

Turn these statistics into meal portions and you come up with more than 25 gallons for a portion of rice, 40 gallons for the bread in a sandwich or a serving of toast, 130 gallons for a two-egg omelet or a mixed salad, 265 gallons for a glass of milk, 400 gallons for an ice cream, 530 gallons for a pork chop, 800 gallons for a hamburger, and 1320 gallons for a small steak. And if you have a sweet tooth, so much the worse: every teaspoonful of sugar in your coffee requires 50 cups of water to grow. Which is a lot, but not as much as the 37 gallons of water (or 592 cups) needed to grow the coffee itself. Prefer alcohol? A glass of wine or beer with dinner requires another 66 gallons, and a glass of brandy afterward takes a staggering 530 gallons.

We are all used to reading detailed technical information about the nutritional content of most food. Maybe it is time that we were given some clues as to how much water it took to

From *When the Rivers Run Dry* by Fred Pearce. Copyright © 2006 by Fred Pearce. Reprinted by permission of Beacon Press, Boston.

grow and process the food. As the world's rivers run dry, it matters.

I figure that as a typical meat-eating, beer-swilling, milk-guzzling Westerner, I consume as much as a hundred times my own weight in water every day. Hats off, then, to my vegetarian daughter, who gets by with about half that. It's time, surely, to go out and preach the gospel of water conservation. But don't buy one of those jokey T-shirts advertised on the Internet with slogans like "Save water, bathe with a friend." Good message, but you could fill roughly twenty-five bathtubs with the water needed to grow the 9 ounces of cotton needed to make the shirt. It gives a whole new meaning to the wet T-shirt contest.

Let's do the annual audit. I probably drink only about 265 gallons of water—that's one ton or 1.3 cubic yards—in a whole year. Around the home I probably use between 50 and 100 tons. But growing the crops to feed and clothe me for a year must take between 1500 and 2000 tons—more than half the contents of an Olympic-size swimming pool.

Where does all that water come from? In England, where I live, most homegrown crops are watered by rain. So the water is at least cheap. But remember that a lot of the food consumed in Britain, and all the cotton, is imported. And when the water to grow crops is collected from rivers or pumped from underground, as it is in much of the world, it is increasingly expensive, and its diversion to fields is increasingly likely to deprive someone else of water and to empty rivers and underground water reserves. And when the rivers are running low, it is ever more likely that the water simply will not be there to grow the crops at all.

The water "footprint" of Western countries on the rest of the world deserves to become a serious issue. Whenever you buy a T-shirt made of Pakistani cotton, eat Thai rice, or drink coffee from Central America, you are influencing the hydrology of those regions—taking a share of the Indus River, the Mekong River, or the Costa Rican rains. You may be helping rivers run dry.

Economists call the water involved in the growing and manufacture of products traded around the world "virtual water." In this terminology, every ton of wheat arriving at a dockside carries with it in virtual form the thousand tons of water needed to grow it. The global virtual-water trade is estimated to be around 800 million acre-feet a year, or twenty Nile Rivers. Of that, two thirds is in a huge range of crops, from grains to vegetable oil, sugar to cotton; a quarter is in meat and dairy products; and just a tenth is in industrial products. That means that nearly a tenth of all the water used in raising crops goes into the international virtual-water trade. This trade "moves water in volumes and over distances beyond the wildest imaginings of water engineers," says Tony Allan, of the School of Oriental and African Studies in London, who invented the term "virtual water."

The biggest net exporter of virtual water is the United States. It exports around a third of all the water it withdraws from the natural environment. Much of that is in grains, either directly or via meat. The United States is emptying critical underground water reserves, such as those beneath the High Plains, to grow grain for export. It also exports an amazing 80 million acre-feet of virtual water in beef. Other major exporters of virtual water include Canada (grain), Australia (cotton and sugar), Argentina (beef), and Thailand (rice).

Major importers of virtual water include Japan and the European Union. Few of these countries are short of water, so there are ethical questions about how much they should be doing this. But for other importers, virtual water is a vital lifeline. Iran, Egypt, and Algeria could starve without it; likewise water-stressed Jordan, which effectively imports between 80 and

90 percent of its water in the form of food. "The Middle East ran out of water some years ago. It is the first major region to do so in the history of the world," says Allan. He estimates that more water flows into the Middle East each year as a result of imports of virtual water than flows down the Nile.

While many nations relieve their water shortages by importing virtual water, some exacerbate their problems by exporting it. Israel and arid southern Spain both export water in tomatoes, Ethiopia in coffee. Mexico's virtual-water exports are emptying its largest water body, Lake Chapala, which is the main source of water for its second city, Guadalajara.

Many cotton-growing countries provide a vivid example of this perverse water trade. Cotton grows best in hot lands with year-round sun. Deserts, in other words. Old European colonies and protectorates such as Egypt, Sudan, and Pakistan still empty the Nile and the Indus for cotton-growing, as they did when Britain ruled and Lancashire cotton mills had to be supplied. When Russia transformed the deserts of Central Asia into a vast cotton plantation, it sowed the seeds of the destruction of the Aral Sea. Most of the missing water for the shrivel-ing sea has in effect been exported over the past half-century in the form of virtual water that continues to clothe the Soviet Union.

Some analysts say that globally, the virtual-water trade significantly reduces water demand for growing crops. It enables farmers to grow crops where water requirements are less, they say. But this is mainly because the biggest trade in virtual water is the export of wheat and corn from temperate lands like the United States and Canada to hotter lands where the same crops would require more water. But for many other crops, such as cotton and sugar, the trade in virtual water looks like terribly bad business for the exporters.

Pakistan consumes more than 40 million acre-feet of water a year from the Indus River—almost a third of the river's total flow and enough to prevent any water from reaching the Arabian Sea—in order to grow cotton. How much sense does that make? And what logic is there in the United States pumping out the High Plains aquifer to add to a global grain glut? Whatever the virtues of the global trade in virtual water, the practice lies at the heart of some of the most intractable hydrological crises on the planet.

Taking the Water to the People

By Fred Pearce

It is the world's largest civil engineering project and aims to remake the natural hydrology of the world's most heavily populated nation. But it began rather inauspiciously, one morning in Beijing in April 2003, when the city's vice mayor, Niu Youcheng, accepted a bottle from a visiting local official. The bottle was filled with water from a reservoir on the Yangtze River 800 miles away in the south of the country. Its handover signaled the start of China's south-to-north transfer project, which is intended to be the ultimate solution to the desiccation of the Yellow River and the North China plain.

Some people see the scheme as an exercise in engineering hubris and a disaster in the making. But Chinese leaders say it is a logical extension of the grand schemes of great societies down the ages to remake their hydrology. Ancient Mesopotamia and Egypt both harnessed their rivers to feed their people. The Romans were famous for their aqueducts. Persian empires were built around laboriously excavated tunnels that delivered water from deep underground. But even at their greatest extent, these ancient works were mild modifications to natural drainage patterns. Today's engineers have bigger ambitions, diverting entire rivers onto distant plains. And China's scheme is the most ambitious ever to have got under way. It will, we are told, enable the Middle Kingdom to continue feeding itself as it has done for thousands of years. Maybe.

The south-to-north scheme will divert part of the flow of the Yangtze, the world's fourth biggest river, to replenish the dried-up Yellow River and the tens of millions of people in megacities that rely on it. The price tag is $60 billion, more than twice the cost of even Colonel Qaddafi's fantasy-world Great Manmade River Project. And it aims to deliver twenty times more water than Qaddafi's pipe dream.

Some of the water will come quite soon. In Beijing, people should be drinking Yangtze water regularly in 2007. Certainly it will be there in time to fill the swimming pools and pretty the streets with fountains as Beijing hosts the Olympic Games in 2008. Some of the water will take longer to get there, but within twenty years, say the planners, the project should annually be siphoning north three times as much water as England consumes in a year. The costs may be colossal, but China says the south-to-north project cannot be allowed to fail.

The project is actually three separate diversions. Two of them are already under construction. The first one will enlarge the existing Danjiangkou reservoir on the Han River, a major tributary of the Yangtze, and take its water north. The reservoir is already Asia's widest artificial expanse of water; enlargement will flood another 140 square miles and displace a quarter of a million more people. The canal north will be 200 feet wide and as long as France. As it crosses China's crowded plains, it will span 500 roads and 120 rail lines and tunnel beneath the Yellow River through a giant inverted siphon.

The second will take water from near the Yangtze's mouth across Shandong Province on the North China plain and deliver it to the megacity of Tianjin, which has suffered chronic

From *When the Rivers Run Dry* by Fred Pearce. Copyright © 2006 by Fred Pearce. Reprinted by permission of Beacon Press, Boston.

water shortages since the 1990s. Part of it will use the 2500-year-old Grand Canal, which was the world's largest artificial river in preindustrial times and the first to have lock gates. Today it is a sump for effluent from China's burgeoning industry, but there are plans to clean it up.

The third, western route is the most ambitious. It alone is expected to cost $36 billion. It will take water from the Yangtze headwaters amid the glaciers of Tibet and push it through tunnels up to 65 miles long into the headwaters of the Yellow River. There is no firm route yet, but several tributaries will be tapped, and there is talk of building the world's highest dam. This route will be the only one to deliver water directly into the Yellow River. The other two are intended to relieve pressure on the river by supplying water for cities and farms on the North China plain that currently take 8 million acre-feet a year from the river. But altogether the plan is to send some 36 million acre-feet of water a year from the Yangtze to northern China.

China's leaders love huge projects. Modernism lives on in their souls. With the World Bank claiming that China has already lost $14 billion in industrial production from water shortages, the scheme seems to them like a sound investment. But even as the first earth was dug, fears were growing about escalating costs. And academics and water planners I met in Beijing in 2004 raised a range of concerns.

The middle route, they said, could cause an ecological crisis on the Han River, taking a third of its water and worsening an already serious pollution problem. Wuhan City, a busy river port with a population of 3 million, could become a cesspit overnight. What, they wondered, about the cost of relocating refugees from the Danjiangkou reservoir? Could the filthy and decrepit Grand Canal really be cleared of pollution? Is the engineering intended for Tibet more than a figment of someone's imagination? And

since China is trying to move to more realistic pricing for water, won't the transferred water be far too expensive for the intended recipients to buy?

China has a vibrant antidam community, which honed its arguments over the Three Gorges project. It sees the scheme as another megalomaniacal folly and wants the billions to be spent instead on improving Chinese water efficiency. Ma Jun, a journalist and campaigner in the mold of Dai Qing, says, "Chinese factories use ten times more water than most developed countries to produce the same products. Chinese irrigation uses twice as much." Even old-fashioned Chinese toilets use much more water than their Western counterparts. The United States has been able to grow its economy for the past thirty years without increasing water use, he says, and so can China. And in the long run, he argues, it would be easier to shift the focus of Chinese food production from the northern plains to the south—where the water is.

But the antidam contingent lost the war over Three Gorges, and they seem set to lose this one too. Already China's scheme is being taken as a template for an even larger project in the world's second most populous nation, India. During 2003, as Chinese earthmovers embarked on their south-to-north project, politicians in Delhi were lining up to back plans for what is known as the River Interlinking Project. It would redraw the hydrological map of India in a quite breathtaking way by harnessing the great monsoon rivers of the north, like the Ganges and the Brahmaputra, and sending their water south and west to the parched lands where the droughts are worst and the underground water reserves are sinking fastest.

The Indian scheme is far more complex than the Chinese plan. It would build dozens of large dams and hundreds of miles of canals to link fourteen northern rivers that drain the

Himalayas. And it would pump their waters south along 1000 miles of canals, aqueducts, and tunnels and through 300 reservoirs to fill a second network, linking the seventeen major rivers of the country's arid south. These rivers include the Godavari, the Krishna, and the Cauvery, each of which has been diminished by heavy overabstraction for irrigation.

The transfer would involve moving 38 million acre-feet a year, very similar in scale to China's scheme. But with so many more rivers and links, the price tag would be two to three times higher, with official estimates ranging from $112 billion to $200 billion, or around 40 percent of the country's GDP. While the Chinese project sounds doable, whatever the pitfalls, the Indian scheme sounds like a great leap into the unknown.

Even so, the River Interlinking Project did not come out of nowhere. It has a long history. The legendary British engineer Sir Arthur Cotton first conceived of something similar in the mid-nineteenth century as a means of improving the country's transportation by linking rivers with canals. His scheme was dashed when the British decided to build railroads instead. But the fantasy never quite died. For a while it was poetically described as providing India with a "garland of canals." But it took a drought across India in the summer of 2002 to bring the idea back to the fore.

The specter of famine returning to India after more than a decade in which the country has had food to spare was a profound shock. Southern India, like northern China, seems to be on the verge of a hydrological crisis. And with water tables tumbling and the country's population predicted to increase by 50 percent within the next half-century, overtaking China to reach a staggering 1.5 billion people, there is a sense that a hydrological holocaust might not be far away. Surely, say many Indian politicians, the only answer is to replumb the nation.

In 2003, the president and prime minister, most state governments, and the Supreme Court—agencies that in India's complex democratic system spend much of their time in internecine warfare—united to promote the River Interlinking Project. Government scientists said it could provide enough water to increase irrigated farmland by more than 50 percent and to power 34,000 megawatts of hydroelectric capacity. On closer inspection, though, the blueprints show that as much as a third of this power would be needed for pumping water around the scheme's network of canals and tunnels.

Will it happen? There are plenty of objections. The rampant pollution in most northern rivers would result in a grand interchange of sewage down the canals. One estimate holds that an area of land the size of Cyprus would have to be flooded for the various structures, leaving 3 million people homeless. Even engineers in the states that apparently stand to gain the most are skeptical. Karnataka, one of the driest, is also one of the highest—often more than 2000 feet above sea level. Engineers there doubt that the water from the north would ever reach them.

A former head of the national water ministry, Ramaswarmy Iyer, calls the whole idea "technological hubris." India already has half-completed water projects that have cost billions of dollars, which should be finished first. He says that across arid India, three quarters of the monsoon rains still evade dams and wash into the sea. Better to try to collect that rain as it falls onto fields than to try to carry water across the country. "The answer is to harvest our rain better," he says.

Bangladesh objects too. It sits downstream of India on both the Ganges and the Brahmaputra. Bangladesh may fear the rivers' monsoon floods in summer, but it also relies on those rivers to irrigate its crops and recharge underground aquifers. It complained angrily in 1974 when India built the Farakka barrage on the Ganges close to the border, diverting valuable dry-season water flows into Indian irrigation canals. It blames the barrage for dried-up fields, disease, and a salty invasion of seawater into the Sunderbans mangrove swamps in the Ganges delta. In 1996, India promised not to reduce the flow further. Yet now it is talking about doing precisely that.

Like China, India is in a bullish mood at present, with annual economic growth at around 8 percent. Its engineers have always thought big, and now its politicians want to turn their dreams into reality. So it could happen. It is at least possible that within two decades, the two most populous countries in the world—with the two fastest-growing economies—will have spent a quarter of a trillion dollars on redirecting their rivers and remaking their hydrology.

And the urge to build big seems to be spreading. Spain spent 2003 lobbying the European Union to foot most of the $10 billion bill for its own north-to-south project. It wanted to build a 600-mile canal from the Ebro, the biggest river in the wet north of the country, taking as much as three quarters of its water to Murcia and Almería in the country's increasingly arid south. There, it was earmarked to irrigate more than a million acres of desert where spaghetti westerns were once filmed and to water golf courses at new tourist resorts.

The project bit the dust late in 2004, when a general election brought in a new government that had listened to critics of the plan, like Pedro Arrojo-Aguda, an economist from the University of Zaragoza. "It's clearly crazy," he told me just before the plug was pulled. For one thing, he said, it would wreck the Ebro delta. The 12-mile tongue of sandbanks, lagoons, and reed beds protruding into the Mediterranean is one of southern Europe's most important wet-

land nature reserves as well as Spain's largest rice-growing area and an important fish nursery. This land of flamingos and paella is already starved of water and silt from the river by upstream dams. The sea is eroding it. The transfer would seal its death warrant, he said. And for what? The golf courses and tourist resorts might be willing to pay for the new water, but the farmers could never pay. "The water will cost more than a dollar for 265 gallons—twice the current cost of the desalination of seawater. By the time it is delivered, few farmers will want it," Arrojo-Aguda said.

For Spaniards like Arrojo-Aguda, the Ebro transfer seems like a return to the bad old days of General Franco, the Fascist dictator who gave Spain more dams than any other similar-sized country. Perhaps that is why, in the heady days of their campaign, angry villagers from valleys in the Pyrenees that would be flooded for new dams joined irate farmers from the Ebro delta, city environmentalists, and political activists in probably the first ever protest to go to Brussels demanding that the EU close its purse. The new government, sworn in in 2004, heard the protests, assessed the economics, and opted to build desalination plants instead. But the project still has powerful backers and is only one general election away from a revival. And the drought that spread across southern Spain in the summer of 2005, reputedly the worst in half a century, brought renewed calls for consideration of the transfer plan.

Europe has other such schemes in the pipeline. The Greek government has a plan to take water out of the country's largest west-flowing river, the Acheloos, and pump it through a tunnel to irrigate tobacco fields on the eastern plains. It would partly destroy the Messolonghi delta, one of the last surviving untouched deltas on the Mediterranean.

In Britain, government agencies have proposed using the eighteenth-century canal system, dug to ship industrial goods around before the age of the railroads, to create a national water grid able to ship water from the wet north and west to the drier south and east. And London's water engineers have long dreamed of tapping the Severn River as it runs out of Wales and through the West Country to pump its water over the Cotswold hills and into the headwaters of the Thames.

Back in the days of heroic Soviet engineering, there was a plan to tap great north-flowing rivers of Siberia like the Ob and the Yenisei and send their water south to refill the canals of the Central Asian cotton industry, and just possibly to help revive the Aral Sea. First proposed by the czars back in the late nineteenth century and revived by Stalin in the 1930s, the idea became a serious proposition in the early 1980s. Thousands of scientists and engineers were recruited to help bring it about. But in the end it fell foul of a mixture of romantic Russian nationalists who did not want to give up their rivers to Muslim states far to the south and the reformist pragmatism of Soviet leader Mikhail Gorbachev.

But you cannot keep a bad megaproject down. In 2003, Igor Zonn, the director of Soyuzvodproject, a Russian government agency in charge of water management and ecology, told me, "We are beginning to revise the old project plans. The old material has to be gathered from more than three hundred institutes." It had won vocal support from ambitious politicians like Moscow's mayor, Yuri Luzhkov, a possible successor to Vladimir Putin as Russian president. If for no other reason, that link makes it a project to be taken seriously again.

The proposal would be roughly equivalent to irrigating Mexico from the Great Lakes, or Spain from the Danube. It would drive a 650-foot-wide canal southward for some 1500 miles, from where the Ob and the Irtysh meet, to re-

plenish the Amu Darya and Syr Darya rivers near the Aral Sea. The canal, according to blueprints shown to me by Russian scientists, would carry 22 million acre-feet of water a year. Though this is just 7 percent of the Ob's flow, it would be equivalent to half the natural flow of the two Central Asian rivers into the Aral Sea.

Down among the "stans," they have always loved the idea. "Although it seems ambitious, it appears to be the only tangible solution to the ecological and other problems caused by the drying of the Aral Sea," says Abdukhalil Razzakov, of the Tashkent State Economic University in Uzbekistan. And early in 2004, Luzhkov visited Kazakhstan to promote the plan. He said that this time around, there would be no handouts from Moscow. Central Asia would have to pay a realistic price for the water. But behind the scenes, Moscow is starting to see the scheme as one of the water projects that could rebuild its political and economic power in the region.

Madness? Certainly. But as Nikita Glazovsky, a leading Russian geographer and former deputy environment minister under Boris Yeltsin, told me when we met in Moscow in 2001, the region's engineers "still find it easier to divert rivers than to stop inefficient irrigation."

In North America, the parched Western states of America have their eyes on Canada's water. It is not very surprising. Canada has some of the largest rivers in the world. When the spring snowmelt gets going, around a tenth of all the water in all the rivers in the world is gushing through British Columbia and Yukon and the Northwest Territories into the Pacific and Arctic oceans. And the Great Lakes, on the border between the two countries, are one of the largest freshwater reserves on the planet. Meanwhile, only a few hundred miles to the south, the High Plains are parched, the reservoirs in the Colorado River sit two thirds empty, and California imposes restrictions on its lawn sprinklers.

In 2003, President George W. Bush raised hackles in Canada by calling for talks about U.S. private companies buying some of Canada's water to supply cities in the American West. It could become the ultimate fulfillment of the old maxim that "water flows uphill to money." Exactly how the water would be shifted economically was not made clear. Bush was less interested in the engineering than in establishing that NAFTA, the North American Free Trade Agreement, could cover the continent's water reserves. But for many north of the border, the issue is highly emotional.

The idea also has unpleasant echoes of vast schemes devised in past decades. One would have drained part of the Great Lakes into the Mississippi. Another, dreamed up back in the 1960s by Donald McCord Baker, an official in the Los Angeles water department, would have captured the waters of the Columbia River in the United States and then, in south-to-north order on the map of Canada, the Fraser, the Liard, the Skeena, and finally the might Yukon and Mackenzie rivers.

Its backers, who included Ralph Parsons, the head of one of the world's largest civil-engineering companies, envisaged building dams up to 1800 feet high in the canyons of British Columbia to funnel water into the Rocky Mountain Trench, a natural depression that would have been turned into a 680-million-acre-foot reservoir—that is, one with three times the total capacity of all the manmade reservoirs in the United States today. The project would, the blueprint proposed, carry south 114 million acre-feet of water a year—three times the capacity of China's entire south-to-north project.

That particular plan is dead and buried. But Canadian water officials say the pressure is growing to allow small water exports, especially from the Great Lakes. And they fear that once a precedent has been established, California and Arizona could come calling. Everything has its price under NAFTA. If the current drought in the American West persists, and if climate predictions that there is worse to come prove right, then who knows?

Africa already knows a bit about harnessing great rivers. The Nile today is as dammed as it could be. Its waters power Egypt and supply its irrigators. Barely a drop reaches the sea in most years. But the continent's other great river— the world's second largest river through the world's second largest rainforest—is a new target. The Congo River runs undiminished throughout the year and has ten times the flow of other major sub-Saharan rivers, like the Zambezi. The veteran British colonial water engineer Henry Oliver, who built the Kariba Dam on the Zambezi, called it "one of the greatest single natural sources of hydroelectric power in the world." He would love to have got to grips with it, he told me after he retired to South Africa.

And now his post-apartheid successors say the great river through what Joseph Conrad called the "heart of darkness" could soon be lighting up Africa. South Africa's state-owned utility, Eskom, is leading a five-country project to upgrade a small and largely moribund hydroelectric plant on the river at Inga and turn it into a dynamo that runs a pan-African electricity grid.

At Inga, just downstream of the Congolese capital, Kinshasa, 34 acre-feet of water a second rush down a series of rapids. Eskom's engineers say the force of this staggering volume of water at this point could generate 40,000 megawatts of power. That's twenty times more energy than comes from the Hoover Dam, ten times as much as Africa's current largest hydroelectric dam, the Aswan High Dam on the Nile, and more than twice that of China's Three Gorges

Dam. It is "enough to light up Africa and export to Europe as well," according to the company's adviser on project developments, Ben Munanga.

The proposed $50 billion Grand Inga hydroelectric project would not even require a large dam, because unlike the Nile, the river is guaranteed to run strongly all year round. So there is no need to store water. Most of the money would be spent connecting this vast power source across Africa's jungle, bush, and desert to the continent's main population centers. The first power lines would link it to South Africa via Angola and Namibia, a distance of 1900 miles. Next, pylons would strut across 2500 miles of rainforest and swamp in the Central African Republic and Sudan to Egypt. Nigeria also wants to take Inga power to West Africa. Its power might even straddle the Sahara and enter Europe via Spain.

The plan is backed by South Africa's president, Thabo Mbeki, who hopes that it could become the flagship project of NEPAD, the New Partnership for Africa's Development, which is being promoted by the G8 governments in Europe and North America as a new Marshall Plan for the continent. It could just happen.

There is a surprisingly strong political push too behind another megaproject to harness the Congo. This time the idea is to send the water itself north to irrigate the fringes of the Sahara and refill Lake Chad. In 2002, several governments met in the rainforests of central Africa to sign an agreement on sharing the waters of the Congo. They said they wanted to raise $5 billion for a dam that would barricade one of the river's major arms, the Ubangi River, at a sleepy port called Palambo in the Central African Republic, and send the water north.

The Lake Chad Basin Commission, representing Nigeria, Niger, Chad, Cameroon, and the Central African Republic, fleshed out the plan in 2004. The dam should, they said, divert 80 million acre-feet of water a year over a narrow watershed into the headwaters of the north-flowing Chari River and down its wide floodplain before ending up 1500 miles away in Lake Chad. The survival of more than 20 million people in the lake basin depends on the Lake Chad Replenishment Project, the commission claimed. It could rehabilitate huge irrigation projects around the lake, such as the South Chad Irrigation Project, which were built in wetter times but are now unused.

"If nothing is done, the lake will disappear," claimed Adamou Namata, the water minister in Niger and the chairman of the commission. But the project would be "an opportunity to rebuild the ecosystem, rehabilitate the lake, reconstitute its biodiversity, and safeguard its people." In late 2004, the Nigerian president, Olusegun Obasanjo, agreed to pay $2.5 million for a feasibility study of the project.

On the Logone and Hadejia rivers, in Cameroon and Nigeria, poor farmers quake at the thought. For them, large engineering projects to remake the rivers have always brought trouble. Wherever the promised water went, it never reached them. Generally they lost water as it was corralled and privatized and sent uphill to money. They want and need very different solutions to their water problems, ones that go with the flow of nature rather than against it.

Discussion Questions

1. What do you perceive as some likely consequences of the global trade in "virtual water?" What are the implications of this water usage for countries that have plentiful water resources, and for those that do not?

2. Does your local community have water supply controversies of its own? What is the source of the controversy, and what are the arguments on both sides of the issue?

3. Civil engineering projects on the scale of the water project proposed in India require massive amounts of capital—an estimated 40 percent of India's GDP, for example. Do you think this type of investment is warranted? Why or why not? What alternatives might a country such as India have to address its water needs? Do the issues—and possible solutions—for a region such as the American Southwest differ from those found in India or China?

4. President George W. Bush talked about privatization of water resources whereby companies might purchase water from Canada for resale in drought-prone areas of the American West. What reasons would you give to support, or to oppose, such a move?

 Supporting Activities

1. Use the CIA *World Factbook* to compare and contrast the size (population and land mass), demographics, economics (including industries and access to energy resources), communication, and transportation statistics of a developed and a lesser-developed country of your choice (https://www.cia.gov/library/publications/the-world-factbook/index.html).

2. Go to the EPA's "Surf Your Watershed" site (http://cfpub.epa.gov/surf/locate/index.cfm) and locate the watershed area for your home. Identify the water sources that are part of this watershed and which of these sources is "impaired" and why; and find out what citizen-based groups are at work on this watershed.

3. View the video *Harvest of Fear* (2001; Frontline/Nova); see also the Web-based materials available that show the arguments on both sides of the genetically modified food debate at: http://www.pbs.org/wgbh/harvest/.

4. Find the source of your community's drinking water supply. How much water does your community consume daily, on average? Where is your community's sewage treatment plant? If you live rurally and depend on well water, find out how deep your well is and what the flow rate from the well is. If you rely on a localized septic system, learn where it is and what kind of maintenance it requires. Tally how many members of the class rely on municipal or individualized water supplies.

5. View Albert Bartlett's classic lectures—billed as "the most IMPORTANT video you'll ever see"—on exponential growth (*Arithmetic, Population, and Energy*) on YouTube (available: http://www.youtube.com/watch?v=F-QA2rkpBSY).

 Additional Resources

1. Review information about other countries of interest on the CIA *World Factbook* (updated biweekly): https://www.cia.gov/library/publications/the-world-factbook/index.html.

2. Access a plethora of Web-based information about population at *World Population: A Guide to the WWW* by Richard Jensen: http://tigger.uic.edu/~rjensen/populate.html.

3. View a short video on New York City's water supply on The Futures Channel Web site: http://www.thefutureschannel.com/dockets/hands-on_math/water_supply/. To learn more about that city's water supply system, visit: http://www.nyc.gov/html/dep/html/drinking_water/history.shtml.

4. Watch a video documentary about China's controversial Yangtze River hydroelectric project, *China's Three Gorges Dam: A Flood of Controversy*. 2009. Video Progressions, Inc. Available at: http://www.chinasthreegorgesdam.com/.

5. For an update on China's South to North water diversion project, see: Oster, Shai. (December 31 2008). China slows water project. *Wall Street Journal*. Available: http://online.wsj.com/article/SB123064275944842277.html.

Hundreds of Man-Made Chemicals . . .

The article by Gay Daly describes efforts that are being made to document the characteristics and effects of synthetic chemicals, most of which have been developed and introduced within the last half-century. These include the synthetic compounds that are used to make plastics, pesticides, herbicides, cosmetics, and dozens of other products. In spite of their relatively recent development, these compounds have become ubiquitous, showing up in thousands of products used every day; traces of these compounds have been found in the soil, water supplies, food, and even in the human bloodstream.

There exist a number of federal and state regulatory entities, such as the Food and Drug Administration (FDA) and the Environmental Protection Agency (EPA). However, some individuals erroneously assume that all products undergo rigorous testing by these agencies, and that products that are shown to have harmful effects are regulated and/or removed from the market. In reality, much of the safety testing that is done is carried out by the very companies that stand to gain from development and sale of a product. Furthermore, even when product testing *is* done by independent agencies there may be conflicting evidence, which can lead to stalemates and further delays in regulating harmful substances. The insecticide DDT is an excellent case in point: it first came into widespread use in the U.S. following World War II and was believed to be a safe, effective way of controlling disease-spreading mosquito populations. The adverse environmental impacts of DDT use became well known following the 1962 publication of the book *Silent Spring* by biologist Rachel Carson. It was not until 1972 that the U.S. banned sale and use of the compound. Although banned more than 30 years ago, numerous studies have shown that this persistent compound can remain in the soil for decades.

Daly highlights the work that has been done by scientist Theo Colborn, whose efforts to catalog the effects of what became termed "endocrine disrupting" chemicals have brought together individuals from across the professional spectrum, including physicians, wildlife biologists, anthropologists, toxicologists, and others. This multidisciplinary approach has been effective for at least two reasons. First, it has allowed pieces of evidence from multiple perspectives to be brought together into what has become a more holistic understanding about the complex nature of the effects of endocrine disrupters. Second, it has made it easier for Colborn and her colleagues to amass a body of research whose scope makes regulatory action more likely.

Still, doubts about direct effects remain, and chemical industry representatives and others maintain that many of these compounds are fundamentally safe. This highlights a basic problem with research of this kind: it's difficult to isolate the effects of any one substance when individuals are exposed to so many chemicals throughout their lives, and the task is particularly hard when the effects can manifest over a lifetime or beyond. Thus, identifying any one compound as the direct cause of a problem is very hard to do; researchers must instead look for a correlation between exposure and effects. In the absence of direct causal evidence, adopting policies to regulate substances is often delayed or not pursued at all.

Author Gay Daly has served as a senior editor at *Discover* magazine, and her work has appeared in *Good Housekeeping, People,* and *Parenting*, among other publications.

Hundreds of Man-Made Chemicals—

In Our Air, Our Water, and Our Food—Could Be Damaging the Most Basic Building Blocks of Human Development

By Gay Daly

Everyone knows that World War II left us, as a legacy, the atomic bomb. Far fewer people are aware that the war also left us a chemical bomb, silently, inexorably ticking away, that may threaten our health, our intelligence, and even our ability to reproduce. It may be exploding as you read.

Before the war, only a few synthetic chemicals—laboratory-made compounds that do not exist in nature—had been invented. With the onset of the war, chemists eager to help their countries achieve victory began inventing plastics, pesticides, solvents, degreasers, insulators, and other materials that could be used to make more effective weapons, increase crop yields, and feed more soldiers. They were, understandably, more focused on success than on safety.

In peacetime, these same labs helped fuel the economic boom of the second half of the twentieth century, formulating new chemicals manufacturers needed to create cheaper, smarter products.

Federal regulation was fragmentary at best, and manufacturers were allowed to provide their own proofs of safety, a situation that remains true today. There are now more than 100,000 synthetic chemicals on the market, and these chemicals are everywhere. They enter our bodies and those of other animals through every possible route of transmission. They are in our food supply, so we eat them. They drift in the air, so we breathe them. (Carried on thermal currents, they have long since reached the Arctic, so polar bears breathe them too.) Present in landfills, they leach into the water supply, so we drink them. Released as effluent into lakes and rivers by factories, they affect the habitat of fish, frogs, and all aquatic life, right down to plankton. Ubiquitous in cosmetics, they are absorbed through our skin. Pregnant women pass them to their fetuses; mothers feed them to their newborns when they breastfeed. A large, uncontrolled scientific experiment has been in progress for the last 60 years, and the question now is: Can we figure out what the results are? And if those results show we are in danger, what we can do about it at this late date?

For almost two decades after the war, our great faith in the new chemistry went untested. It seemed as if one miracle after another emerged from the labs, providing abundant, cheap food, drugs to cure disease, and technology that made life easier and more pleasurable: televisions, dependable cars, inexpensive, reliable refrigerators to replace the icebox.

Rachel Carson pushed Americans to question these miracles when she published *Silent Spring* in 1962, and legislation was passed to address concerns she and others raised about environmental toxins. By the early 1970s, more warning signs had showed up on the radar. DDT, the pesticide that had saved American soldiers

From *Onearth, 27(4), Winter 2006* by G. Daly. Copyright © 2006 by Natural Resources Defense Council. Reprinted by permission.

who fought in the South Pacific from malaria and been sprayed on millions of acres of cropland, was fingered as a killer of birds, especially the beloved bald eagle. Eggshells thinned by exposure to the compound meant fewer hatchlings survived. DES, a drug believed to prevent miscarriage, was found to cause cancer in the young women whose mothers took it during pregnancy; emergency hysterectomies saved many of the daughters' lives, but at a terrible cost. PCBs, highly effective lubricants and insulators used in electrical capacitors, transistors, hydraulic fluids, plasticizers, inks, waxes and adhesives, were deforming and killing birds and fish; by 1971, Monsanto had voluntarily stopped making them. Each of these problems was seen as an isolated case: A few rogue chemicals had wreaked havoc, but havoc could be contained. Ban DDT, ban DES, ban PCBs—perhaps we couldn't undo the damage already done, but we thought we could stop it in its tracks and breathe a sigh of relief.

The average person still thinks about chemicals as single entities, and our system of federal regulation still decides on a case-by-case basis whether chemicals are safe enough to circulate in our world. But a paradigm shift is underway among some scientists, who have over the last 30 years quietly begun to wonder: By introducing so many substances that did not evolve along with living organisms over hundreds of millions of years, have we unwittingly initiated changes in our biology that may be damaging it profoundly?

She Went Looking

One of the researchers most responsible for raising this question and pressing to find answers is Theo Colborn, a woman whose career path has been anything but conventional. Colborn got her Ph.D. at 58, an age at which most people are beginning to think about retirement.

By then, she had raised four children while working as a pharmacist, a job that required her to know a great deal about chemistry, biology, and health. In the 1970s she began to see disturbing patterns of illness in the six Colorado communities where she worked as a pharmacist. Eventually, she hypothesized that everybody drank from the local creek or river and each water source had its own unique set of toxins. She went to a number of conferences on water in the Western states and was shocked to find that all anybody talked about was the quantity of water—and who owned it.

Divorced, without a mortgage, her children grown and gone, Colborn decided to go back to school to make herself an expert on the quality of water. A master's degree in freshwater ecology led to a doctorate in zoology, then two years as a Congressional Fellow in the Office of Technology Assessment in Washington.

Then, in 1987, she landed at the Conservation Foundation, where her new boss asked her to take on a survey of research on the impact of pollution in the Great Lakes, a study that deter-

Theo Colborn, 78, has worked for almost 20 years to understand endocrine disruption. "Theo is a Rachel Carson of our day," says Gina Solomon, an expert in the field. "She has none of the trappings of a hero, but she is one."

mined the course of her life's work. A younger scientist would probably have wanted to make her own mark rather than reading over other people's work. There is little glory in this kind of analysis, no tenure. One of Colborn's gifts was that she enjoyed looking for patterns. She was, and is, one of those rare people who can hold thousands of details in her head, shuffling and reshuffling them, able to tolerate the uncertainty of not knowing where they will take her. For six months, she worked seven days a week, reading more than 2,000 research papers and 500 government reports. She developed a primitive filing system: 43 boxes of documents, one for each species that had been studied.

At first, Colborn went looking for increases in cancer, but she found, instead, other problems that disturbed her. Where hundreds of bald eagles had nested on the Great Lakes' shorelines, only 45 pairs remained. Inland, these birds had rebounded in the years since DDT had been banned; near cleaner lakes they also flourished. But on the shores of the Great Lakes, deformed birds were showing up across species with missing eyes, crossed bills, clubfeet. A startling number of gull and tern nests sheltered twice the number of eggs they should, which suggested that females were sharing nests, apparently for lack of a male companion. Many males were not mating or not parenting. Some birds were abandoning their nests altogether. Chicks seemingly born healthy quickly developed a wasting disease and died. Creepy stuff, but what did it mean? She sought out wildlife biologists who told her that they, too, sensed something was wrong, but none of them could put a finger on what it was. Tissue analyses of the animals kept turning up the same chemicals, including DDT, dieldrin, chlordane, lindane, and PCBs. Everyone knew that hundreds of chemicals had been discharged into the lakes, many of them persistent but impossible to measure with methods available at the time.

To tame the data, Colborn made an electronic spreadsheet for species that were most profoundly affected to figure out where the patterns lay. Before long, she realized that something fundamental had to be happening to explain such a wide range of symptoms: reproductive failures, genital deformities, thyroid malfunctions, behavioral abnormalities, and immune suppression. Eventually she decided the most likely probability was endocrine damage.

Her knowledge of endocrinology was sketchy, so she set herself the task of mastering it. Endocrinology is the science of hormones, the chemical signals that, in myriad delicate and subtle ways, manage an organism's most vital functions. Hormones tell the ovaries and testes how to make eggs and sperm, tell the lungs how to breathe, the intestines how to digest, and the heart how to pump; they direct neurons in the brain. The way they do their work is an extraordinarily complicated dance that scientists are still working to comprehend. Estrogens, the female sex hormones, have been accorded the most attention so they are best understood; the male hormones, androgens, run second; and the thyroid, which controls brain development, is a distant third. If hormones cannot do their job properly, the consequences are legion—some subtle, some disastrous. The wrong balance of estrogens and androgens, for instance, can lead to reproductive failure. If a fetus suffers even a small drop in thyroid hormone levels, learning disabilities may be the consequence, IQ points may be lost.

Colborn drew up a list of world-class scientists from different fields—endocrinology, biology, immunology, toxicology, psychiatry, ecology, anthropology—whose work gave them, collectively, the expertise to test her suspicions, and invited them to the Wingspread Conference Center in Racine, Wisconsin, in the summer of 1991. "I was scared to death! There I was, a brand-new Ph.D. who knew only a handful of wildlife biologists." She did her best to set up conditions in which this wary bunch could find common ground. "I kept them working from morning till night so they had to get to know each other," she says. "Thank God there were no cell phones back then." Right away, people began to see surprising connections between their work. They stayed up talking into the small hours.

The term endocrine disruption was coined at the meeting. As the fruit of their work, the group issued a consensus statement that has stood up well to the test of subsequent research. The participants agreed that many man-made chemicals had the potential to disrupt the endocrine system of animals, including humans, by mimicking the activity of a hormone, by blocking it, or through other mechanisms, and that many wildlife populations had already been affected. Even more disturbing, they emphasized that the fetus and newborn are at greatest risk, and that the effects might not be manifested until the animal was mature. Perhaps the greatest bombshell was the statement that "the concentrations of a number of synthetic sex hormone [disruptors] measured in the U.S. human population today are well within the range and dosages at which effects are seen in wildlife populations." Suddenly, this was not about cleaning up a few lakes; the health of all the creatures in our care was at stake—including the health of our unborn children.

Mountains of Data

In the years since that conference, research on endocrine disruption has picked up speed; Colborn and her staff have built a database of 33,000 articles to make that research accessible. Chemical manufacturers have funded many studies that have almost uniformly concluded that endocrine disruption does not occur or, if it

does, is not harmful. This is hardly surprising because a great deal of money is at stake. (To offer just one example: In 2002 U.S. companies produced 2.8 million tons of bisphenol A [BPA], a synthetic estrogen used to make baby bottles, plastic water bottles, dental sealants, and resin liners for metal food cans. At 94 cents a pound, this translates to sales of more than $5.3 billion in that year alone.) By contrast, federally funded academic researchers, who have no financial stake in the outcome of their work, have found much compelling evidence that synthetic chemicals, including BPA, do cause endocrine disruption and that the damage can be serious.

One discovery in particular changed the ground of all endocrine disruption research. Frederick vom Saal, a reproductive endocrinologist at the University of Missouri, established in 1997 that significant effects can be seen at extremely low levels of exposure, parts per billion and even per trillion. These levels are present in the blood of humans as well as animals.

The next logical step would be to expose human subjects to these chemicals, but it is considered unethical to subject humans to substances that might damage their endocrine function. So rats and mice have had to stand in for humans, just as they do in cancer research.

Over the last 10 years, vom Saal has studied the effects of BPA on mice, and others have followed his lead. Collaborating with Wade Welshons, a veterinary medical researcher also at the University of Missouri, he established in 1997 that male mice whose mothers were exposed to BPA during gestation routinely developed enlarged prostates. Further research found that BPA has many other impacts. In male offspring, exposure of the mother results in decreased sperm counts, decreased motility of sperm, an increase in malformed sperm, and smaller testes. In females, researchers have observed early onset of puberty, larger uteri, polycystic ovaries, deformed and incomplete vaginal structures and tissues, enlargement of mammary ducts and milk glands in the breast, and an increase in miscarriages. Damage by BPA, vom Saal notes, is not limited to reproductive effects. Structural changes in the brain; immune-system damage; learning problems; hyperaggression; and changes in sexual behavior, social interactions, and play behavior have also been documented.

Chemical manufacturers have worked hard to counter this academic research, hiring chemists to study and discredit the results. Vom Saal and others have had to spend enormous amounts of time and money defending their work, resources better devoted to moving forward onto new ground. Researchers funded by industry, curiously, tend to find that every chemical is safe. In 2004, vom Saal tallied up results of all the studies he could find on BPA. He discovered that of 104 studies done by independent researchers, 94 found adverse effects and 10 found no effects. Of the 11 studies conducted by industry-supported researchers, zero identified adverse effects. Marian Stanley, a spokesperson for the American Chemical Council, which represents the interests of chemical manufacturers, says, "We are unaware of any big discrepancies between the experimental research supported by industry and by others. Animal studies—that is, credible experimental research—from all sectors show basically the same results across the board."

In fact, Colborn observes, academic researchers have been able to demonstrate the effects of chemicals at very low doses, but industry labs have not been able to replicate their work, and use their lack of results to claim that the chemicals are safe. Colborn says that independent researchers have identified possible causes of these discrepancies. Diet is key; animal chow that has more soy, which itself is mildly estrogenic, may skew results. Housing rats in plastic cages or stainless steel may throw things off since some plastics disrupt endocrine levels but metal does not. Intrauterine position can affect results: For instance, a male rat that grew in utero between two female rats will be born with higher levels of estrogen in its blood than one that grew between two male rats. Controlling for all these variables is hard and expensive. The most contentious variable has been breed of rat. Early in the process, researchers determined that the Charles River Sprague Dawley rat was so tough that it barely responded to estrogenic compounds. Many scientists whose work is funded by chemical manufacturers have continued to use this strain, a practice deplored by Colborn and other independent researchers.

Pat Hunt, a geneticist at Washington State University, was shocked when she discovered how great a difference a worn-out plastic cage could make. Suddenly, 40 percent of the healthy control mice in an experiment began to make eggs with grossly abnormal chromosome behavior where she expected to see a rate of 1 to 2 percent. She traced the problem back to BPA they were exposed to when it leached out of their cages and water bottles. She spent five years on the problem, making certain of her results before publishing "because I was going to say exposure to this chemical used in plastics can cause miscarriages." Today, at conferences, Hunt urges fellow scientists to take endocrine disruption seriously. "The mouse is an incredibly robust breeder while we humans are, comparatively, so fragile." She is concerned about delay. "If we wait till we see an increase in chromosomally abnormal [human] miscarriages or a sharp drop in sperm count, by the time that big an effect comes up on the radar screen, we need to ask ourselves if we are going to be reproducing as a species or not."

Research on male sex hormones, or androgens, has shot forward in the past decade, and the man most responsible for this progress is Earl Gray, a toxicologist who works for the Environmental Protection Agency in Research Triangle Park, North Carolina. In 1995, he started by administering very low doses of the fungicide vinclozolin to pregnant rats.

Vinclozolin was widely used until 2002, when the EPA began to restrict it because of its potential health effects. Gray found that the rats' male offspring were born with nipples, malformed scrota and testes, vaginal pouches, and cleft phalluses with hypospadias (urethral openings in the wrong place, along the shaft of the penis or in the scrotum). This finding is particularly resonant for human health, since the rate of hypospadias in human infants doubled for no known reason between 1968 and 1993. The animals in this experiment also displayed delayed puberty, lower sperm counts, and reduced fertility.

Gray went on to examine trenbolone acetate, a synthetic steroid used as a growth promoter in beef cattle in the United States and as a performance-enhancer by athletes who purchase it illegally over the Internet. Trenbolone, excreted in animal waste, shows up in rivers and streams where, Gray believes, it may affect aquatic animals. After experiments on the fathead minnow, Gray concluded that trenbolone was a powerful androgen: Female offspring of mothers exposed to the compound grew tubercles, part of the reproductive system usually seen only in males, and had fewer babies. Observers of wildlife are beginning to report similar effects around the world. Effluents from pulp and paper mills are sufficiently androgenic to sex-reverse female fish in Florida, the Baltic Sea, and New Zealand.

Gray is an extraordinarily productive researcher, at the top of his field. One can only wonder how much more he might discover if he had more resources. Because of a hiring freeze at EPA, Gray's staff of technicians has shrunk from three to one, limiting the number of experiments he can do.

Threats to Our Health

It is extremely difficult to obtain direct evidence that endocrine-disrupting chemicals cause reproductive damage in humans, for reasons beyond the ethical one. For instance, determining the effect of any particular chemical on an individual is nearly impossible because it is so difficult to figure out which chemicals the individual's mother was exposed to during pregnancy. However, Shanna Swan, director of the Center for Reproductive Epidemiology at the University of Rochester School of Medicine and a researcher who is at the forefront of this effort, published last May the first study to link prenatal exposure to phthalates to outcomes in offspring.

She had recruited a group of pregnant women and measured nine phthalate metabolites in their urine. This chemical group had already been shown to disrupt the endocrine system in rodents and is ubiquitous in our world—in plastics, nail polish, perfumes, toothbrushes, pesticides, paint, and the coating on time-release pills. Then Swan asked pediatricians who knew nothing about the maternal exposure levels to measure the distance between the genitals and the anus in the male babies. Then this distance was divided by the infant's weight to establish an anogenital index (AGI), a biomarker animal researchers have long used because it is predictive of the healthy development of the genitals in rodents. Short AGI correlates with smaller penises, smaller, ill-defined scrota, and incomplete testicular descent.

Swan found that a boy born to a mother with a high exposure to dibutyl phthalate (DBP), for example, was 10 times more likely to have a short AGI than a child of a mother with a low exposure to DBP. Swan points out that this was a small study of 85 infants; she has proposed a larger study of 600 families to investigate these effects further. She believes the research is necessary because the mothers of babies with short AGIs had been exposed to levels of phthalates that, according to estimates from the Centers for Disease Control and Prevention, are present in the bodies of one-quarter of all American women.

It is already clear that synthetic chemicals can also powerfully affect the thyroid gland, which is critical to brain development and function, according to Thomas Zoeller, an endocrinologist at the University of Massachusetts Amherst. But work is still in an early stage; much remains to be understood about how the thyroid functions and how that functioning can be disrupted. Zoeller's lab works with PCBs even though they were banned in 1979, largely because the behavior of these chemicals is well understood, which makes it easier both to predict their behavior in the lab and to interpret it. Moreover, although PCB levels dropped at first after the ban, these chemicals have such a long half-life that the rate of decline leveled off in the mid-1990s, which means they will belong to our bodies' burden of toxins for a long time to come.

Zoeller has determined that exposing a fetus to PCBs leads to profound changes in the brain. "The corpus callosum is a big bridge of white matter that connects the two hemispheres, and in our experimental animals, the PCBs cause a reduction in the size of the corpus callosum," he says. This may prove to be a very important finding, he explains, because "a number of neuropsychological diseases in humans have been linked to the development of the corpus callosum—for example, autism and Tourette's." However, he emphasizes that we don't know yet if the link is causative. Zoeller also suspects that disruption of the thyroid may be contributing to the sharp spike in learning disabilities observed over the past two decades, a spike that cannot, he says, be explained away by improvements in diagnosis.

A careful study published in 1996 by Joseph and Sandra Jacobson suggests Zoeller is right to be concerned. Testing children of mothers who ate Great Lakes fish contaminated by PCBs, they found that children whose mother's blood and breast milk, along with umbilical cord blood, showed the highest concentrations of PCBs had lower IQs—on average six points lower—than children of mothers with the lowest concentration. Joe Jacobson points out that what he and his wife documented was a correlation between exposure and a drop in IQs rather than proof that PCBs caused the drop. The children with greatest exposure also exhibited memory and attention deficits and were twice as likely to be at least two years behind kids in the lowest exposure group in reading comprehension. None of these impacts sounds catastrophic, but they could mean more kids who can't sit still in class and are miserable in school. The Jacobsons followed these children only until they were 11 so they do not know how those exposures affected them later in life. But children who have difficulty in school may well grow up less able to read, write, or think clearly.

> Two brooding questions have hung over endocrine-disruption research. One: are the effects of endocrine-disrupting chemicals additive—if you are exposed to many of them, will their effects add up to produce greater changes in hormonal activity? And two: are the effects handed down from one generation to the next? The first attempts to study these questions suggest that the answers are likely to be: yes and yes.

In 2005 Kevin Crofton, a neurotoxicologist who works for the EPA at Research Triangle Park in North Carolina, published a finding that helped to confirm many researchers' worst fears. Crofton gave rats different doses of mixtures of three classes of chemicals—dioxins, PCBs, and dibenzofurans—at concentrations ranging from approximately those that would be found in humans to levels 100 times higher. The chemicals in the mixture were chosen because they are found in foods people eat, from fish to breast milk. The highest dose he used for each chemical was still so low that he had seen no endocrine-disrupting effects for that chemical at that level. At the lower doses, Crofton found that the effect of the mixture was additive and that it significantly reduced the animals' level of thyroxine, the most common thyroid hormone. At higher doses, he observed that the mixtures reduced thyroxine synergistically so that the sum of their effect was slightly greater than simple addition. A fetus must have enough thyroxine for the brain to develop properly; adults need thyroxine to regulate metabolism and heart rate.

This and many other recent studies of mixtures up the ante considerably. They cut right through the endless debates about whether the levels of exposure to a chemical in any given experiment accurately reflect the levels at which humans or animals are actually exposed to that compound in the environment. These studies suggest that we can't solve the problem by taking a handful of the most dangerous chemicals off the market; instead, we will have to consider whether all endocrine disruptors need to go. The European Union has already begun to move in this direction.

The second question, whether effects are handed down from one generation to the next, got an answer almost by accident. Michael Skinner, a molecular and cellular biologist who focuses on reproductive biology at Washington State University, wanted to look at how cells communicate during the development of ovaries and testes. He dosed a group of pregnant rats at mid-gestation with vinclozolin, an anti-androgen (a substance that blocks androgenic hormonal activity), and another group with the pesticide methoxychlor, which is estrogenic, to see if either would alter the development of their offspring. A research fellow in his lab bred that first generation of babies, which was not part of the plan. She apologized, but Skinner told her not to worry, to seize it instead as an opportunity to examine the impact on a second generation. Everyone in his lab was stunned when they found that both chemicals wreaked significant damage. According to Skinner, of those exposed to vinclozolin, "greater than 90 percent of the males developed subfertility with a dramatic increase in developing sperm undergoing cell death" for not one but four generations. Further analysis established that the rats in both experiments had suffered germ-cell defects, the result of a chemical modification of their DNA. Both males and females developed various diseases as they aged. For example, female offspring of the first generation developed a condition equivalent to pre-eclampsia in human mothers, which can result in severe complications for the baby and death for the mother. In humans, incidence of pre-eclampsia has risen sharply over the last 20 years, and no one knows why. Skinner points out that he used a level of

•• WHAT YOU CAN DO •••••••••••••••••••••••••••••••••••

In the fight to rid the environment of endocrine-disrupting chemicals, your purchasing power is your greatest weapon. You can start to make informed choices about what to buy only after you identify the sources of exposure—not an easy task.

For baby products, take a look at www.oeconline.org/kidshealth/tinyfootprints. Cosmetics are a tough area because the federal government doesn't require that manufacturers list all ingredients. But the Environmental Working Group's website, www.ewg.org/reports/skindeep, is a good place to start. For pesticides, log on to www.pesticide.org. If you would like a fuller list of websites that have been vetted by Theo Colborn and her staff, send an email to tedx@tds.net asking for their self-help list. Manufacturers fear what they call product deselection. If you write to tell them why you have stopped buying a product, you exercise even greater power in the marketplace. You can also multiply that power by telling your relatives and friends what you're doing and why; at the same time, you will be helping to protect them.

To learn more about the science and politics of endocrine disruption, go to www.ourstolenfuture.org, the work of John Peterson Myers, one of the coauthors of Colborn's book.

toxins higher than what people would be exposed to in ordinary circumstances, but he believes that "women in their mid-gestation pregnancies should be very cautious about their environmental exposures."

We Are Unprotected

Fewer than a thousand of the 100,000 synthetic chemicals have been tested for endocrine disruption by anybody, but even the little we know is alarming. Sadly, the government's effort to mount a response has been checked continually by insufficient funding for research and regulation, by the complexity of the science that must be done, and by industry's well-funded efforts to delay the EPA's plans to test chemicals.

After the Wingspread conference, Colborn worked to raise awareness of endocrine disruption in citizens and legislators. With two gifted collaborators, John Peterson Myers and the science writer Dianne Dumanoski, Colborn wrote *Our Stolen Future*, a book for the lay reader. In 1996, the year it was published, Congress passed ambitious legislation mandating the testing of all synthetic chemicals to determine whether they cause endocrine disruption. The Endocrine

Disruptor Screening and Testing Advisory Committee (EDSTAC) was charged to recommend a testing protocol within two years.

From the start, EDSTAC faced considerable obstacles. One was its size: 39 members, including chemical company representatives and environmental activists, but only five bench scientists. Gina Solomon, a Harvard-trained physician who had just started work at the Natural Resources Defense Council (NRDC), where she is now a senior scientist, remembers, "It was often hard to get a word in edgewise, let alone talk through anything." She adds, "These were public meetings with audiences of up to 100, held in anonymous airport hotels around the country so there could be local participation and comment, which is a good thing, but it created a disconnect. The committee was charged to do a very technical scientific task."

Discussions were contentious. Representatives of some chemical manufacturers were accompanied by teams of lawyers who had to consult on every issue. At one point, the committee reached a seemingly hopeless impasse on how to define an endocrine disruptor. A compromise was finally achieved when Colborn suggested that they "describe" rather than "define" the term. How to define an adverse effect of an endocrine disruptor also ate up oceans of time. The law required an investigation of estrogenic effects of synthetic chemicals but did not limit the investigation to estrogen alone. Industry wanted to look only at estrogens, while Colborn and others believed all hormones should be studied. Eventually androgens were included, and later thyroid hormones were added as well, but it took months to reach these agreements. (Other hormonal systems that are not yet part of the testing include the pancreas, where malfunction can lead to diabetes or obesity; the pituitary gland; the pineal gland, which controls sleep; and the thymus, critical to the immune system.)

The committee was also divided about whether the goal was to protect human health or the health of wildlife. Colborn considered this a false dichotomy because she does not see animals and humans as two groups with separate fates. If wildlife suffers, so do humans. Yet, while evidence of harm to wildlife was mounting, how to pin down causal connections to human health remained a vexed question. Representatives of industry were quick to exploit the dilemma inherent in the research: They argued that anything less than the gold standard of experiments conducted with human control groups would be "unsound science," experiments that everyone agreed could never be conducted for ethical reasons.

Despite these difficulties, EDSTAC met its deadline: In August 1998, its final report recommended 14 assays, or tests, and a plan for making decisions about how many of these tests a chemical had to pass before it could be deemed safe.

Not even one assay has been approved as we go to press. Before testing can begin, protocols have to be agreed upon for conducting each assay and then each assay has to be validated by running trials in multiple labs to prove that results are reproducible from one lab to the next. Establishing protocols and validating them has proved to be extraordinarily difficult and time-consuming.

But the work is all the more important because the chemical companies themselves will be responsible for conducting these tests. Still, the process of validating the government's battery of assays has eaten up seven years. Colborn says that lack of resources has been the biggest deterrent to progress: "With the lack of funding and the limited staff provided to the EPA, we could not have expected much more." Solomon of the NRDC is cautiously optimistic but warns that validation has seemed within reach several times before, only to be disrupted by unforeseen difficulties. Colborn fears that money and time will be thrown away testing high doses instead of low doses, on adult rats rather than embryos, on Charles River Sprague Dawley rats that won't react.

Gray is, like Colborn, keenly impatient with the delays, but he believes the proposed assays will tell us what we need to know. "We have reliable screening assays for identifying estrogens and anti-estrogens and androgens and anti-androgens that have been used in the scientific community for decades," Gray says. "These assays are reproducible, and they're diagnostic of endocrine effect. They produce valid, interpretable results."

Show Us the Money

Given the strength of the science and the risks in play, it would seem that it is time to spend the money to do the testing and move the regulatory process forward. Unfortunately, the reverse seems to be happening. In 2003, 2004, and 2005, the Bush administration tried to cut all EPA funding for independent scientists who do endocrine-disruptor research. While these efforts failed, the total budget for those three years was still less than $15 million. (By contrast, Japan recently spent $135 million on a research program and has identified some 70 chemicals as endocrine disruptors.)

Spokespeople for chemical companies maintain that the levels at which humans are exposed to endocrine disruptors are not dangerous. Marian Stanley at the American Chemical Council states: "The consensus of the research is clear that there is no evidence that humans have been adversely affected by environmental exposures to endocrine active substances . . . and there is not convincing evidence of a growing human health issue." Still, there are signs that manufacturers have read the handwriting on the wall and are making changes to avoid liability suits down the line. Procter & Gamble has removed dibutyl phthalate (DBP) from all products that it sells around the world. Unilever, Revlon and L'Oréal have pledged to take chemicals banned in Europe out of any products they sell here. Baxter International is developing an alternative to phthalates for its medical bags and tubes. And methoxychlor, one of the pesticides Michael Skinner tested that showed endocrine damage through four generations, quietly disappeared from the U.S. market last year when Drexel Chemical failed to re-register it with the EPA.

Colborn is encouraged by these developments, but she is still extremely worried because these few withdrawals "don't begin to clean up the womb environment." Solomon worries, too, particularly with regard to food production and supply. "Every time a pesticide is re-registered by the EPA, the registration contains a boilerplate statement that there is no evidence that this chemical causes endocrine disruption, but that after tests are approved there may need to be additional testing. In the meantime, that chemical may be affecting the health of hundreds of thousands of farm workers or millions of people who eat the crops that are sprayed with that chemical."

In addition to the chemicals already released into the environment, 2,000 new chemicals go to market every year, and each may have the potential to be another DDT, a DES, a PCB, all of which turned out to be powerful endocrine disruptors. The biggest hurdle to solving the problem is funding. Colborn and others have proposed that those who profit from these chemicals be made financially responsible for determining the environmental safety of their products. Money could be paid by manufacturers into a trust, or directly to the government, so that manufacturers could not influence the outcome of the testing.

Instead of drifting along for years, nibbling away at the problem of how to remove endocrine disruptors from the environment, Colborn hopes we will throw our collective will and enough resources into finishing the job as quickly as possible. "Think of how many billions we've spent on cancer research. If these chemicals threaten our ability to reproduce, then we ought to be spending at least as much money on understanding how they work and whether we need to get them out of our environment," she says. "If we can't reproduce, whether we get cancer or not will be a moot point."

Discussion Questions

1. Daly discusses what she calls a "paradigm shift" in the way some scientists are thinking about the effects of synthetic chemicals on the environment. What is the nature of this paradigm shift, and how does it differ from prior thinking?
2. On the issue of the effects of endocrine disruptors, as with other contentious issues, there are two diametrically opposed points of view: one camp holds that there is no evidence of adverse effects; the other maintains that the evidence is compelling and that more research, and more regulatory oversight, is needed. How is it possible for a society to move forward with responsible policy decisions when there is so little agreement on who is "right" and who is "wrong?" What strategies could be used to overcome this type of stalemate?
3. What do you see as the most important concerns associated with the widespread use of synthetic chemicals? What two to three responses do you think would be most effective for responding to these concerns?

 Supporting Activities

1. Read and discuss the book *Silent Spring* by biologist Rachel Carson, originally published in 1962. This book has long been heralded as a major contributor to the modern environmental movement because it documented direct effects of human impacts on the environment.
2. While DDT has been irrefutably linked to adverse health effects in humans and other species, it remains an effective insecticide. Uncover some global statistics on malaria. If you were a policymaker responsible for reducing malarial deaths in sub-Saharan Africa, what recommendations would you make?
3. View the movie *The Estrogen Effect: Assault on the Male,* which details the search for endocrine-disrupting synthetic chemicals and highlights the work of scientist Theo Colborn and others. The video, first published in 1993, is distributed through Films for the Humanities and Sciences in Princeton, NJ.
4. Go to the Web site *Our Stolen Future* (http://www.ourstolenfuture.org/). Select and read one of the research studies presented there, and prepare a one-page summary of the research.

 Additional Resources

1. Visit the Web page of The Endocrine Exchange, a non-profit organization founded by Dr. Theo Colborn and dedicated to compiling and disseminating evidence about chemicals that act as endocrine disruptors: http://www.endocrinedisruption.com/home.php.
2. For more information about chemicals and safety, see: Rodricks, Joseph V. 2007. *Calculated Risks: The Toxicity and Human Health Risks of Chemicals in Our Environment (2nd ed.).* Cambridge: Cambridge University Press.
3. The report *Environmental Threats to Healthy Aging* (2008) by Jill Stein, Ted Schettler, Ben Rohrer, and Maria Valenti summarizes research on the effects of environmental pollutants, among other factors, on overall health, with a particular focus on Alzheimer's and Parkinson's disease. Available at: http://www.agehealthy.org/.

4. For differing points of view about the safety of plastics, particularly its use in food and beverage containers, see the Frequently Asked Questions at a plastics industry information site: http://www.plasticsinfo.org/ and compare this with the article *Pots, pans, and plastics: A shopper's guide to food safety*, which can be found on the WebMD site: http://www.webmd.com/health-ehome-9/plastics-food-safety.

5. Learn more about the chemicals used in cosmetics at the FDA site: http://www.fda.gov/Cosmetics/default.htm.

The Case of the Vanishing Frogs

There is cause for growing concern about species loss. Although species decline has always occurred, often due to massive climate changes leading to great extinctions, scientists believe that the rate and extent of species loss in the absence of such a climate change is occurring at a rate faster than at any other time in the Earth's history.[14] Halliday and Heyer, both active scientists in the field, discuss the mounting evidence of alarming declines in amphibian populations worldwide, even in areas considered untouched by development.

Two features of this article are important to highlight. First is the clear and concise way the authors lay out a rationale for why we should care about these declines. Their arguments apply equally well to other species as they do to frogs, and these arguments provide excellent grounds for discussion about when, whether, and why steps should be taken to preserve biodiversity. Second, these authors provide a useful illustration of how and why it can be difficult to pinpoint the factors that cause species decline (and similar biological catastrophes such as those described in the Daly article). The ongoing international efforts to document and study decline in amphibian species that both authors continue to be engaged in represent important steps in understanding, and addressing, this decline. The implications of this work extend to other species as well.

Timothy R. Halliday is a Professor in the Department of Life Sciences at The Open University in Milton Keynes, U.K. He is a member of the Board of Directors of the Declining Amphibian Populations Task Force (DAPTF) and has written extensively on amphibian biology. W. Ronald Heyer is Chair of the DAPTF, and works out of the Biodiversity Programs Office of the Smithsonian Institution in Washington, D.C.

The Case of the Vanishing Frogs

By Timothy R. Halliday and W. Ronald Heyer

Are the world's amphibians—vulnerable to ecological changes in water and on land—acting like canaries in a coal mine, warning us of environmental dangers below the threshold of human perception?

In the summer of 1982, David Wake, director of the Museum of Vertebrate Zoology at the University of California, Berkeley, set out to solve a little mystery. Several months earlier he had pointed David Green, then a postdoctoral fellow, to a site in the nearby Sierra Nevada that Wake knew to be abundant in *Rana muscosa*, a mottled yellow and brown frog Green was studying because of its unusually broken distribution patterns. But when Green reached the designated location, he couldn't find a single specimen.

Image © worldswildlifewonders, 2009. Used under license from Shutterstock, Inc.

Used with permission of MIT Technology Review, from *Technology Review, Vol. 100, No. 4,* by T.R. Halliday & W.R. Heyer, 1997; permission conveyed through Copyright Clearance Center, Inc.

Puzzled by Green's account, Wake decided to accompany him to the site, assuming he had simply missed it the first time. But when they arrived, Wake, too, was surprised to find that all the adults had disappeared and only a couple of tadpoles remained.

Wake and his other students soon began to notice similar disappearances at other popular frog localities in central and northern California. Wake wondered if he had stumbled upon a bigger puzzle: Was this decline in amphibian populations occurring only in California, or was it part of some larger pattern?

By coincidence, the First World Congress of Herpetology was scheduled to take place later that year in Canterbury, England. So Wake seized the opportunity to discuss his disturbing observations with other herpetologists. What he discovered, to his dismay, was that many of the attendees had witnessed the same phenomenon in scattered areas around the globe.

Wake took their reports and his own to the next meeting of the National Academy of Sciences Board of Biology, to which he belonged, and convinced its members to assemble a group of leading international amphibian experts to evaluate the evidence. The group, which convened in February 1990 in Irvine, Calif., quickly concluded that although most of the evidence for amphibian declines was anecdotal, the sheer number of widely dispersed informal reports indicated that the situation could be an environmental emergency, and that an international working group should conduct a full scientific investigation.

By the end of the year, after approaching several potential sponsors, Wake created the Declining Amphibian Populations Task Force (DAPTF) under the aegis of the Species Survival Commission of the World Conservation Union, an international organization comprising more than 500 environmental groups including the U.S. Fish and Wildlife Service and the U.S. National Park Service. Based at the Open University in Milton Keynes, England, the task force recruited more than 1,200 scientists to determine whether declining amphibian populations will simply rebound as part of some normal cycle or whether they truly are disappearing from the face of the earth.

Why We Care about the Victims

One reason so many amphibian biologists were eager to join the task force was simply because they were worried they might be losing their objects of study. But they were even more concerned for other reasons that everyone can appreciate. The first is the ethical consideration that amphibians have the right to exist. If people are responsible for amphibian disappearances, then people have a moral obligation to prevent them. Most religious traditions assign value to all living organisms. Even Judeo-Christianity, which espouses that humans are a special creation of God and are given dominion over the rest of the living organisms on earth, teaches that this relationship should be a stewardship, not a slaughter.

Second, amphibians are fascinating organisms that interact in complex ways with each other and their environments. Consider the life history of the Central American strawberry poison frog *Dendrobates pumilio*. At the beginning of their reproductive cycle, males call for females from perches on the tropical forest floor. After mating, the female lays her eggs in the forest's leaf litter. The father then revisits the eggs and keeps them moist with bladder water. When the eggs hatch into tadpoles, the mother carries them on her back and deposits each one into a tiny pool of water, often dew that collects at the base of bromeliad leaves. Because there is seldom enough food for even a single tadpole in these pools, the mother revisits each one every few days and lays an unfertilized egg for her offspring to eat. As the frogs mature, they synthesize poison toxins in their brightly colored skin from compounds found in the native arthropods on which they feed. If such frog species disappear, we lose valuable information about life on earth.

Third, amphibians may provide direct benefit to humans. One example is the gastric brooding frog, *Rheobatrachus silus*, of Queensland, Australia. After the female's eggs are fertilized, she swallows them and uses her stomach as a brood pouch, somehow switching off her digestive enzymes during the incubation period. Knowledge of such an enzyme-suppression mechanism might have proven helpful to people suffering from gastric ulcers. Unfortunately, while these and other biological aspects of *R. silus* were being investigated, the species disappeared from its natural environment, and all specimens in the laboratory died. For a rough idea of what we'd be missing if many such species disappeared, consider some benefits that have already been realized, including a pain killer recently derived from poison-frog toxins and a nonirritating vaginal cream made from frog skin that prevents pregnancy and protects against sexually transmitted diseases (see "All Natural AIDS Protection?" *TR* August/September 1996).

The fourth and primary reason that the task force was established is that amphibians are important indicators of general environmental health. Because most amphibians have a biphasic life cycle—they spend their early stages in water and their adult life on land—and have extremely thin, permeable skin, any changes in either aquatic or terrestrial environments may significantly affect these creatures. Thus, amphibians may provide early warnings of deteriorating environments that appear unaltered to human perception.

Gathering Evidence

A concerted effort by the enlisted scientists has provided us with far greater documentation of amphibian decline than we had in 1990 when the task force was formed. One suspicion that researchers confirmed is that most amphibian declines and disappearances are directly related to habitat modification. Furthermore, when the habitat change is dramatic, so are the effects. For example, in the United Kingdom, where many—in some areas 80 percent—of breeding ponds have been filled in over the past 50 years, all six native amphibian species have suffered dramatic population declines. Elsewhere, along a well-studied area on Volcan Tajumulco, the highest mountain in Guatemala, only 1 of 8 species of salamanders was able to survive after cattle ranchers converted the upper cloud forest zone into grazing pastures. Herpetologists also discovered that seemingly modest changes in habitats can also have profound effects. For instance, to the casual observer, it would appear that the arroyo toad (*Bufo microscaphus californicus*), whose habitat now exists entirely within uninhabited parks in California, is well protected. But the major streams that fed the best breeding sites have been dammed, and what remains of the stream bed plains is now being overrun by all-terrain sport vehicles. Because the larvae cannot live in the silty conditions that result from these modifications, toad populations have decreased alarmingly.

Perhaps the most disturbing finding, however, is that amphibian declines are occurring in diverse locations in relatively undisturbed habitats. Consider the following cases:

- In Australia, herpetologists have known since the late 1970s that populations of *R. silus*, the gastric brooding frog, were declining in pristine sites. After learning at the First World Congress of Herpetology that the decline might be symptomatic of a worldwide problem, the Australians launched a campaign to inventory all known amphibian localities throughout their rainforests, and to initiate long-term monitoring programs in some key areas. The researchers had since counted 14 frog species from remote habitats whose once-abundant populations had either completely vanished or had been reduced to only a few frogs.

- In California, biologists Charles Drost and Gary Fellers, both of whom are now with the U.S. Geological Survey, devised a clever approach to evaluate the status of amphibian populations in Yosemite National Park. Using extensive field notes of biologists Joseph Grinnell and Tracy Storer—who recorded detailed descriptions of the area's amphibian breeding sites between 1915 and 1919—Drost and Fellers were able to reassess the amphibian populations at the same sites. The fact that the researchers were able to relocate every site proved that no obvious change had occurred in the habitat during the intervening 75 years. Sadly, they also found that most of the amphibians were gone: whereas Grinnell and Storer counted 7 different amphibian species at 70 locations, Drost and Fellers could now find only 4 at 26 sites.

- The elfin forests on the ridge crest at Monteverde, Costa Rica, have witnessed perhaps the most notorious disappearance of an amphibian population from an undisturbed habitat—that of *Bufo periglenes*, the golden toad. Among the world's most colorful amphibians, the brilliant golden males differ dramatically from the equally flamboyant black, red, and yellow females. Largely because of their spectacular beauty, golden toads——known to science only since the 1960s (although the Quakers who colonized the Monteverde area were aware of their

existence before then)—served as the focus of concerted efforts to conserve the local habitat. In fact, a golden toad is depicted on the same sign with a panda to mark the entrance to a 328-hectare preserve established in 1972 by the Tropical Science Center of Costa Rica and the World Wildlife Fund for Nature. Later endeavors by other conservation groups tripled the size of the preserve to 10,500 hectares and finally more than doubled it again by adjoining it to the 16,000-hectare Children's International Rainforest.

Despite these conservation efforts, the golden-toad population crashed in 1988. During April and May of 1987, "more than 1,500 toads gathered to mate in temporary pools at Brillante, the principal known breeding site," report biologists Martha Crump and Alan Pounds, in the March 1994 issue of *Conservation Biology*. "But in 1988 and again in 1989, only a single toad appeared at Brillante, and a few others gathered 4 to 5 kilometers [to the southeast]. During 1990 to 1992," the researchers note, "despite our intense surveys, no golden toads were found." Nor have any been seen since.

- In Puerto Rico, researchers have discovered that two species, including *Eleutherodactylus jasperi*—one of the world's few viviparous frog species (which, like mammals, produce live young instead of eggs)—have apparently become extinct though their habitat still appears suitable.

- In Ecuador and Venezuela, eight species have been reported absent from the cloud forests of the Andes mountains. One genus in particular, the *Atelopus*, was once incredibly abundant (researchers could collect hundreds in an hour). But in 1990, Enrique LaMarca, a biologist at the University of the Andes in Venezuela—having spent more than 300 hours during 34 separate field trips searching for the frogs—reported finding only one specimen of *A. mucabajiensis* and two *A. soriani*. Another species in the genus, *A. oxyxrhynchus*, which LaMarca reported observing walking by the dozens on the forest floor, has not been seen since 1978.

- In the Atlantic Forests of southeast Brazil, specifically at a well-studied site in Boraceia, São Paulo, seven common amphibian species disappeared in 1979. The site has since been revisited numerous times by several herpetologists including Jaime Bertolucci, a doctoral student at the University of São Paulo, who conducted an intensive year-long study of the ecology of tadpoles. But none of the species that disappeared in 1979 have ever been found.

Similarly well-documented studies have found amphibian disappearances or declines from relatively undisturbed habitats elsewhere in these and other regions, including the U.S. Rocky Mountains and the Cascade Mountain Range in Washington, Oregon, and California.

Possible Suspects

Though more work must be done to plug the gaps in our knowledge of amphibian declines, these studies allow us to draw an important conclusion: amphibian populations, in far-flung locations, are indeed disappearing even in seemingly virgin environments. The challenge, therefore, is no longer merely to preserve habitat, though that is still a vital task. We must also discover and address the less obvious reasons for the demise of these creatures as well as determine what fate they might portend for other species, including ourselves.

Prominent among the suspects thought responsible for declining amphibian populations, at least in specific locales, include agri-

cultural chemicals and pesticides. In many parts of the world, certain amphibian species have thrived in agricultural areas, taking advantage of artificial water bodies used for irrigation and watering livestock. But the chemicals found in farmland breeding sites interfere with normal amphibian development. Michael Tyler, a biologist at the University of Adelaide in Australia and a board member of the Declining Amphibian Populations Task Force, explains that the problem with some herbicides is not the active ingredient itself, for example glyphosate, but rather a detergent additive that acts as a dispersant or wetting agent. The detergent breaks down the surface tension at the leaf surface to enable spray droplets to completely cover the leaf. However, the agent also interferes with respiration in frogs through the skin and even more so with respiration of tadpoles through gills. Michael Lannoo, a biologist at Ball State University, also points out that some pesticides such as methoprene (used for mosquito control) break down into a compound resembling retonic acid, which has been shown in the laboratory to produce severe amphibian limb deformities that would render individuals incapable of escaping predators.

Other pollutants under investigation are being blamed for more regional amphibian declines. Among the leading culprits for these losses may be acid rain. In fact, researchers have found that almost all amphibian eggs or larvae tested so far cannot survive in water with a pH of less than 4.5. Yet acid rains, commonly in the 3.5 range, can lower the pH of ponds and streams from a normal average of about 7.0 to lethal levels. In fact, acid rain has been identified as a cause of amphibian declines in lakes and ponds in Canada, Scandinavia, and Eastern Europe.

Chief among the candidates likely to be responsible for amphibian declines on an even wider, perhaps global, basis is ozone depletion.

Recent studies in Oregon have shown that rising levels of ultraviolet-B (UV-B) radiation resulting from the depletion of the earth's ozone layer have undermined the hatching success of eggs in some native amphibian species. The researchers suggest that other amphibians most likely to be affected by increased UV-B radiation —which, at elevated levels, breaks down the DNA molecule—are those living at cooler, higher elevations and extreme latitudes, where the ozone layer is thinnest but where amphibians must bask in the sunlight to regulate body temperature.

Environmental estrogens may also be responsible for global declines. Researchers believe that these pollutants, which result from the chemical breakdown of pesticides such as DDT, are likely to severely affect the reproductive biology of amphibians, as they have been shown to do in other aquatic organisms, such as fish and alligators. In fact, in laboratory studies, Tyrone Hayes, an endocrinologist at the University of California, Berkeley, found that such environmental estrogens masculinized female Japanese tree frogs, *Buergeria buergeri*, and feminized male pine woods tree frogs, *Hyla femoralis*, causing both populations to become sterile. These estrogens, whose molecules do not break down easily in the environment, stockpile in silt on the bottoms of ponds and lakes, where they are ingested by bottom-feeding amphibian larvae. Some of these agents are effective in very small concentrations and are easily wind-borne, making them a global threat regardless of their point of origin.

Inconclusive Evidence

We must conduct more research to determine which, if any, of these factors are responsible for declining amphibian populations in relatively pristine habitats. One approach would be to compare undisturbed sites where amphibian populations are healthy to similar habitats where the populations are in serious decline. One such grouping exists in the Andes mountains in Ecuador, Colombia, and Venezuela. While amphibians continue to thrive in high-elevation habitats in Colombia, they have disappeared from virtually identical habitats in Ecuador and Venezuela. Might something as straightforward as introducing predators such as trout into the waters of Ecuador and Venezuela, but not Colombia, be responsible? Or might atmospheric transport of agricultural chemicals applied in lowland regions of Ecuador and Venezuela be causing problems? An elegant set of comparative studies and experiments could be designed to address such questions at these and other promising groups of undisturbed sites in lowland and cloud forest habitats of Africa, South America, southeast Asia, and Madagascar.

Another approach would include studies aimed at rejecting regional or global factors as causes of amphibian declines. Most research has tried to verify the link between reduced frog populations and factors such as high UV-B concentrations. But some studies suggest that UV-B, as a single factor, is not responsible for all amphibian declines, since several species, such as the golden toad of Costa Rica, are never exposed to the sun's ultraviolet rays. In fact, golden toads lived underground all year long, except for a few days at the end of the dry season when they emerged to breed. But even then they were protected under the canopy of Monteverde's elfin forest, which (even though short by tropical lowland standards) effectively filters out the ultraviolet radiation. Moreover, because females chose to lay their eggs in well-shaded pools, the now-extinct golden toads were never exposed to UV-B even as eggs or larvae.

Such an analysis doesn't mean that rising UV-B levels are not killing off amphibians elsewhere. In fact, studies of amphibians exposed to such radiation are under way in the mountains of Chile and Argentina. It does, however, suggest that no single factor may be responsible for all declines. Perhaps more significant, the analysis also raises the possibility that more than one factor may be at play at each location. For example, if an amphibian population is subject to sublethal stresses from habitat fragmentation and acid rain, might it be more likely to succumb to an additional stress from some regional or global factor such as climate change or estrogen mimics?

Some research shows that such scenarios are possible. A study of the western toad *Bufo boreas*, common to the Elk and West Elk Mountains of Colorado, serves as one example. Cynthia Carey, a biologist at the University of Colorado, who began studying these toads in 1974, discovered that they had contracted "red leg" disease, a normally nonfatal illness caused by *Aeromonas hydrophila*, a naturally occurring bacterium. Over the next eight years, Carey found that the toads, once common in the mountains, had almost completely disappeared. Her conclusion was that some environmental factor, or the synergistic effects of several factors, may have caused the toads to secrete elevated levels of hormones that compromised their immune system and led to their infection and eventual death.

Studies such as these demonstrate that the underlying causes of amphibian declines may be far more complex than anyone originally imagined. Thus, studies that examine possible synergistic effects and help us tease out the relative contribution of each must be among our research priorities.

Interim Recommendations

Though much research lies ahead, we can take some practical steps immediately to halt the decline of amphibian populations. Perhaps the most obvious is to preserve remaining amphibian habitats. One novel approach would be to consider the health of amphibians in environmental impact assessments. In fact, this practice proved highly successful at a highway-construction site in British Columbia recently. Typically, whenever highways are built in the forested Canadian province, workers create roadside ditches and scour them of all vegetation. But in this case, thanks to a herpetologist included on the environmental-impact study team, the road builders added parts of fallen trees to the ditches, enabling native amphibians to use them as breeding sites.

Another simple but valuable step would be to consider amphibians in environmental assessment programs as bioindicators of overall ecosystem health. Because the eggs of many amphibians lack a protective covering and are laid at or near the surface of a body of water, they are very sensitive to both air- and water-borne pollutants. Also, because the climatic factors typically determine the onset, duration, and intensity of amphibian mating activity, careful monitoring of breeding populations can provide an extremely sensitive assay of climate change.

Finally, the latest findings regarding causes of amphibian declines need to be communicated both to international policymakers, who are in a position to set research priorities and fund additional studies, and to the public at large, which can influence their decisions. Americans are now much more aware of issues concerning amphibians than they were even a decade ago, thanks in large part to a number of excellent television documentaries that have focused on dwindling amphibian populations. But scientists and the media must continue to spread the word to convince people around the world that these precious creatures are worth their concern.

Discussion Questions

1. Halliday and Heyer discuss four reasons why humans should, or do, care about the declines of certain animal species. What are they? Which of these reasons do you personally find most compelling, and why?
2. Why are biologists particularly concerned about declines in frog species even in areas considered to be undisturbed?
3. What are considered to be the primary factors leading to decline of frog species? Are there other likely causes?
4. Do you consider the recommendations suggested by these authors to be useful and appropriate? What other types of steps might be needed to address this problem?

 Supporting Activities

1. Watch the short video *Worldwide amphibian declines: How big is the problem, what are the causes and what can be done?* May 2008. Available on AmphibiaWeb at: http://amphibiaweb. org/declines/declines.html.
2. Read more about what is required in order for a species to be listed by the U.S. Fish and Wildlife Service as threatened or endangered under the Endangered Species Act guidelines, and what that protection entails: http://www.fws.gov/Endangered/wildlife.html.

 Additional Resources

1. Visit the Global Biodiversity Information Facility, which seeks to make information about global species diversity accessible and serves as an open source clearinghouse for biodiversity data: http://www.gbif.org//.
2. Learn all about frogs at the American Museum of Natural History frog exhibit web site: http://www.amnh.org/exhibitions/frogs/.
3. Read more about the amphibians in literature, history, and the natural and social sciences in *Nature's Fading Chorus: Classic and Contemporary Writings on Amphibians*. 2000. Gordon L. Miller (Ed.). Washington, DC: Island Press.

House Proud *and* Building Materials: What Makes a Product Green?

The idea of creating a pre-fabricated, environmentally friendly, affordable home is one that has been tried without success before. One of the more interesting and groundbreaking approaches was proposed in the late 1920s by designer and visionary R. Buckminster Fuller. His "Dymaxion House" was designed to be completely self-sufficient, energy efficient, and even recyclable. The house was round, supported by a central mast, and made of aluminum, and Fuller's concept was that the home could be shipped anywhere in the world inside a tube.[15] The idea was definitely ahead of its time, and the Dymaxion House never achieved any kind of commercial acceptance.

One of the latest designers to attempt the goal of a "green" prefab home is architect Michelle Kaufmann, the subject of Booth's article. Although the advantages of factory-built over site-built homes are well documented (and briefly described in this article), the modular home concept has yet to break free of its image as a shoddy substitute for the real thing. Unfortunately, even this much-heralded effort at innovative design appears to have folded, a consequence of the financial downturn.[16]

Even as some efforts falter, consumer demand for products and materials in their homes that use less energy and are less damaging environmentally continues to increase. The aforementioned building standards such as LEED and Energy Star are just two of many attempts to achieve the significant environmental benefits that are believed to be well within reach through changes in the built environment. As author Alex Wilson points out, however, defining what approaches and materials are best is not always a clear-cut process. Some materials are simply "less bad" than others, an achievement that architect William McDonough would cite as woefully insufficient[17] in the quest for environmentally responsible design. Moreover, as being green is increasingly seen as a good business strategy the prevalence of, and incentives for, "greenwashing" also increase, making it harder for consumers to know whether they are really making the best choices. Nevertheless, Wilson's overview of the current strategies and terminology used in the building industry provides a useful introduction for those interested in reducing the overall impact of buildings.

House Proud

High Design in a Factory-Made Home? Michelle Kaufmann Believes She Holds the Key

By William Booth

Like the robot maid and the flying car, the perfect prefab house seems like one of those futuristic promises that never quite come true. You know the house: a light and airy, clean and green 3 BR, 2 BA constructed of renewable, energy-efficient materials—delivered to your doorstep. A modern house you can buy the way you buy almost everything else, with a click of the mouse. A modular house that can be assembled in an afternoon and comes complete, right

From *Smithsonian, Vol. 37, No. 10, January 2007* by William Booth. Copyright © 2007 by William Booth. Reprinted by permission.

William Booth is a Los Angeles-based staff writer for the *Washington Post* who covers culture and the arts.

down to the towel racks in the bathroom. Just plug in the utilities.

This is the house that Michelle Kaufmann believes she has designed—a young architect's answer to the challenge of bringing good design to the masses. "We want to create sustainable homes, of high quality, for a reasonable price, for the middle classes," says Kaufmann, 38. And to do that, she says, "you need an assembly line."

Not too long ago, Kaufmann bumped into her old boss, architect and design maestro Frank O. Gehry. "You know," he said, "some pretty smart people have tried this and failed." Indeed, several masters of 20th-century architecture saw the promise of prefab—giants such as Walter Gropius, Charles and Ray Eames and Joseph Eichler—but they could not redeem it.

But where others have failed, Kaufmann sees a way. Gropius or the Eameses could have built the factories to make their prefabricated homes, she says, but they lacked a crucial piece of technology. "The Internet is the key," she says. "A house is not a toothbrush," meaning a one-size-fits-all, perishable good. "You need and want to interface with the customer," to get a sense of how your building might be tailored to individual needs.

But instead of taking a dozen meetings with an architect, pinning down a hundred details, a Kaufmann prefab buyer meets with her once and then communicates with her through a Web site and by e-mail, selecting from a limited menu of options. "If you had to take meetings, you could never have mass production," says Kaufmann, who grew up in Iowa and holds degrees in architecture from Iowa State and Princeton universities. "But with e-mail, we can make the changes, we can tweak in an instant. You can keep the process moving forward."

The prefab house is hot again, at least in the pages of shelter magazines, and Kaufmann's designs are some of the smartest around; she has "definitively answered the question, 'Why prefab?'" wrote Allison Arieff when she was editor of *dwell* magazine. One of them is on view through June 3 at the National Building Museum in Washington, D.C., in an exhibit titled "The Green House: New Directions in Sustainable Architecture and Design." Another one, a demonstration project Kaufmann did with *Sunset* magazine in 2004, went up in a parking lot in Menlo Park, California, and was visited by some 25,000 people over two days. On her own she has designed a third, called mkSolaire, tailored more for urban than suburban lots. Kaufmann's firm's Web site (mkd-arc.com) has received some 15,000 inquiries for information on her modular homes.

How many prefabs has Kaufmann built? A dozen. Which hardly constitutes a revolution—high design, tailored prefab still remains more of an idea than a product line, but Kaufmann vows to change that.

She came to her "eureka" moment through personal experience. In 2002, she and her then-new husband, Kevin Cullen, a carpenter and contractor, began to look for a place to live in the San Francisco Bay Area; they quickly confronted the brutal realities of a real estate market gone bananas. Their choices were as frustrating as they are familiar: pay a gazillion dollars for a tear-down in close-in Oakland (and end up with no money to rebuild) or move to the far reaches of former farmland for a long commute from a soul-sucking tract of mini-mansions.

They looked for six months. "It was really depressing," Kaufmann recalls. "I seriously thought about what kinds of bad decisions had I made in my life to end up in a place where we could not afford a home. We actually went into therapy."

So they decided to build a house themselves. They found a narrow lot in suburban Marin County, and Cullen went to work on a

Kaufmann design with a simple but beguiling floor plan of connected rectangles, just 1,560 square feet, with an easy flow from space to space—a curtain of glass doors under a shed roof covered with solar panels. They called it the Glidehouse. Friends took a look at the plans and said: Make us one too. "This is the thing," Kaufmann says. "They didn't want me to design them another house. They wanted *our* house, the exact same house. And that's when I thought, hmm, could we make this in mass production?"

To hear her preach the prefab gospel, building a home from scratch, on-site—with what she calls "sticks"—makes little sense, while a factory committed to punching out Glidehouses provides nothing but advantages. There is quality control and little waste. Because the house moves down an assembly line, shuttled from station to station with overhead cranes and constructed on a grid with precision cuts, the joinery is plumb, the angles true.

"The factory reuses; the stick builder throws trash in the dumpster. With prefab, you build only what is needed," says Kaufmann. "The wood and other materials are not exposed to rain and the elements. There is also the human element: you know people are going to show up for work. There's no waiting for the subcontractor."

To prove the idea's benefits, Kaufmann performed an experiment in 2003 and 2004. While Cullen built the Glidehouse prototype from scratch on their Marin County lot, she worked with a manufacturer to complete an identical Glidehouse in a factory. The results: the site-built Glidehouse took 21 months to design, engineer and permit, and 14 months to build. The modular version was built in four months. (Kaufmann thinks she can shave this down to six weeks or less.) The site-built home cost $363,950 to build, or $233 per square foot, while the modular house cost $290,500, or $182 per square foot, including shipping. Both required additional spending for lots, foundations, landscaping, driveways, decks and garages.

After the experiment, Kaufmann dedicated her firm exclusively to prefab construction. "I was just young and naive enough not to know how hard this would be," she says.

Kaufmann soon learned that there were established companies already manufacturing modular structures for oil-field workers or temporary classrooms—decent boxes for temporary shelter, though hardly Glidehouses, with their lightweight paperstone kitchen countertops made of recycled paper, their roofs ready for clip-on solar panels and their clerestory windows. But her efforts to reach them were unavailing—she would discover that they wouldn't even call her back because they considered architects too difficult, and too time-consuming, to work with.

Undeterred, she says, "I basically became a stalker" and got through to a few manufacturers, enough to persuade them that "the future can be much more than what they had been doing." She contracted with them to make 11 Glidehouses and one Breezehouse, but she was still frustrated by the length of time the revolution was taking. So in 2006, she took the plunge and bought her own factory, 25,000 square feet east of Seattle, from a retiring modular house builder. She moved in this past October, with a goal of producing 10,000 prefabs over the next ten years. That's close to the number of post-

and-beam houses—still considered jewels of mid-century modernism—that Joseph Eichler built in California between 1949 and 1974.

For Kaufmann, prefab offers something else worth celebrating: a truly green building. "We've already done all the homework to find the most sustainable materials," she says. A client may like a bathroom to be blue or green, but either way it will be lined with recycled glass tiles, finished with nontoxic paint, lit by energy-efficient fluorescent bulbs and equipped with low-flow faucets and a tankless water heater.

"I think about the house like I think about a hybrid car," says Kaufmann, who drives a Toyota Prius. "You can be more efficient, but you don't have to change your life. With the hybrid, you still go to the gas station and fill it up. With the prefab houses, you make it easier to go green."

Her most cherished insight? "You have to stop thinking like an architect and start thinking like a manufacturer," Kaufmann says. "When I started on this, I didn't realize that the way to do it was to do it all."

Building Materials: What Makes a Product Green?

By Alex Wilson

Quite a bit of attention has been focused on the issue of green building materials. What makes a given product "green"? How do you evaluate the relative greenness of different products? How do you find green products? More important, perhaps, manufacturers are asking, "How can we make our products greener?"

There are several directories of green building products available, some national in focus, some regional. In compiling any directory of green building products, the authors have to figure out what qualifies a product for inclusion. That was an exercise the *EBN* editorial staff went through when we began developing the *GreenSpec®* directory, our own entry into the products directory field, in the late 1990s. This article is an attempt to lay out for public examination and discussion our standards for what makes a building product green. Our standards and thresholds have evolved over time, and this article lays out for public examination and discussion our current standards for "what makes a product green." These criteria will continue to change, and as they do, the products included in future editions of *GreenSpec* will also change. We welcome input in this process of determining just what is green.

The Challenges in Defining What Is Green

The Holy Grail of the green building movement would be a database in which the life-cycle environmental impacts of different materials were fully quantified and the impacts weighted so that a designer could easily see which material was better from an environmental standpoint. Though efforts are afoot along these lines we are not even close to realizing that goal. Very often, we are comparing apples to oranges. We are trying to weigh, for example, the resource-extraction impacts of one product with the manufacturing impacts of another, and the indoor-air-quality impacts of a third.

These issues were addressed in an earlier article on material selection (see *EBN* Vol. 6, No. 1), but in that article we were addressing the broader issue of material selection for a given project—not determining which materials should be considered green in general. This distinction is subtle but important. In building a house or office building, a great many materials and products will be used. Even in the greenest of projects it is likely that many products will be used that are not themselves green—but they are used in a manner that helps reduce the overall environmental impacts of the building. A particular window may not be green, but the way it is used maximizes collection of low winter sunlight and blocks the summer sun. So even a relatively conventional window can help make a house green. Creating a green building means matching the products and materials to the specific design and site to minimize the overall environmental impact.

This article examines products in isolation —not how to use a product to make a building green, rather what makes a certain product

From *Environmental Building News, 9(1), January 2006* by Alex Wilson. Copyright © 2006 by Building Green, Inc. Reprinted by permission.

green. Green products, including virtually all of those found in *GreenSpec*, could be used in dumb ways that result in buildings that are far from environmentally responsible. In a well-thought-out building design, however, substituting green products for conventional products can make the difference between a good building and a great one.

Defining Standards When Feasible

Our tactic with the *GreenSpec* directory is to identify quantifiable, easily verifiable, standards where those could be defined, then base other decisions about what should be included on the collective wisdom of our editorial staff. In a few product categories, such as energy-consuming appliances and VOC-emitting paints, specific thresholds can be established relatively easily. But for many criteria, the lines are much fuzzier and judgment calls are required.

It is important also to note that multiple criteria often apply—in other words, a product may be considered green for more than one reason. Take recycled plastic lumber, for example: it's made from recycled waste, it's highly durable, and it can obviate the need for pesticide treatments. Straw particleboard products are made from agricultural waste materials, and they are free from formaldehyde offgassing. A product with multiple benefits could qualify for *GreenSpec* on the basis of its overall environmental performance, even if it doesn't meet a threshold in any one category alone. Conversely, a product with one or more green attributes might not qualify if it also carries significant environmental burdens. For example, wood treated with toxic preservatives has advantages in terms of durability, but it would not be listed in *GreenSpec* due the health and environmental hazards it represents.

This article reviews the criteria—not listed in any order of priority—used to designate building products as green and therefore suitable for inclusion in our *GreenSpec* directory.

1. Products Made with Salvaged, Recycled, or Agricultural Waste Content

The materials used to produce a building product—and where those materials came from—is a key determinant of green.

1A. SALVAGED PRODUCTS. Whenever we can re-use a product instead of producing a new one from raw materials—even if those raw materials are recycled—we save on resource use and energy. Many salvaged materials used in buildings (bricks, millwork, framing lumber, plumbing fixtures, and period hardware) are sold on a local or regional basis by salvage yards. Fewer salvaged materials are marketed widely, and it is generally only these that are profiled in a national directory such as *GreenSpec*. Local and regional green product directories can really shine when it comes to finding salvaged materials.

1B. PRODUCTS WITH POST-CONSUMER RECYCLED CONTENT. Recycled content is an important feature of many green products. From an environmental standpoint, post-consumer is preferable to pre-consumer recycled content, because post-consumer recycled materials are more likely to be diverted from landfills. For most product categories, there is currently no set standard for the percentage of recycled content required to qualify for inclusion in *GreenSpec*, but such standards will increasingly be developed in the future.

In some cases, products with recycled content are included with caveats regarding where they should be used. Rubber flooring made from recycled automobile tires is a good example—the caveat is that these products should not be used in most fully enclosed indoor spaces due to offgassing concerns.

In certain situations, from a life-cycle perspective, recycling has downsides. For example, energy consumption or pollution may be a concern with some collection programs or recycling processes. Also, closed-loop recycling is generally preferable to downcycling, in which a lower-grade material is produced. As more complete life-cycle information on recycled materials—and the process of recycling—becomes available, we intend to scrutinize recycled products more carefully.

1C. PRODUCTS WITH PRE-CONSUMER RECYCLED CONTENT. Pre-consumer (also called "post-industrial") recycling refers to the use of industrial by-products, as distinguished from material that has been in consumer use. Iron-ore slag used to make mineral wool insulation, fly ash used to make concrete, and PVC scrap from pipe manufacture used to make shingles are examples of post-industrial recycled materials. Usually excluded from this category is the use of scrap within the same manufacturing process from which it was generated—material that would typically have gone back into the manufacturing process anyway. While post-consumer recycled content is better than pre-consumer recycled content, the latter can still qualify a product for inclusion in *GreenSpec* in many product categories—especially those where there are no products available with post-consumer recycled content.

1D. PRODUCTS MADE FROM AGRICULTURAL WASTE MATERIAL. A number of products are included in *GreenSpec* because they are derived from agricultural waste products. Most of these are made from straw—the stems left after harvesting cereal grains. Citrus oil, a waste product from orange and lemon juice extraction, is also used in some green products, but such products usually include other agricultural oils as well and are lumped under 2d–Rapidly renewable products.

2. Products That Conserve Natural Resources

Aside from salvaged or recycled content, there are a number of other ways that products can contribute to the conservation of natural resources. These include products that serve a function using less material than the standard solution, products that are especially durable and therefore won't need replacement as often, products made from FSC-certified wood, and products made from rapidly renewable resources.

2A. PRODUCTS THAT REDUCE MATERIAL USE. Products meeting this criteria may not be distinctly green on their own but are included in *GreenSpec* because of resource efficiency benefits that they make possible. For example, drywall clips allow the elimination of corner studs, engineered stair stringers reduce lumber waste, pier foundation systems minimize concrete use, and concrete pigments can turn concrete slabs into attractive finished floors, eliminating the need for conventional finish flooring.

2B. PRODUCTS WITH EXCEPTIONAL DURABILITY OR LOW MAINTENANCE REQUIREMENTS. These products are environmentally attractive because they need to be replaced less frequently, or their maintenance has very low impact. Sometimes, durability is a contributing factor to the green designation but not enough to distinguish the product as green on its own. This criterion is highly variable by product type. Included in this category are such products as fiber-cement siding, fiberglass windows, slate shingles, and vitrified-clay waste pipe.

2C. CERTIFIED WOOD PRODUCTS. Third-party forest certification, based on standards developed by the Forest Stewardship Council (FSC), is the best way to ensure that wood products come from well-managed forests. Wood products must go through a chain-of-custody certification process to carry an FSC stamp.

Manufactured wood products can meet the FSC certification requirements with less than 100% certified wood content through percentage-based claims. With a few special-case exceptions, any nonsalvaged solid-wood product and most other wood products must be FSC-certified to be included in *GreenSpec*. A few manufactured wood products, including engineered lumber and particleboard or MDF, can be included if they have other environmental advantages—such as absence of formaldehyde binders. Engineered wood products in *GreenSpec* do not qualify by virtue of their resource efficiency benefits alone (for more on this, see *EBN* Vol. 8, No. 11).

2D. RAPIDLY RENEWABLE PRODUCTS. Rapidly renewable materials are distinguished from wood by the shorter harvest rotation—typically 10 years or less. They are biodegradable, often (but not always) low in VOC emissions, and generally produced from agricultural crops. Because sunlight is generally the primary energy input (via photosynthesis), these products may be less energy-intensive to produce—though transportation and processing energy use must be considered. Examples include linoleum, form-release agents made from plant oils, natural paints, geotextile fabrics from coir and jute, cork, and such textiles as organic cotton, wool, and sisal. Note that not all rapidly renewable materials are included in *GreenSpec*—non-organic cotton, for example, is highly pesticide-intensive. In some cases, even though a product qualifies for *GreenSpec* by virtue of its natural raw materials, it may have negatives that render it inappropriate for certain uses—such as high VOC levels that cause problems for people with chemical sensitivities.

3. Products That Avoid Toxic or Other Emissions

Some building products are considered green because they have low manufacturing impacts, because they are alternatives to conventional products made from chemicals considered problematic, or because they facilitate a reduction in polluting emissions from building maintenance. In the *GreenSpec* criteria, a few product components were singled out for avoidance in most cases: substances that deplete stratospheric ozone, and those associated with ecological or health hazards including mercury and halogenated compounds. In a few cases, these substances may be included in a "green" product if that product has significant environmental benefits (for example, low energy or water use).

These substitutes for products made with environmentally hazardous components may not, in themselves, be particularly green (i.e., they may be petrochemical-based or relatively high in VOCs), but relative to the products being replaced they can be considered green. Most of the products satisfying this criterion are in categories that are dominated by the more harmful products—such as foam insulation categories in which most products contain HCFCs. We have created several subcategories here for green products:

3A. NATURAL OR MINIMALLY PROCESSED PRODUCTS. Products that are natural or minimally processed can be green because of low energy use and low risk of chemical releases during manufacture. These can include wood products, agricultural or nonagricultural plant products, and mineral products such as natural stone and slate shingles.

3B. ALTERNATIVES TO OZONE-DEPLETING SUBSTANCES. Included here are categories where the majority of products still contain or use HCFCs: rigid foam insulation and compression-cycle HVAC equipment.

3C. ALTERNATIVES TO HAZARDOUS PRODUCTS. Some materials provide a better alternative in an application dominated by products for which there are concerns about toxic constituents, intermediaries, or by-products. Fluorescent lamps with low mercury levels are included here, along with form release agents that won't contaminate water or soils with toxicants. Also included here are alternatives to products made with chlorinated hydrocarbons such as polyvinyl chloride (PVC) and brominated fire retardants.

3D. PRODUCTS THAT REDUCE OR ELIMINATE PESTI-CIDE TREATMENTS. Periodic pesticide treatment around buildings can be a significant health and environmental hazard. The use of certain products can obviate the need for pesticide treatments, and such products are therefore considered green. Examples include physical termite barriers, borate-treated building products, and bait systems that eliminate the need for broad-based pesticide application.

3E. PRODUCTS THAT REDUCE STORMWATER POLLUTION. Porous paving products and green (vegetated) roofing systems result in less stormwater runoff and thereby reduce surface water pollution. Stormwater treatment systems reduce pollutant levels in any water that is released.

3F. PRODUCTS THAT REDUCE IMPACTS FROM CONSTRUCTION OR DEMOLITION ACTIVITIES. Included here are various erosion-control products, foundation products that eliminate the need for excavation, and exterior stains that result in lower VOC emissions into the atmosphere. Fluorescent lamp and ballast recyclers and low-mercury fluorescent lamps reduce environmental impacts during demolition (as well as renovation).

3G. PRODUCTS THAT REDUCE POLLUTION OR WASTE FROM OPERATIONS. Alternative wastewater disposal systems reduce groundwater pollution by decomposing organic wastes or removing nutrients more effectively. Masonry fireplaces burn fuel-wood more completely with fewer emissions than conventional fireplaces and wood stoves. Recycling bins and compost

systems enable occupants to reduce their solid waste generation.

4. Products That Save Energy or Water

The ongoing environmental impacts that result from energy and water used in operating a building often far outweigh the impacts associated with building it. Many products are included in *GreenSpec* for these benefits. There are several quite distinct subcategories:

4A. BUILDING COMPONENTS THAT REDUCE HEAT-ING AND COOLING LOADS. Examples include structural insulated panels (SIPs), insulated concrete forms (ICFs), autoclaved aerated concrete (AAC) blocks, and high-performance windows and glazings. As these energy-saving products gain market acceptance, our threshold for inclusion in *GreenSpec* may become more stringent. For example, we may begin including only SIPs and ICFs with steady-state R-values above a certain threshold or with other environmental features, such as recycled-content foam insulation. Some products, such as insulation, clearly offer environmental benefits but are so common that they need other environmental features to qualify for *GreenSpec*.

In the case of windows, the base standard for energy performance of windows is an NFRC-rated unit U-factor of 0.25 or lower for at least one product in a listed product line. If the windows are made from an environmentally attractive material (e.g., high recycled content or superb durability), the energy standard is less stringent: U-factor of 0.30 or lower. If the frame material is nongreen, such as PVC (vinyl), the energy standard is more stringent: U-factor of 0.20 or lower. There are a few exceptions to these standards, such as high-recycled-content windows made for unheated buildings.

4B. EQUIPMENT THAT CONSERVES ENERGY AND MANAGES LOADS. With energy-consuming

Sample *GreenSpec* Standards for Selected Equipment

Product Type	GreenSpec *Standard*
Domestic water heaters	Energy Factor = 0.80 or higher
Residential clothes washers	Minimum modified Energy Factor of 1.8 and maximum Water Factor of 5.5 (as defined by the Consortium for Energy Efficiency)
Residential refrigerators	Exceed 2004 National Energy Standards by 20% (full size) or 25% (compact)
Residential dishwashers	Energy Factor = 0.67 or higher
Central AC and heat pumps	Product line must have at least one model with a SEER rating of 16 or greater

equipment, such as water heaters and refrigerators, we have good data on energy consumption and can set clear standards accordingly. In most product categories—e.g., refrigerators, dishwashers, and clothes washers—we set higher thresholds than ENERGY STAR®: for example, exceeding those standards by 10% or 20%. With lighting and lighting control equipment, certain generic products qualify, such as compact fluorescent lamps and occupancy/daylighting controls, while in other categories only a subset of products qualify. (See table for *GreenSpec* standards for certain types of equipment.) In some cases, products that meet the energy efficiency requirements are excluded, because of evidence of poor performance or durability. Microturbines are included here because of the potential for cogeneration (combined heat and power) that they offer. Ice- or chilled-water thermal energy storage (TES) equipment is also included because it helps reduce peak loads, which in turn can reduce energy costs and lower the impact of electricity generation.

4C. RENEWABLE ENERGY AND FUEL CELL EQUIPMENT. Equipment and products that enable us to use renewable energy instead of fossil fuels and conventional electricity are highly beneficial from an environmental standpoint. Examples include solar water heaters, photovoltaic systems, and wind turbines. Fuel cells are also included here, even though fuel cells today nearly always use natural gas or another fossil fuel as the hydrogen source—they are considered green because emissions are lower than combustion-based equipment and because the use of fuel cells will help us eventually move beyond fossil fuel dependence.

4D. FIXTURES AND EQUIPMENT THAT CONSERVE WATER. All toilets and most showerheads today meet the federal water efficiency standards, but not all of these products perform satisfactorily. With toilets and showerheads we include products that meet the federal standards and have dependably good performance. We include in *GreenSpec* only toilets that offer at least 20% water savings, compared with the federal standard of 1.6 gallons per flush (gpf), and we have adopted the Maximum Performance (MaP) standard for the performance of most toilets—requiring a minimum rating of 65 grams of test media removal per liter of flush volume. Some other products, such as rainwater catchment systems, are also included.

5. Products That Contribute to a Safe, Healthy Built Environment

Buildings should be healthy to live or work in and around, and product selection is a significant determinant of indoor environment quality. Green building products that help to ensure a healthy built environment can be separated into several categories:

5A. PRODUCTS THAT DO NOT RELEASE SIGNIFI-CANT POLLUTANTS INTO THE BUILDING. Included here are zero- and low-VOC paints, caulks, and adhesives, as well as products with very low emissions, such as nonformaldehyde manufactured wood products. Just how low the VOC level needs to be for a given product to qualify for inclusion in *GreenSpec* depends on the product category. Ideally those standards should be based not on simple VOC content, but on resultant VOC concentrations in the space after a given period of time—EPA is working on such data for paints (including a way to factor in higher impacts for more toxic VOCs), but this information is not yet available.

5B. PRODUCTS THAT BLOCK THE INTRODUCTION, DEVELOPMENT, OR SPREAD OF INDOOR CONTAMINANTS. Certain materials and products are green because they prevent the generation or introduction of pollutants—especially biological contaminants—into occupied space. Duct mastic, for example, can block the entry of mold-laden air or insulation fibers into a duct system. "Track-off" systems for entryways help to remove pollutants from the shoes of people entering. Coated ductboard—compared with standard rigid fiberglass ductboard—prevents fiber shedding and helps control mold growth. And linoleum helps to control microbial growth because of the ongoing process of linoleic acid oxidation.

5C. PRODUCTS THAT REMOVE INDOOR POLLU-TANTS. Qualifying for inclusion here are certain ventilation products, filters, radon mitigation equipment, and other equipment and devices that help to remove pollutants or introduce fresh air. Because ventilation equipment is now fairly standard, only products that are particularly efficient or quiet, or that have other environmental benefits are included.

5D. PRODUCTS THAT WARN OCCUPANTS OF HEALTH HAZARDS IN THE BUILDING. Included here are carbon monoxide (CO) detectors, lead paint test kits, and other IAQ test kits. Because CO detectors are so common, other features are needed to qualify such products for *GreenSpec*, such as evidence of superb performance.

5E. PRODUCTS THAT IMPROVE LIGHT QUALITY. There is a growing body of evidence that natural daylight is beneficial to our health and productivity (see *EBN* Vol. 8, No. 9). Products that enable us to bring daylight into a building, including tubular skylights, specialized commercial skylights, and fiber-optic daylighting systems, are included in *GreenSpec*. Some other products, such as full-spectrum lighting systems and highly reflective ceiling panels, could also be included in *GreenSpec* under this criterion.

5F. PRODUCTS THAT HELP CONTROL NOISE. Noise, both from indoor and outside sources, adds to stress and discomfort. A wide range of products are available to help absorb noise, prevent it from spreading, masking it, and even reducing it with sound-cancellation technologies.

5G. PRODUCTS THAT ENHANCE COMMUNITY WELL-BEING. Looking beyond the walls of a building, many products can contribute to safer neighborhoods, increasing walkability and making high-density communities appealing.

Final Thoughts

The primary intent with any green building products directory is to simplify the product selection process. Such directories, including *GreenSpec*, are designed to save you time. For a directory to properly serve your needs, you must be able to trust it—you must have confidence that the process used to select products for inclusion is logical and based on good information and careful analysis. In this article, we have attempted to lay out our process for selecting products for the *GreenSpec* directory.

We are also providing this information so that you can critique it. We print updated copies of *GreenSpec* periodically, and we update the online version every week. That means not just ensuring that we have up-to-date contact information and product descriptions, but also regularly reexamining our standards for what should (and should not) be included. In the next edition of *GreenSpec* certain products will be kicked out—not because they have gotten worse from an environmental standpoint, but because we have reevaluated our standards for inclusion. As more low-VOC paints reach the market, we will likely tighten our standards because we want to include only the very best products. As we consider modifying our standards, we'd like to hear from users of this information. Are our standards too tight in a given area? Are they too lax? What other criteria should we consider adding to our product-evaluation process? We welcome your suggestions and comments by e-mail at: greenspec@BuildingGreen.com.

Finally, we have laid out our standards for *GreenSpec* to advance the development of new, greener products. We want to make it as easy as possible for manufacturers to understand what we consider to be green—so that they can strive to meet those criteria. Doing so will make more green building products available to us all and help to reduce the overall impacts of construction.

Environmental Building News' Checklist for Environmentally Responsible Design and Construction*

Design
- Smaller is better
- Design an energy-efficient building
- Design buildings to use renewable energy
- Optimize material use
- Design water-efficient, low-maintenance landscaping
- Make it easy for occupants to recycle waste
- Look into the feasibility of graywater
- Design for durability
- Design for future reuse and adaptability
- Avoid potential health hazards—radon, mold, pesticides

Land Use and Site Issues
- Renovate older buildings
- Create community
- Encourage in-fill and mixed-use development
- Minimize automobile dependence
- Value site resources
- Locate buildings to minimize impact
- Provide responsible on-site water management
- Situate buildings to benefit from existing vegetation
- Protect trees and topsoil during sitework
- Avoid use of pesticides and other chemicals that may leach into the groundwater

Materials
- Use durable products and materials
- Choose low-maintenance building materials
- Choose building materials with low embodied energy
- Buy locally produced building materials
- Use building products made from recycled materials
- Use salvaged building materials when possible
- Seek responsible wood supplies

*From *Environmental Building News*, 9(1), January 2006. Copyright © 2006 by Building Green, Inc. Reprinted by permission.

- Avoid materials that will offgas pollutants
- Minimize use of pressure-treated lumber
- Minimize packaging waste

Equipment

- Install high-efficiency heating and cooling equipment
- Avoid ozone-depleting chemicals in mechanical equipment and insulation

- Install high-efficiency lights and appliances
- Install water-efficient equipment
- Install mechanical ventilation equipment

Business Practices

- Minimize job-site waste
- Make your business operations more environmentally responsible
- Make education a part of your daily practice

Discussion Questions

1. What are the advantages to factory built homes as compared to conventionally-build homes?
2. The concept of life-cycle environmental assessment of a product or material is increasingly being seen as necessary for understanding the overall impact of that product. What does this mean? What are the challenges of conducting an accurate life-cycle assessment?
3. What do you perceive as obstacles to the use of environmentally responsible building components? What are the incentives for doing so?
4. Which of the product standards cited in the "Green Building Materials" article do you feel are most important—or most feasible—to incorporate in buildings at this time, and why?

 Supporting Activities

1. Take an online tour of the only surviving prototype of Fuller's Dymaxion House and learn more about its history at the Henry Ford Museum Web site: http://www.thehenryford.org/exhibits/dymaxion/index.html.
2. Look for examples of greenwashing in television or print advertisements for products. What is the product? Why do you think it represents an example of greenwashing?
3. Review the suggestions provided on the U.S. Department of Energy's Energy Efficiency and Renewable Energy site for how to save energy in your home: http://www.energysavers.gov/your_home/. Conduct an "audit" of your house or apartment, and then make a list of three to five strategies you can/will implement to save energy in your home.

 Additional Resources

1. The Forest Stewardship Council Web site provides more information about certified wood products, sources for green building supplies, and wood use in the paper and printing industry: http://www.fscus.org/.
2. Read about the LEED certification process, buildings that are LEED certified, and the components of the LEED standards at the U.S. Green Building Council Web site: http://www.usgbc.org/.
3. There are a host of books devoted to the topic of green building. For the neophyte, see *Green Building and Remodeling for Dummies* (2008) by Eric Corey Freed (Hoboken, NJ: Wiley). For more advanced reading see Jerry Yudelson's work, which includes *Green Building Through Integrated Design* (2009; McGraw-Hill) and *The Green Building Revolution* (2008; Island Press).
4. View a variety of building-related topics on the National Association of Home Builders' NAH-BTV, accessible via: http://www.youtube.com/nahbtv.

 Endnotes

1. Nugent, Walter. 1992. *Crossings: The Great Transatlantic Migrations, 1870–1914.* Bloomington, IN: Indiana University Press.

2. UNICEF. 2009. *Water, sanitation and hygiene.* Available: http://www.unicef.org/wash/.

3. United Nations World Food Programme. 2009. *Hunger.* Available: http://www.wfp.org/hunger/stats.

4. To learn more, see: Peter Rogers. August 2008. Facing the freshwater crisis. *Scientific American,* 299 (2): 46–55; and Joel K. Bourne, Jr. 2009. The End of Plenty. *National Geographic,* 215 (6): 26–59.

5. U.S. Census Bureau. 2008. *International Data Base—World Population.* Available: http://www.census.gov/ipc/www/idb/worldpopinfo.html.

6. World Resources Institute. 2007. *Earth Trends—The Environmental Information Portal.* Available: http://earthtrends.wri.org/searchable_db/index.php?theme=6&variable_ID=351&action=select_countries.

7. See, for example, an interview in *The Guardian* with Nigel Lawson, former British energy minister, whose 2008 book *An Appeal to Reason: A Cool Look at Global Warming* is one of several such books in print that challenge the scientific evidence on climate change (http://www.guardian.co.uk/environment/2008/may/03/climatechange.greenpolitics).

8. See, for example, the 2002 report, *Green Revolution: Curse or Blessing?*, published by the International Food Policy Research Institute, which provides a short but effective summary of the effects of the agricultural green revolution (http://www.ifpri.org/pubs/ib/ib11.pdf) that resulted in significantly higher food yields worldwide beginning in the mid-twentieth century.

9. For more information, view and listen to *Behind the ever-expanding American dream home* (July 4, 2006) on National Public Radio: http://www.npr.org/templates/story/story.php?storyId=5525283.

10. U.S. Department of Energy. 2009. *Buildings energy data book: Buildings share of U.S. primary energy consumption* (Table 1.1.3). Available: http://buildingsdatabook.eren.doe.gov/TableView.aspx?table=1.1.3.

11. For more information, visit the Energy Star Web site (http://www.energystar.gov/); the U.S. Green Building Council Web site (http://www.usgbc.org/); and resources such as Susan Saranka's book *The Not-So-Big House* and companion materials (for more information, go to: http://www.notsobighouse.com/).

12. The changes in Lake Powell water levels over a 10-year period can be seen at the NASA Earth Observatory Web site, which also includes an explanation of the changes: http://earthobservatory.nasa.gov/Features/WorldOfChange/lake_powell.php.

13. United States Environmental Protection Agency. May 31 2007. *Landmark settlement aims to clean up raw sewage discharges in Allegheny County.* Available: http://yosemite.epa.gov/opa/admpress.nsf/a883dc3da7094f97852572a00065d7d8/e3ddfc9b9a111c0a852572ec005d6356!OpenDocument.

14. The International Union for Conservation of Nature (IUCN), considered a global authority on species extinction, estimates that species loss is occurring at a rate 1,000 to 10,000 times higher than would be expected naturally. For more information about the IUCN "Red List" visit: http://www.iucn.org/about/work/programmes/species/red_list/about_the_red_list/.

15. There are numerous sources of information about the Dymaxion House; two good starting points for more information include the Henry Ford Museum site (http://www.thehenryford.org/exhibits/dymaxion/index.html) and a 2008 critique in *Architectural Digest* (http://archrecord.construction.com/features/critique/0811critique-1.asp).

16. See more information on Michelle Kaufmann's blog: http://blog.michellekaufmann.com/?p=2147.

17. McDonough, William, and Braungart, Michael. 2002. *Cradle to Cradle: Remaking the Way We Make Things.* New York: North Point Press.

Fueling the Technological Revolution

Energy, while hard to define, is the most critical ingredient of our existence. The basics of life—food, water, clothing, shelter—all require the accumulation and expenditure of energy. When your diet includes fresh fruit in winter washed down with imported Perrier, the shirt on your back is made of polyester (a petroleum product), and your 3,000 square foot suburban home is located 50 miles from your work or school, the energy requirement is enormous. You may say you can't live without your cell phone or iPod or computer or car, but a seemingly endless supply of cheap energy is really what you can't live without. In fact, as you'll read, access to energy is strongly correlated to "standard of living"—a quantity difficult to rigorously define, but whose general meaning is clear enough. A somewhat dated but still relevant study by the Lawrence Livermore National Laboratory[1] suggests an annual per capita electricity consumption of 4,000 kilowatt-hours (kWh) as the minimum necessary to achieve a "Western" lifestyle, as seen in Figure 1. Two points deserve emphasis. The first is that below this threshold, *incremental* increases in electricity consumption yield *significant* increases in standard of living. Secondly, above this threshold, *vast* increases in electricity consumption result in *virtually no* standard of living improvement. It's worth noting that U.S. electricity consumption is three times this threshold level. More recently, the concept of the 2,000 Watt Society has been promoted in Europe. The goal of this movement is to achieve worldwide per capita energy consumption levels that represent the current global per capita average of 2,000 watts. Figure 1 illustrates the broad disparity in current consumption levels (today's levels remain roughly similar to this 1997 data). The 2,000 Watt Society would see citizens of India (at around 1,000 watts per capita) and citizens of the U.S. (at around 12,000 watts per capita) consuming at equal levels—a goal that would require drastic changes on the part of citizens in developed nations, but would substantially add to the standard of living in other nations.

What has made possible the lifestyle that developed countries enjoy and developing countries envy is cheap, abundant energy. For the past 150 years, cheap and abundant energy has been made possible through the harvesting and burning of fossil fuels: petroleum powers our cars and planes, coal provides electricity, and natural gas heats our homes. A high standard of living, for many in the West, has come to mean a house, two cars in the garage, and access to goods from every corner of the globe. Humanity has developed incredible technologies to locate, extract, and process vast quantities of fossil fuels to provide energy with which to operate even more technological gadgets. According to the U.S. Department of Energy (USDOE), humans

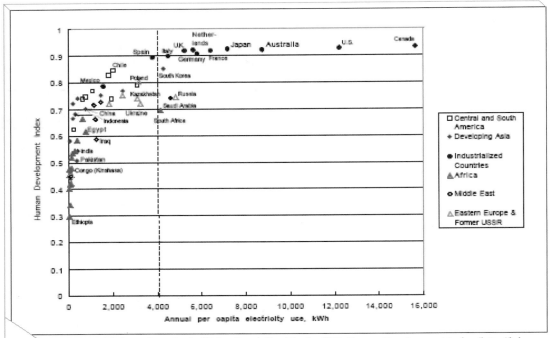

Figure 1. This graph[1] shows "standard of living," as defined by the UN's Human Development Index (http://hdr.undp.org/en/statistics/indices/hdi/) as a function of per capita electricity consumption for a range of countries. Data is from 1997.

consume over 84 million barrels of oil[2] and over 17 million tons of coal[3] every single day! And the U.S., with 5% of the world's population, is responsible for around 25 percent of this consumption.

As important as energy is, most people are unaware of its critical role in our daily lives, and fail to appreciate the unique value of fossil fuels. To many, electricity comes "out of the wall" and gasoline comes from the gas station. Even fewer people stop to wonder about the consequences of extracting a staggering amount of resources from the Earth and returning an equally staggering amount of pollution. Although these consequences are numerous, the single most significant impact may be climate change. According to the USDOE, worldwide around 80 million tons of CO_2, a known greenhouse gas,

are emitted into the atmosphere every single day.[4]

Ironically, these problems may soon be solved for us. Supplies of fossil fuels are undeniably finite. At some point in the not-too-distant future, the demand for fossil fuels will surpass supply, and fossil fuels will price themselves out of reach. Citizens of developing countries, with a recently acquired addiction to energy and little tolerance for price volatility, will be hit first and hardest. People in developed countries will feel entitled to continue their energy-intensive lifestyle, and their governments will struggle to address the problems caused by a dwindling supply of energy. Competition for energy will become intense. Addressing the problem of growing scarcity of fossil fuel supplies is further complicated by the fact that many individuals challenge the entire notion of scarcity, as illustrated in the excerpt by Cavaney that is included here.

The transition away from fossil fuels doesn't need to be cataclysmic. There are technologies available today that can dramatically reduce our need for energy, and provide the balance at an affordable price with reduced or zero carbon emission. Energy-efficient cars and buildings, thoughtful urban planning, and renewable energy technologies are a few examples.

In this unit, readings have been selected to provide context to humanity's energy situation, to highlight some problems with the status quo, and finally, to offer some solutions that may allow us as a species to minimize the impact of the transition that will surely accompany the decline of cheap fossil fuels. Specifically, you are asked to think about the relationship between energy and society within the following conceptual framework:

- What are the challenges of estimating fossil fuel energy supplies?
- Is the weight of evidence to support global climate change compelling?
- *All* energy technologies, particularly fossil fuels, lead to environmental problems, as we use increasingly devastating methods to recover them.
- What are the obstacles that prevent the widespread adoption of increasingly viable strategies to displace dependence on fossil fuel-based energy technologies?

Razing Appalachia

The article "Razing Appalachia" by Maryanne Vollers appeared in the July/August 1999 issue of *Mother Jones* magazine. It highlights the social, environmental, and economic implications of mountain-top removal coal mining in West Virginia. Mountaintop removal (MTR), a particularly devastating form of surface mining, is now the preferred method to mine coal, replacing the more expensive and more dangerous method of underground mining. The reading highlights two sides to the story.

One side is fighting to stop MTR from destroying their generations-old lifestyle. Communities that live in the shadows of these mega-projects are subjected daily to blasting, polluted air and ground water, and the fear of toxic slurry spills. Regionally, the Appalachian people have contended with an ever-growing number of lost mountains and valleys, and are trying to put an end to it.

On the other side are coal miners and owners struggling to maintain their generations-old lifestyle, and to satisfy the nation's growing demand for electricity. Increasingly restrictive environmental regulations squeeze their profit margins. Community leaders, desperate for any jobs, tout the economic development of coal mining. Coal miners simply want to feed their families. Coal mine operators say "we're obeying the law"—and in most cases they are.

Maryanne Vollers is an author and journalist who has written and ghostwritten several books as well as articles for *Time*, *Esquire*, and *Rolling Stone*. This article was the motivation for the award-winning documentary of the same name released in 2003. It was directed by Sasha Waters for Room 135 Productions and is available through Bullfrog Films.

Razing Appalachia

By Maryanne Vollers

First they dug out the land. Then they strip mined it. Now Big Coal is leveling the mountains themselves—and tearing communities apart.

"Hear that quiet?" Larry Gibson asks as he climbs through the highland cemetery where nearly 300 of his kin lie buried. "You know they're about to set off a shot when they shut down the machines." Gibson, a 53-year-old retired maintenance worker and evangelist of the environmental cause, hunkers down with some visitors to wait for the blast.

Gibson knows the routine by heart. After all, the Princess Beverly Coal Company has been blowing up the hills around his family's 50-acre "homeplace" in West Virginia for more than a decade. When the demolition team is ready down below, the "Ukes"—heavy shovel trucks—back away from a line of high explosives drilled into solid rock. Then the warning horn sounds: two minutes.

The graveyard sits atop Kayford Mountain, a modest, leafy peak that sticks out of the shattered landscape like a fat, green thumb. The view from the edge of the cemetery looks more like the Tunisian outback than a West Virginia mountain range: The ground drops 300 or 400 feet into a dust bowl of raw coal and rubble,

From *Mother Jones, 24(4), July/August 1999* by M. Vollers. © 1999, Foundation for National Progress. Reprinted by permission.

crosscut by dirt tracks. In the distance, what used to be forested ridges now resemble flat-topped buttes crusted over with rough grass and a few stunted trees.

West Virginia has been mined since the mid-18th century, but nobody has seen annihilation like this before. In the past 20 years, environmentalists claim, 500 square miles of the state have been stripped and gutted for their coal. In the most apocalyptic form of strip mining, called mountaintop removal, whole peaks are razed to extract layers of relatively clean-burning low-sulfur coal, while the excess rock and earth "overburden" is dumped into the valleys. Hundreds of miles of streams have been buried under these "valley fills," and dozens of mountains have been flattened into synthetic prairies.

Now, an environmental group called the West Virginia Highlands Conservancy and seven coalfield residents are taking state and federal regulators to court for the first time, claiming not only that mountaintop removal devastates the environment, but that existing laws designed to mitigate the damage are not being enforced. Coal companies and their proxies defend the practice as necessary for the economy, and assert that there is no proof it permanently damages the environment. Since last year, both sides have been presenting their cases in a federal court. What's at stake is the future of surface coal mining in West Virginia, the economies of several counties, the way of life of thousands of people, and, environmentalists contend, the ecological health of the northern Appalachian watershed.

Whatever the outcome of the lawsuit, most of Kayford Mountain is destined to be strip-mined one way or another. But Larry Gibson won't let the coal companies take it all. He represents the large extended clan that owns that 50-acre parcel atop Kayford, the remnant of a mountaintop farm dating back to the 18th cen-

tury. It's one of the rare private holdings in West Virginia's southern highlands, where most land is owned by corporations and leased to coal companies. Millions of dollars in coal lie beneath the picnic ground and vacation cabins, but the family trust won't sell.

"The man from the coal company told me, 'We haven't seen anything we can't buy,'" Gibson recalls. "I said, 'You're not buying this land.' If we sell, we sell our heritage. We have no past after that. Where can we show our family where their roots are?"

As we watch, a huge explosion wallops a coal-streaked bench below the cemetery, flinging up plumes of yellow dust and sending cascades of dirt and shale overburden into the valley. The hillside shudders with the shock wave. "That warn't nothing," observes Gibson's cousin, Carl "Red" Fraker, a 70-year-old retired miner who lives in a half-deserted village along Cabin Creek, below Kayford. "The big ones roll the ground like an earthquake." Fraker was born on Kayford Mountain, and he intends to be buried here some day.

But most of his friends and neighbors have moved on. Aside from the environmental damage caused by mountaintop removal, the practice is killing a way of life in West Virginia's hollows. Explosions shower dust and rocks down on people who live below the mountaintop mines. The foundations of their houses crack and their wells dry up. Whole towns are disappearing as people sell their homes and move away.

Machines do almost all the work in these modern mines; the coal miners and their communities are now an inconvenience. Thousands of people once lived in simple wood-frame houses along Cabin Creek. Now the road that follows the streambed is lined with ghost towns with names like Red Warrior and Acme and White Row, casualties of the conversion from underground mining to strip mining and now mountaintop removal. After the shops and movie theaters were shuttered and shacks were emptied, the bulldozers came. All that remains now are worn patches in the mountainside, and a few stubborn clusters of daffodils planted long ago in now-vanished gardens.

Up above, when the dust clouds settle after the latest blast, the Ukes start chugging up the hill to scrape out the exposed coal. Red Fraker takes another look out at the black wasteland below. "I want to ask, what's gonna happen to West Virginia when all the coal's gone?" he says. "Ain't no timber on it. No dirt left. Nothin'. What's it gonna be?"

That was precisely the question members of Congress were asking when they passed the Surface Mining Control and Reclamation Act, SMCRA (familiarly known as smack-ra), back in 1977. The gist of the law is this: If you mine it, you have to restore the land to the same or better condition than it was in before you got there. The law also provides detailed regulations designed to reduce the environmental impact of such destructive mining. According to SMCRA, strip mines, including mountaintop mines, cannot be allowed within 100 feet of active streams unless it can be shown that the streams won't be damaged. The law further requires "contemporaneous reclamation"—meaning that soil replacement and reseeding must occur soon after the coal is removed. The land must be returned to its "approximate original contour," or AOC. The permit holder can be granted a variance from the AOC rule only after submitting a detailed plan for post-mining flatland development, such as a school, airport, or shopping center that would benefit nearby communities.

West Virginia's Department of Environmental Protection (DEP) is charged with enforcing SMCRA, with the oversight of the federal Office of Surface Mining. Unfortunately, there has

been very little regulation by the DEP, whose ranks are filled with former coal-industry employees, and even less supervision from the weak and understaffed federal agency.

When SMCRA was written, mountaintop removal was still an unusual practice. It became more prevalent in the 1980s, when 20-story-tall, rock-eating machines called draglines were brought in to make the technique profitable. Ironically, it was stricter environmental laws that increased the demand for West Virginia's low-sulfur coal. More than 80 percent of America's coal is consumed by coal-burning electric power plants, which in turn provide the nation with 56 percent of its electricity. Following passage of 1990's Clean Air Act, power plants were forced to reduce the sulfur content of smokestack emissions, which react with the atmosphere to cause acid rain. Some of the purest and hottest-burning coal in the nation is found in thin, multiple seams high in West Virginia's southern mountains. Rather than mine this coal out of the mountains, industry accountants found, it's cheaper and faster to take the mountains off the coal.

In recent years, the DEP has kept up with the demand for low-sulfur coal by granting permits for more and bigger surface mines. Since 1995, the agency has approved permits subjecting 27,000 new acres to mountaintop removal. (In contrast, journalist Ken Ward, Jr. discovered while researching a prizewinning series of articles for the *Charleston Gazette*, the state's largest and most influential newspaper, fewer than 10,000 acres were permitted during the 1980s.) Anywhere from a tenth to two-thirds of the mining permits issued in West Virginia in 1997 (the number depends on whether you consult state regulators or the *Gazette's* Ward) are for mountaintop-removal mines, which account for 16 percent of the state's coal output. Environmentalists assert that some mountaintop mining areas are now 10 miles wide, and that the largest will eventually gobble up 20,000 acres.

But it is not just the size of a given mining area that's worrisome; nobody has studied what the cumulative impact of so much disruption will be on the environment of northern Appalachia. "It might be a different story if it was a 200-acre plot here, and 500 acres in another county," says Cindy Rank of the West Virginia Highlands Conservancy. "But mountaintop removal is spreading and connecting all through the areas where there are coal reserves." If permits continue to be approved at the pace set over the past decade, environmentalists say, half the peaks in some southern counties could be lopped off.

Despite assurances from coal companies that the technique is perfectly safe, environmentalists are focused on an array of problems associated with mountaintop removal. They worry about increased acid runoff from these giant gashes, particularly since they estimate that 75 percent of West Virginia's streams and rivers are already polluted by mining and other industries. They fear the loss of groundwater in the land below flattened mountains that were once laced with springs and aquifers. And even though coal-industry technicians insist that the gargantuan valley fills behave "like sponges" and are actually a form of flood control, other experts remain skeptical. "What you see in a lot of these valley fills has no engineering method to it at all," says Rick Eades, a hydrogeologist who used to work in the mining industry and is now an environmental activist. "It's just dirt and rock being pushed over the side of a hill and filling in vertically several hundred feet." Although none of the valley fills has failed since they became a part of West Virginia's landscape 25 years ago, Eades fears a disastrous flood within the next 25. "Nature will cut those valley fills right out of there, given time. And there's

no way that the mountains can heal in a way that will resemble the original ability of the land to hold back the water during heavy rains, hold back sediments, and retain groundwater." Such concerns led two West Virginia conservation groups to put the DEP on notice in January of this year of their intent to sue the agency for not assessing the "cumulative hydrological impacts" of mountaintop removal during the permitting process.

Still more problems exist. "Mountaintop removal destroys the beauty of the state, which is somewhat intangible," says William Maxey, West Virginia's former chief forester. "More tangible is the fact that it deforests the state." Maxey says that, as of 1997, 300,000 acres of hardwood forest had been destroyed by mountaintop removal. He characterizes the mining industry's preferred reforestation methods as "bogus," saying they are "totally superficial and will not work." After Maxey failed to convince the DEP to require adequate reforestation of mountaintop mines, he resigned from his job in disgust.

King Coal rules West Virginia like a petulant monarch, one used to getting its way. Coal production accounts for 13 percent of West Virginia's gross state product, commands an annual payroll of $900 million, and provides more than a third of the state's business-tax revenues. King Coal also finds campaign contributions a good investment, and is famously generous with them. For instance, Gov. Cecil Underwood, a former coal executive, is the recent beneficiary of $250,000 in campaign donations from coal companies. (An additional quarter-million was contributed to cover the cost of his inauguration party.) It was Underwood who pushed a bill through the state legislature last year to make mountaintop-removal mining even easier and more profitable. It allowed companies to obliterate up to 480 acres of the drainage above any stream (up from 250 acres) before paying mitigation costs to the state—of $200,000 per buried acre.

But the blatant coal-industry giveaway backfired—leading to the bill's repeal—when it roused public interest, even outrage. City people started paying more attention to what was going on out of sight, up in the remote coalfields. A 1998 opinion poll showed that 53 percent of West Virginians opposed mountaintop removal, versus 29 percent in favor.

At the same time that Underwood was lobbying for the pro-industry bill in March 1998, the *Charleston Gazette* was employing the Freedom of Information Act to obtain 81 mining permits issued by the DEP, which it then reviewed against federal laws such as SMCRA and the Clean Water Act. The investigation revealed some startling facts: The DEP didn't keep complete records of how many permits it issued, so there was no way to track the cumulative effects of mining. The U.S. Army Corps of Engineers routinely gave general "nationwide" permits for valley fills that should have required more rigorous individual permits. And in almost all cases, mountaintop-removal AOC variances were issued without post-mining development plans. In those cases when plans were submitted, most of them were for "timberland" or "wildlife habitat"—uses not recognized by SMCRA.

The Office of Surface Mining conducted its own investigation, which essentially confirmed the newspaper's findings. In other words, for 20 years the DEP had been stretching the law to please the coal companies, and the U.S. government had been letting them get away with it.

In response to an increasing public outcry over mountaintop removal, Gov. Underwood appointed a task force to investigate the issue. It came up with recommendations for more studies and increased vigilance by the regulators. But old hands at this game don't believe coal companies can be regulated. Ken Hechler, West Virginia's 84-year-old secretary of state, is a longtime nemesis of the coal industry. As a West Virginia congressman from 1959 to 1977, Hechler tried to abolish strip mining altogether.

"I still feel that it is impossible to have either strip mining or mountaintop removal and have adequate reclamation, which I characterize as putting lipstick on a corpse," he says. He recently appeared at an environmental rally at the capital and sang a song, to the tune of John Denver's "Take Me Home, Country Roads." It began: "Almost level, West Virginia/Scalped-off mountains, dumped into our rivers."

Meanwhile, Arch Coal, the country's second-largest coal company, was trying to push through a 3,100-acre mountaintop-removal permit to expand its giant Dal-Tex mine in Logan County. It would be the largest permit ever granted—amounting to about five square miles of what the DEP calls "total extraction." The Dal-Tex mine had already filled in dozens of hollows on the west side of the Spruce Fork River along state Highway 17. All but 40 of the 200 families that once lived in the hamlet of Blair had already moved away. That was when James Weekley, a 58-year-old grandfather and former miner, began to fear that Arch Coal wanted the rest—including the headwaters of Pigeonroost Branch, in the leafy hollow where he and his family have lived for generations.

In July 1998, Weekley and nine other coalfield residents joined with the West Virginia Highlands Conservancy to sue the Army Corps and the DEP for ignoring SMCRA, the Clean Water Act, and other laws. (Three of the original plaintiffs have since dropped out.) Although no coal companies were specifically sued, the purpose of the lawsuit was to make sure the mines comply with the law.

Pro-coal letter writers to West Virginia newspapers labeled Weekley and the other plaintiffs environmental radicals. "I'm not an environmentalist—I'm a citizen!" says Weekley. "I was born in this hollow and I'm gonna die here. They'll have to bulldoze me out before I go."

Last December, the plaintiffs decided to settle part of the case against the federal government. They agreed that the Army Corps, in conjunction with other federal and state agencies, would conduct a two-year environmental impact study to assess and deal with the cumulative damage caused by mountaintop removal in West Virginia. Meanwhile, new permits, and ones already in the pipeline, would be subjected to closer scrutiny to ensure their compliance with existing regulations and standards. But after Arch Coal, responding to pressure from the U.S. Environmental Protection Agency that was unrelated to the lawsuit, made significant changes in its permit application—including reducing the lifetime of the Dal-Tex expansion mine from 12 to five years and scaling back its proposed valley fills—the federal defendants argued that the Dal-Tex permit should be exempted from new, stricter scrutiny, and that mining should be allowed to begin.

But Weekley and the other plaintiffs balked at exempting the Dal-Tex mine. They asked U.S. District Chief Judge Charles Haden for a preliminary injunction to delay the permit until the rest of the lawsuit could be resolved in a trial scheduled for this July.

To the astonishment of almost everyone, the conservative Republican judge—who had visited Pigeonroost Hollow and flown over the coalfields—granted the preliminary injunction. In doing so, he cited the "imminent and irreversible" harm that would be done to the Weekleys, and to the stream flowing through Pigeonroost Hollow, if the mining were to proceed, and distinguished it from the "purely temporary economic harms" that Arch would endure from the delay in its operations. The judge then noted

that the other legal questions the plaintiffs had raised regarding the conduct of mountaintop removal would be addressed in the future trial. Meanwhile, Arch Coal would have to wait for its permit.

The coal company responded to the ruling by laying off 30 miners at its Dal-Tex mine, and promising to shut down its operation and put 300 more employees out of work by summer. The loss of jobs and tax revenues would poleax the economy of Logan County, one of the poorest counties in a poor state. Less money would be available for schools, police—everything would be affected. The president of the Logan County Commission declared, "It's a war!" and the commission vowed to fight to keep the mine open. Days after the Haden decision, 1,500 miners, along with union and business leaders from Logan County, marched on Charleston to protest.

The United Mine Workers of America (UMWA) found itself in a terrible position. The stark reality of labor in West Virginia is this: At the end of World War II there were more than 100,000 union coal miners in the state. Now, of the fewer than 19,000 who remain, only 40 percent belong to the UMWA. The union's president, Cecil Roberts, perceived as a moderate on the issue of mountaintop removal, had already come out in favor of protecting communities from the technique's excesses. But the imminent loss of one of the biggest union mines in the state was more than he could take. Roberts called for observation of April 2, 1999, as a "memorial day" without pay for the nation's 35,000 union miners to protest the situation in West Virginia. He was hoping that up to 10,000 would attend a rally in Charleston. Perhaps because it was the Easter weekend, only about 500 miners and family members showed up at the Capitol steps.

Roberts, a wiry, bearded, native West Virginian, shouted like a preacher at the modest crowd that day, telling them they'd all been "kicked in the teeth again by the environmental community. We're fed up and we're fired up!" Roberts has been busy leading the union in its fight with the Clinton-Gore administration over U.S. support for the Kyoto treaty on global warming, which he fears will put the nation's coal industry out of business and cost his workers their jobs. He told the crowd, "You can't say 'Don't burn it' in Washington and 'Don't mine it' in West Virginia and say you're not trying to take the jobs of every coal miner in the United States. And I'm here to say no, no, and hell no!"

Some in West Virginia have accused Roberts of stirring up an already volatile situation in the coalfields. Roberts responds that he's been reasonable for the past year, trying to negotiate a solution to the mountaintop-removal problem. "We were working to find a compromise for workers to keep their jobs and at the same time protect the environment. I believe you can do both," he told *Mother Jones*. "We argued that we shouldn't eliminate mountaintop mining at that moment. It wasn't fair to the workers, wasn't fair quite frankly to the companies that had invested literally millions and millions of dollars in West Virginia."

Secretary of State Hechler, who has a long history of supporting the UMWA, is disappointed in Roberts' stance. "Like all wars," he says, "a war against the mountains creates employment. But you don't keep fighting just to supply jobs. In any event, we ought to start diversifying our economy early on instead of making such a heavy dependence on coal, which pollutes the streams, pollutes the politics, and is a finite resource."

The coal hasn't quite run out yet. In fact, the last two years have set new records for West Virginia coal production, with 182 million tons extracted in 1997 alone. Furthermore, most of the mining jobs eliminated over the past half-

century were lost to mechanization of the mines and a conversion to surface mining—not a decline in coal production.

But Hechler is right: The coal will run out some day. And the big lie of Big Coal is that West Virginia depends on mining for its prosperity. Skeptics ask: What prosperity? West Virginia is 49th among the 50 states in household income. And in this very poor state, the poorest counties are the ones with the most coal mines.

"No state has given more to the American Dream and gotten less back from it than West Virginia," says Norm Steenstra, director of the West Virginia Citizen Action Group and a former coal operator himself. "The corrupt political system, the dead streams, the severed mountains, the fraud, the dust, the noise, the air pollution—what for? All to supply the voracious American appetite for cheap electricity."

It's a risky business calling up a coal company and saying you're with *Mother Jones*. But David Todd, vice president and spokesman for Arch Coal, is a good sport, and he agrees to a tour of the Hobet 21 mine near Madison, West Virginia. The mine is a cousin of the Dal-Tex operation, 40 miles south of here, and a showcase for mountaintop removal.

We climb into a 4 x 4 truck to have a look at a section that was mined 20 years ago. In fact, the reclaimed parts of Hobet 21 are quite handsome. There are rolling, grassy hills, stands of small trees here and there, a number of ponds where ducks like to nest. To my eyes, it looks more like western Nebraska than West Virginia. But to Todd, and to the regulators who approved this reclamation, this is a fine example of restoring the approximate original contour of the land. "The hills are smaller but with similar rolls as the original mountains," says Todd, sweeping his hand across the pastures to the forested bumps on the horizon. "This is just more manicured-looking." Secretary of the Interior Bruce Babbitt (who oversees the Office of Surface Mining) took a similar tour of the Hobet 21 mine in the summer of 1996. Impressed, he announced that the Hobet mine was "a rebuke to those who say, Jobs or the environment. This landscape shouts out: You can have both!" Babbitt also said something that continues to haunt the foes of mountaintop removal: "The landscape has changed. It is a better landscape in many ways, a different landscape—a savanna of forests coming back, of fields." The local headline read "Landscape improved, Babbitt says." And Arch Coal helpfully provides copies of the story in its press kit.

Before we wrap up the afternoon tour, Todd wants to get something off his chest about the mountaintop-removal controversy and the Dal-Tex permit problem. "If you detect a level of frustration, sometimes even anger, I don't deny it," says Todd, a fair-haired man in a white hard hat. "Because, dammit, we've done everything and more that people have asked us to do throughout the years." He says Arch Coal has bent over backward to get the right permits and keep the mine running, taking a loss of $1 million a month since September 1998 in the process. "All we ask is, tell us what the standard is, how we should comply with the law, the permits we need, and we will do that!" he says, throwing up his hands. "Meantime, shutting us down and costing 300 jobs at Dal-Tex is unconscionable!"

It's touching to hear a coal executive so concerned about the loss of jobs. In the past year, 900 union miners have been laid off in West Virginia due to reduced domestic demand (after a pair of mild winters) and a general consolidation in the coal industry. Nobody marched on Charleston when those cuts were announced, and no corporate vice presidents expressed their anger and frustration. Most of the coal-mining jobs are moving to the Powder River Basin of Wyoming, where there are no

unions, and where seams 75 feet thick lie right below the gentle, rolling surface of the land. Arch Coal recently purchased Atlantic Richfield Company's giant strip mine there and, a few days after Judge Haden's decision, began to dismantle one of its 340-ton coal shovel trucks to ship to Wyoming.

Ricky Light of Sharples, West Virginia, used to drive that truck. Light, 32, who has a wife, three young daughters, and payments to make on a new modular home, was one of the first to be laid off at Dal-Tex. He used to make $55,000 a year; now he receives unemployment income of $1,200 a month, though his bills amount to $1,800, not including groceries. He and his wife, Samantha, may be shutting off the phone soon, and are considering moving in with her mother. "We planned our life around 15 more years of mining," says Light, a slender, dark-haired man in a Nike swoosh cap. "I didn't believe it'd go this far. I thought they'd get the permits."

Light says he has a "few good possibilities" for another job. He's been told he could relocate to Arch's new mine, near Gillette, Wyoming, but Light doesn't want to leave his hometown. Like the business leaders in Logan, Ricky Light doesn't fault Arch Coal or the grim realities of mining for his predicament. He blames the people who brought the lawsuit, some of them his neighbors. "There's a lot of hard feelings here," he says. "It's just getting started. 'Cause you don't take things off people's tables. You don't mess with people's livelihoods."

Pigeonroost Hollow is just a mile or so east of Blair Mountain, which was the site of the biggest union battle in the history of West Virginia. That was in 1921, when a young firebrand named Bill Blizzard—whose great-nephew happens to be UMWA president Cecil Roberts—led 15,000 men on a march to unionize the southern coalfields. Famed organizer Mary Harris "Mother" Jones herself tried to stop the confrontation, but she couldn't turn them back. The union men met the sheriff's private army on the slopes of Blair Mountain. As many as 20 people were killed; nobody knows the exact number. Blizzard ended up in jail. It took another decade and still more blood to organize the West Virginia mines.

Another war is now being fought in the shadow of Blair Mountain. The barriers seem harder to define, and the sons and daughters of those union foot soldiers are dug in on both sides of the line. It's a battle over jobs and the environment, tradition and change—a fight that is going on here in the coalfields, and out in the redwood forests of California, and in the copper mines of Montana, and overseas where the natural resources are running dry.

There used to be a historical marker at the foot of Blair Mountain describing the great union war. But somebody stole it, and the sign was never replaced. Soon the mountain itself will be gone, consumed by the dragline and converted into an artificial pasture big enough for a hundred future Wal-Marts, although there will be hardly anyone left to shop there. There may not even be a marker to commemorate the battle, or the times when Mother Jones walked up the creeks to organize the coal camps because the coal company owned the roads. The creeks themselves will be buried under tons of dirt and rock, buried like the mountain and the memory of a time when the people of the coalfields and their union knew which side they were on.

Discussion Questions

1. What conclusions can you draw from the absence of discussion about global warming, acid rain, and other "hot" environmental topics? Is MTR an "Appalachian" issue? A national issue? An international issue?

2. According to the Department of Energy's Energy Information Administration (EIA), the productivity of a U.S. surface miner (in tons mined per worker-hour) is close to four times higher than that of an underground miner. Surface mining accounts for around 100 times fewer mine fatalities per unit of coal than does underground mining. How do you think these statistics should be factored into the MTR debate?

3. One potential solution to the MTR debate is strict enforcement of existing environmental and reclamation laws. Do you think this is an effective approach? Why or why not?

4. How much do you pay per kWh for electricity? If you're not sure, then check your electricity bill. Would you support a 10 percent increase in your electricity bill to subsidize more environmentally benign coal mining in West Virginia? What about 50 percent? 100 percent? 200 percent?

 Supporting Activities

1. On Google Earth, fly to Logan County, West Virginia and locate a surface mine. Use the measuring tool to estimate the area of the operation.

2. Find out coal consumption levels for your state and for the U.S. in the last year. A good resource is the Department of Energy's Energy Information Administration (www.eia.doe.gov).

3. Look into another very revealing fact at EIA. At current consumption rates, how long will the coal *at currently producing* mines last?

4. Where is the nearest coal-fired power plant to where you live? What's the name and "nameplate capacity" of this facility?

5. What is the current status of Kayford Mountain? Of the Blair Mountain preservation efforts?

 Additional Resources

1. A regional environmental group: West Virginia Highlands Conservancy: www.wvhighlands.org.
2. Another regional environmental group: Appalachian Voices: www.appvoices.org.
3. A coal lobbying group: Friends of Coal: www.friendsofcoal.org, www.friendsofcoalky.com.
4. A Great YouTube parody of coal: http://youtube.com/watch?v=71kckb8hhOQ.

Lights Out: Approaching the Historic Interval's End

No one can dispute that fossil fuels are a finite resource. However, our technological capacity to satisfy global demand for cheap energy has allowed consumers and policy makers to "plan" for a future with more of the same. But this really isn't a plan. It's an example of misguided "cornucopian" thinking that defies well-accepted science. Fossil fuels will not satisfy global demand forever.

So when will oil "run out"? As it turns out, that's really not what matters. It's not how much of this or that fuel is left, but rather the price. Price, as any economist will tell you, depends on supply and demand. Energy has been historically cheap (except for brief exceptions) because supply has been able to satisfy demand, and both have risen dramatically. There is now a scientific consensus, however, that the supply of petroleum is unlikely to keep pace with demand for much longer. Oil production, or the rate at which oil is extracted from the ground, will soon peak and decline. The greater the demand, and the greater the extraction efficiency, the sooner the peak will occur. This peak is predicted to occur sometime between now and 2020. At that point, prices will invariably rise. At that point, as Heinberg puts it, the party will truly be over.

Do we have time to act? Can a timely, cheap alternative be found that will simply replace oil without a hitch? The answer is, most likely, no. Historically cheap oil in the U.S. has resulted in an economy and infrastructure that relies heavily on the automobile and large quantities of oil. Cheap energy has also discouraged the search for alternatives to fossil fuels. A transition will not be easy.

In this reading, which is excerpted from Richard Heinberg's book *The Party's Over*, the author presents the scientific case for peak oil by explaining the observations and arguments that support the claim. While not himself a scientist, Heinberg has the ability to readily identify the salient points. Be warned, however, he often employs biased language and perhaps occasionally stretches the facts a bit thin. Be a healthy skeptic of "facts" offered up on both sides of the debate (good advice to consumers of any information) and "when in doubt, check it out." While reading, try to form your own opinion based on the material presented, and consider what type of further information you need in order to establish a well-informed position.

Richard Heinberg is a Senior Fellow of the Post Carbon Institute in Sebastopol, California. The sequel to *The Party's Over* is titled *Powerdown: Options and Actions for a Post-Carbon World*.

Lights Out: Approaching the Historic Interval's End

By Richard Heinberg

The Ground Giving Way

In nearly every year since 1859, the total amount of oil extracted from the world's ancient and finite underground reserves had grown—from a few thousand barrels a year to 65 million barrels per day by the end of the 20th century, an increase averaging about two percent per annum. Demand had grown just as dramatically, sometimes lagging behind the erratically expanding supply. The great oil crises of the 1970s—the most significant occasions when demand exceeded supply—had been politically-based interruptions in the delivery of crude that

From *The Party's Over: Oil, War, and the Fate of Industrial Societies, 2nd Edition* by Richard Heinberg. Copyright © 2005 by New Society Publishers. Reprinted by permission.

was otherwise readily available; there had been no actual physical shortage of the substance then, or at any other time.

In the latter part of the year 2000, as Al Gore and George W. Bush were crisscrossing the nation vying for votes and campaign contributions, the world price of oil rose dramatically from its low point of $10 per barrel in February 1999 to $35 per barrel by mid-September of 2000. Essentially, Venezuela and Mexico had convinced the other members of OPEC to cease cheating on production quotas, and this resulted in a partial closing of the global petroleum spigot. Yet while Saudi Arabia, Iraq, and Russia still had excess production capacity that could have been brought on line to keep prices down, most other oil-producing nations were pumping at, or nearly at, full capacity throughout this period.

Meanwhile, a wave of mergers had swept the industry. Exxon and Mobil had combined into Exxon-Mobil, the world's largest oil company; Chevron had merged with Texaco; Conoco had merged with Phillips; and BP had purchased Amoco-Arco. Small and medium-sized companies—such as Tosco, Valero, and Ultramar Diamond Shamrock Corp—also joined in the mania for mergers, buyouts, and downsizing. Nationally, oil-company mergers, acquisitions, and divestments totaled $82 billion in 1998 and over $50 billion in 1999.

Altogether, the oil industry appeared to be in a mode of consolidation, not one of expansion. As Goldman Sachs put it in an August 1999 report, "The oil companies are not going to keep rigs employed to drill dry holes. They know it but are unable . . . to admit it. The great merger mania is nothing more than a scaling down of a dying industry in recognition that 90 percent of global conventional oil has already been found."[4]

Meanwhile the Energy Information Agency (EIA) predicted that global *demand* for oil would continue to grow, increasing 60 percent by the year 2020 to roughly 40 billion barrels per year, or nearly 120 million barrels per day.[5]

The dramatic price hikes of 2000 soon triggered a global economic recession. The link between energy prices and the economy was intuitively obvious and had been amply demonstrated by the oil crises and accompanying recessions of the 1970s. Yet, as late as mid-2000, many pundits were insisting that the new "information economy" of the 1990s was impervious to energy-price shocks. This trend of thought was typified in a comment by British Prime Minister Tony Blair, who in January 2000 stated that "[t]wenty years on from the oil shock of the '70s, most economists would agree that oil is no longer the most important commodity in the world economy. Now, that commodity is information."[6] Yet when fuel prices soared in Britain during the last quarter of the year, truckers went on strike, bringing commerce within that nation to a virtual standstill. Though energy resources now *directly* accounted for only a small portion of economic activity in industrialized countries—1.2 percent to 2 percent in the US—all manufacturing and transportation still required fuel. In fact, the *entire* economy in every industrial nation was completely dependent on the continuing availability of energy resources at low and stable prices.

As the world economy slowed, demand for new goods also slowed, and manufacturing and transportation were scaled back. As a result, demand for oil also decreased, falling roughly five percent in the ensuing year. Prices for crude began to soften. Indeed, by late 2001, oil prices had plummeted partly as the result of market-share competition between Russia and Saudi Arabia. Gasoline prices at the pump in California had topped $2 in late 2000, but by early 2002 they had drifted to a mere $1.12 per gallon.

Such low prices tended to breed complacency. The Bush administration warned of future energy shortages, but proposed to solve the problem by promoting exploration and production within the US and by building more nuclear power plants—ideas that few with much knowledge of the energy industry took seriously. Now that gasoline prices were low again, not many citizens contemplated the possible future implications of the price run-ups of 2000. In contrast, industry insiders expressed growing concern that fundamental limits to oil production were within sight.

This concern gained public recognition in 2004, as oil prices again shot upward, this time attaining all-time highs of over $55 per barrel. *National Geographic* proclaimed in its cover story that this was "The End of Cheap Oil"; *Le Monde* announced "The Petro-Apocalypse;" while Paul Erdman, writing for the CBS television magazine *Marketwatch,* proclaimed that "the looming oil crisis will dwarf 1973." In article after article, analysts pointed to dwindling discoveries of new oil, evaporating spare production capacity, and burgeoning global demand for crude. The upshot: world oil production might be near its all-time peak.

If this were indeed the case—that world petroleum production would soon no longer be able to keep up with demand—it would be the most important news item of the dawning century, dwarfing even the atrocities of September 11. Oil was what had made 20th-century industrialism possible; it was the crucial material that had given the US its economic and technological edge during the first two-thirds of the century, enabling it to become the world's superpower. If world production of oil could no longer expand, the global economy would be structurally imperiled. The implications were staggering.

There was every reason to assume that the Bush administration understood at least the essential outlines of the situation. Not only were many policy makers themselves—including the President, Vice President, and National Security Advisor—former oil industry executives; in addition, Vice President Dick Cheney's chief petroleum-futures guru, Matthew Simmons, had warned his clients of coming energy-supply crises repeatedly. Moreover, for many years the CIA had been monitoring global petroleum supplies; it had, for example, subscribed to the yearly report of Switzerland-based Petroconsultants, published at $35,000 per copy, and was thus surely also aware of another report, also supplied by Petroconsultants, titled "The World's Oil Supply 1995," which predicted that the peak of global oil production would occur during the first decade of the new century.

It would be an understatement to say that the general public was poorly prepared to understand this information or to appreciate its gravity. The *New York Times* had carried the stories of the oil company mergers on its front pages, but offered its readers little analysis of the state of the industry or that of the geological resources on which it depended. Mass-audience magazines *Discover* and *Popular Science* blandly noted, in buried paragraphs or sidebars, that "early in [the new century] . . . half the world's known oil supply will have been used, and oil production will slide into permanent decline"[7] and that "experts predict that production will peak in 2010, and then drop over subsequent years"[8]—but these publications made no attempt to inform readers of the monumental implications of these statements. It would be safe to say that the average person had no clue whatever that the entire world was poised on the brink of an economic cataclysm that was as vast and unprecedented as it was inevitable.

Yet here and there were individuals who did perfectly comprehend the situation. Many were petroleum geologists who had spent their careers searching the globe for oil deposits, honing the theoretical and technical skills that enabled them to assess fairly accurately just how much oil was left in the ground, where it was located, and how easily it could be accessed.

What these people knew about the coming production peak—and how and when they arrived at this knowledge—constitutes a story that centers on the work of one extraordinary scientist.

M. King Hubbert: Energy Visionary

During the 1950s, '60s, and '70s, Marion King Hubbert became one of the best-known geophysicists in the world because of his disturbing prediction, first announced in 1949, that the fossil-fuel era would prove to be very brief.

Of course, the idea that oil would run out eventually was not, in itself, original. Indeed, in the 1920s many geologists had warned that world petroleum supplies would be exhausted in a matter of years. After all, the early wells in Pennsylvania had played out quickly; and extrapolating that initial experience to the limited reserves known in the first two decades of the century yielded an extremely pessimistic forecast for oil's future. However, the huge discoveries of the 1930s in east Texas and the Persian Gulf made such predictions laughable. Each year far more oil was being found than was being extracted. The doomsayers having been proven wrong, most people associated with the industry came to assume that supply and demand could continue to increase far into the future, with no end in sight. Hubbert, armed with better data and methods, doggedly challenged that assumption.

M. King Hubbert had been born in 1903 in central Texas, the hub of world oil exploration during the early 20th century. After showing a childhood fascination with steam engines and telephones, he settled on a career in science. He earned BS, MS, and Ph.D. degrees at the Univer-

sity of Chicago and, during the 1930s, taught geophysics at Columbia University. In the summer months, he worked for the Amerada Petroleum Corporation in Oklahoma, the Illinois State Geological Survey, and the United States Geological Survey (USGS). In 1943, after serving as a senior analyst at the Board of Economic Warfare in Washington, DC, Hubbert joined Shell Oil Company in Houston, where he directed the Shell research laboratory. He retired from Shell in 1964, then joined the USGS as a senior research geophysicist, a position he held until 1976. In his later years, he also taught occasionally at Stanford University, the University of California at Los Angeles, the University of California at Berkeley, the Massachusetts Institute of Technology, and Johns Hopkins University.

During his career, Hubbert made many important contributions to geophysics. In 1937 he resolved a standing paradox regarding the apparent strength of rocks that form the Earth's crust. Despite their evident properties of hardness and brittleness, such rocks often show signs of plastic flow. Hubbert demonstrated mathematically that, because even the hardest of rocks are subject to immense pressures at depth, they can respond in a manner similar to soft muds or clays. In the early 1950s, he showed that underground fluids can become entrapped under circumstances previously not thought possible, a finding that resulted in the redesign of techniques employed to locate oil and natural gas deposits. And by 1959, in collaboration with USGS geologist William W. Rubey, Hubbert also explained some puzzling characteristics of overthrust faults—low-angle fractures in rock formations in which one surface is displaced relative to another by a distance on the order of kilometers.

These scientific achievements would have been sufficient to assure Hubbert a prominent place in the history of geology. However, his greatest recognition came from his studies of petroleum and natural gas reserves—studies he had begun in 1926 while a student at the University of Chicago. In 1949, he used statistical and physical methods to calculate total world oil and natural gas supplies and documented their sharply increasing consumption. Then, in 1956 on the basis of his reserve estimates and his study of the lifetime production profile of typical oil reservoirs, he predicted that the peak of crude-oil production in the United States would occur between 1966 and 1972. At the time most economists, oil companies, and government agencies (including the USGS) dismissed the prediction. The actual peak of US oil production occurred in 1970, though this was not apparent until 1971.[9]

Let us trace just how Hubbert arrived at his prediction. First, he noted the production from a typical reservoir or province does not begin, increase to some stable level, continue at that level for a long period, and then suddenly drop off to nothing after all of the oil is gone. Rather, production tends to follow bell-shaped curve. The first exploratory well that punctures a reservoir is capable of extracting only a limited amount; but once the reservoir has been mapped more wells can be drilled.

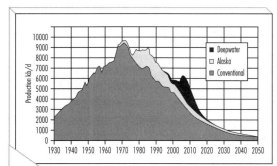

Figure 1. US oil production, history and projection, including lower 48, Alaska and Gulf of Mexico (deep water).

Source: ASPO.

During this early phase, production increases rapidly as the easiest-accessed oil is drained first. However, beyond a certain point, whatever remains is harder to get at. Production begins to decline, even if more wells are still being drilled. Typically, the production peak will occur when about half of the total oil in the reservoir has been extracted. Even after production has tapered off, some oil will still be left in the ground: it is economically impractical—and physically impossible—to remove every last drop. Indeed, for some reservoirs only a few percent of the existing oil may be recoverable (the average is between 30 and 50 percent).

Hubbert also examined the history of discovery in the lower-48 United States. More oil had been found in the 1930s than in any decade before or since—and this despite the fact that investment in exploration had increased dramatically in succeeding decades. Thus discovery also appeared to follow a bell-shaped curve. Once the history of discovery had been charted, Hubbert was able to estimate the total ultimately recoverable reserves (URR) for the entire lower-48 region. He arrived at two figures: the most pessimistic reasonable amount (150 billion barrels) and the most optimistic reasonable amount (200 billion barrels). Using these two estimates, he calculated future production rates. If the total URR in the lower-48 US amounted to 150 billion barrels, half would be gone—and production would peak—in 1966; if the figure were closer to 200 billion barrels, the peak would come in 1972.

These early calculations involved a certain amount of guesswork. For example, Hubbert chose to chart production rates on a logistic curve, whereas he might have employed a better-fitting Gaussian curve.[10] Even today, according to Princeton University geophysicist Kenneth S. Deffeyes, author of *Hubbert's Peak: The Impending World Oil Shortage*, the "numerical methods that Hubbert used to make his prediction are not crystal clear."[11] Despite many conversations with Hubbert and ensuing years spent attempting to reconstruct those original calculations, Deffeyes finds aspects of Hubbert's process obscure and "messy." Nevertheless, Hubbert did succeed in obtaining important, useful findings.

Following his prediction of the US production peak, Hubbert devoted his efforts to forecasting the global production peak. With the figures then available for the likely total recoverable world petroleum reserves, he estimated that the peak would come between the years 1990 and 2000. This forecast would prove too pessimistic, partly because of inadequate data and partly because of minor flaws in Hubbert's method. Nevertheless as we will see shortly, other researchers would later refine both input data and method in order to arrive at more reliable predictions—ones that would vary only about a decade from Hubbert's.

Hubbert immediately grasped the vast economic and social implications of this information. He understood the role of fossil fuels in the creation of the modern industrial world, and thus foresaw the wrenching transition that would likely occur following the peak in global extraction rates. In lectures and articles, starting in the 1950s, Hubbert outlined how society needed to change in order to prepare for a post-petroleum regime. The following passage, part of a summary by Hubbert of one of his own lectures, conveys some of the breadth and flavor of his macrosocial thinking:

> The world's present industrial civilization is handicapped by the coexistence of two universal, overlapping, and incompatible intellectual systems: the accumulated knowledge of the last four centuries of the properties and interrelationships of matter and energy; and the associated monetary culture which has evolved from folkways of prehistoric origin.

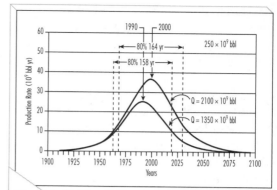

Figure 2. M. King Hubbert's projected cycles for world crude production for the extreme values of the estimated total resource.

Source: M. K. Hubbert, *Resources and Man.*

> The first of these two systems has been responsible for the spectacular rise, principally during the last two centuries, of the present industrial system and is essential for its continuance. The second, an inheritance from the prescientific past, operates by rules of its own having little in common with those of the matter-energy system. Nevertheless, the monetary system, by means of a loose coupling, exercises a general control over the matter-energy system upon which it is superimposed.

> Despite their inherent incompatibilities, these two systems during the last two centuries have had one fundamental characteristic in common, namely exponential growth, which has made a reasonably stable coexistence possible. But, for various reasons, it is impossible for the matter-energy system to sustain exponential growth for more than a few tens of doublings, and this phase is by now almost over. The monetary system has no such constraints, and, according to one of its most fundamental rules, it must continue to grow by compound interest.[12]

Hubbert thus believed that society, if it is to avoid chaos during the energy decline, must give up its antiquated, debt-and-interest-based monetary system and adopt a system of accounts based on matter-energy—an inherently ecological system that would acknowledge the finite nature of essential resources.

Hubbert was quoted as saying that we are in a "crisis in the evolution of human society. It's unique to both human and geologic history. It has never happened before and it can't possibly happen again. You can only use oil once. You can only use metals once. Soon all the oil is going to be burned and all the metals mined and scattered."[13]

Statements like this one gave Hubbert the popular image of a doomsayer. Yet he was not a pessimist; indeed, on occasion he could assume the role of utopian seer. We have, he believed, the necessary know-how; all we need do is overhaul our culture and find an alternative to money. If society were to develop solar-energy technologies, reduce its population and its demands on resources, and develop a steady-state economy to replace the present one based on unending growth, our species' future could be rosy indeed. "We are not starting from zero," he emphasized. "We have an enormous amount of existing technical knowledge. It's just a matter of putting it all together. We still have great flexibility but our maneuverability will diminish with time."[14]

Reading Hubbert's few published works—for example, his statement before the House of Representatives Subcommittee on the Environment on June 6, 1974—one is struck by his ability to follow the implications of his findings on oil depletion through the domains of economics and ecology.[15] He was a holistic and interdisciplinary thinker who deserves, if anyone does, to be called a prophet of the coming era.

Hubbert died in 1989, a few years before his predicted date for the global production peak. That all-important forecast date was incorrect, as the rate of world oil production continued to increase through the first months of 2005. But

by how far did he miss the mark? It would be up to his followers to find out.

Zeroing in on the Date of the Peak

As a growing community of scientists applies itself to the task of determining exactly when the world's oil production will begin to decline, four principle methods for doing so are emerging.

1. Estimate the total ultimately recoverable resource (URR) and calculate when half will have been extracted. This is the original method developed and used by Hubbert himself, beginning in the 1950s. As we have seen, Hubbert noted that for a typical oil-producing region, a graph of extraction over time tends to take on a bell-shaped curve: the more cheaply and easily accessed portion of the resource is depleted first, so that when about half is gone the rate at which extraction can proceed tends to diminish.

The method is relatively simple, and it worked well for predicting the U.S. production peak. However, it relies on the availability of accurate discovery and reserve data so that URR can be accurately estimated, and on accurate extraction data as well. For the US, these figures were not problematic, but for some other important oil-producing regions this is not the case: reserve data for Saudi Arabia, for example, are controversial.

Moreover, there is no natural law stating that the extraction curve must be precisely bell-shaped or symmetrical. Indeed, political, economic, and technological factors can deform the curve in an infinite number of ways. In reality the actual production curves from producing nations never conform to a simple mathematical curve, and are characterized by bumps, plateaus, valleys, and peaks of differing sizes and durations. A war, a recession, the application of a new recovery technology, or the decision by a government to restrain extraction can reshape the curve arbitrarily.

Nevertheless, what comes up must come down: for every oil-producing region, extraction starts at zero, increases to a maximum, and declines, regardless of the tortuous bumps in between. And, in general, the latter half of the resource will require more effort and time to extract than the first half. Moreover, experience shows that if actual production strays far from the predicted curve because of political or economic factors, it will tend to return to it once the influence of those factors subsides.

The Hubbert model is therefore a good way of providing a first-order approximation: it gives us a general overview of the depletion process, and (depending on the accuracy of the available reserve and production data) yields a likely peak year, with a window of uncertainty. However, it cannot be used to forecast actual production for the next month or even the next decade.

Using this method (with various refinements), Kenneth Deffeyes, in his book *Hubbert's Curve,* arrives at a peak date of 2005. Other researchers, such as Jean Laherrère, using more optimistic reserve estimates, place the peak further out, up to 2020.

2. Count the number of years from peak of discovery. Hubbert realized that, when graphed over time, the *discovery* of oil within any given region tends to peak and decline, just as production does. Understandably, discovery always peaks first—since it is necessary to find oil before it can be extracted.

In the US, discoveries of oil peaked in the early 1930s with the stupendous finds in east Texas; production peaked almost exactly 40 years later. Are we likely to find a similar time lag for other oil producing regions? If so, this could provide a basis for predicting the timing of the global production peak.

The duration of the lag between discovery and production peaks depends on a number of factors: the geological conditions (some fields can be depleted more quickly than others); the extraction technology being used (new recovery methods can deplete a reservoir more quickly and efficiently, but can also increase the total amount recoverable and thus extend the life of the field); and whether the resource is being extracted at maximum possible rate (as already noted, economic or political events can intervene to reduce production rates).

The North Sea provides an example of a relatively brief lag between discovery and extraction peaks: there, discoveries peaked in the early 1970s, while production peaked only 30 years later, at the turn of the new century. The latest exploration and extraction technologies were applied, and the resource base was drawn down at virtually the maximum possible rate because North Sea oil was in high demand throughout this period.

Iraq provides a counterexample: there, two principal periods of major discovery occurred—in the early 1950s and the mid-1970s. For that country, political and economic events have constrained production to a very significant degree: first, the Iran-Iraq war of the 1980s, then the US-led embargo of the 1990s, and finally the turmoil surrounding the US invasion and occupation have reduced extraction rates well below levels that would otherwise have been achieved. Consequently, Iraqi oil production may not peak until 2015 at the earliest, though more likely a decade or so later, yielding a discovery-to-production-peak lag of 45 to 60 years.

Will other discovery-to-production-peak lag times tend to more closely match those of the North Sea countries, or that of Iraq? Chances are that, as individual anomalies cancel each other out, lag times are on average likely to cluster around that of the US—roughly 40 years.

Global oil discoveries peaked in 1963. This is not a controversial fact: both the oil industry and the US Department of Energy acknowledge that this is the case.

Given this, we might expect that the global peak in the rate of oil extraction would occur roughly 40 years later—i.e., in 2003.

However, we must take into account intervening economic and political events that might have tended to reduce extraction rates below their potential, and thus increase the time lag. The principal such events were the Arab OPEC embargo of the early 1970s, the fall of the Shah of Iran, and the subsequent Iran-Iraq war a few years later. The consequent oil price spikes reduced demand for oil, and led to a decline in extraction rates. The effect may have been to add up to ten years to the global discovery-to-production-peak time lag, yielding a likely peak date window of 2005 to 2013.

3. Track the reserve and production data of individual countries. For the past few years, both Colin Campbell (Association for the Study of Peak Oil) and Richard C. Duncan (Institute on Energy and Man) have been keeping close track of production data for individual producing nations.

Campbell's detailed discussions of oil statistics nation by nation are available in the archived newsletters of the Association for the Study of Peak Oil (www.asponews.org), and in his book, *The Essence of Oil & Gas Depletion* (MultiScience, 2003).

Duncan uses a "graphical-heuristic-iterative (GHI)" method to forecast world oil production, repeating the entire modeling and forecasting process annually to give a series of consistent but unique world oil forecasts. According to Duncan, *heuristic* means "a method of computer programming in which the modeler and machine proceed along empirical lines, using data, other information, and rules of thumb to find solutions or answers." *Iterative* means "repetitious; repeating or repeated." The

Graphical Input Device (used in system dynamics programs such as Stella) enables the modeler "to quickly create and/or edit an oil production forecast of a nation just before each trial run (iteration) of the model." The *Scatter Graph* (system dynamics) is used to depict "the forecasted peak year of oil production (x-axis) *versus* the forecasted peak production rate (y-axis) of our ongoing series of world oil forecasts." Duncan describes this as a work in progress "that will eventually converge on Peak Oil—whether the Peak is near at hand or far in the future."[24]

Many countries are now clearly past their individual all-time extraction peaks. The list includes not only the US, but also Indonesia, Gabon, Great Britain, and Norway. Altogether, according to Duncan, of 45 significant oil-producing countries, 25 are past-peak (*BP Statistical Review of World Energy* currently estimates the latter number at 18, indicating that there is some uncertainty on this point, but also that oil companies are keenly aware of the peaking phenomenon and are keeping score).[25]

Some of the pre-peak nations are major producers with huge reserves (e.g., Iraq and Saudi Arabia). Thus it would be unwise to assume that the global peak will occur when exactly half of all producing nations have undergone their individual peaks. Clearly, more complex calculations are necessary, and this is the work that Duncan and Campbell are undertaking.

The countries in decline account for about 30 percent of the world's total oil production. Further, according to *Oil & Gas Journal,* as demand for oil expanded and prices rose during 2004, all of the added supply came from Russia and a few OPEC nations. Evidently, all of the nations outside of Russia and OPEC, when taken together, have already peaked in production (though there are individual exceptions, such as Brazil).

By examining the geology, history, and economic-political circumstances of each oil-producing country, it is possible to encircle the remaining uncertainties and pick away at them. How much oil has been discovered in each given nation? How long ago did discoveries peak? Are significant future discoveries likely? What kinds of recovery methods are being used?

Duncan summarizes his method as follows:

I make a separate computer-based model to forecast the oil production for each of the major oil-producing nations in the world; 2) The latest oil data and related information on each nation are gathered from journals, the internet, and colleagues just before each national model is run; 3) Then both a Low oil forecast and a Medium oil forecast are made for each nation; 4) Next all of the Medium oil forecasts are combined (added up) to give the world oil forecast; 5) This process is repeated annually as soon as new oil data and related information become available; 6) A Scatter Graph indicates that the eight world oil forecasts that we've completed so far seem to be converging on Peak Oil in 2006 or 2007; 7) One new forecast (point) will be added to the Scatter Graph each year until Peak Oil is confirmed.

Campbell's analysis of likely future oil production by individual producing nations yields a global peak date of 2008.

4. Compare the amount of new production capacity likely to be available over the coming years with the amount of production capacity needed to offset decline rates from existing fields. The global oil industry needs to develop new production capacity yearly, in order to meet new demand and offset declines in production rates from individual wells and producing regions already past their all-time peaks. Currently, the world produces about 83 million barrels per day of all petroleum liquids combined (conventional oil plus oil from tar sands, natural gas liquids, and so on). The IEA estimates that in 2005 the world will need another 1.5 million barrels per day of new production capacity in order to meet new demand, plus another 4 mb/d to offset declines from existing fields—a total of about 5.5 mb/d. In 2006, a slightly greater new quantity will be needed, and in 2007, more still. In the five years from 2005 to 2010 a total of over 35 mb/d of new production capacity will need to come online. (These figures are agreed upon by both industry and various governmental agencies.) A substantial effort is necessary, to say the least.

But where will all this new production capacity come from?

In general, new production capacity arises from three sources: the discovery of new resources; the development of previously discovered resources (including reserve growth and infill drilling); or the development of unconventional resources (which sometimes depends on the invention and implementation of new technologies).

It takes time and investment to develop new production capacity. Thus it is possible—though no simple matter!—to gather the necessary data, analyze it, and project how much new production capacity is likely to emerge over the next five years, given current rates of investment, the available technology, and the discoveries in place. (Even if a huge new discovery were to be made next year, it would probably be impossible to bring the oil from it into production before 2010.) Chris Skrebowski, editor of *Petroleum Review,* has done just that in his 2004 report, "Oil Field Megaprojects," sponsored by the Oil Depletion Analysis Centre (ODAC).

Skrebowski compiles and regularly updates the details of planned major production projects, as reported by the oil companies. The list contains data on all announced fields with at least 500 million barrels of estimated reserves, and on projects with the claimed potential to produce 100,000 barrels a day or more.

Skrebowski and ODAC analyzed 68 production projects with announced start-up dates ranging from 2004 through 2010, and found that they are likely to add about 12.5 million barrels per day of new production capacity. In a press release, he stated: "This new production would almost certainly not be sufficient to offset diminishing supplies from existing sources and still meet growing global demand," and that "even with relatively low demand growth, our study indicates a seemingly unbridgeable supply-demand gap opening up after 2007."[27]

"It is disturbing to see such a dramatic fall-off of new project commitments after 2007, and not more than a handful of tentative projects into the next decade," Skrebowski said. "This could very well be a signal that world oil production is rapidly approaching its peak, as a growing number of analysts now forecast, especially in view of the diminishing prospects for major new oil discoveries."

At the end of the day, there are still uncertainties. Major new oil discoveries are always possible, though increasingly unlikely. Probably the greatest uncertainty with respect to the timing of the global oil production peak is future demand. If the global economy fares well, then demand will increase and the peak will come sooner; if the economy falters, then the peak will come later. If the world stumbles into a full-fledged depression, the peak could be delayed significantly, and the effects of the phenomenon could be masked by other events.

Nevertheless, as we have seen, the results of the possible forecasting methods tend to converge. We are within only a few years of the all-time global oil production peak. We are virtually at the summit now, with almost no time left for maneuvering before the event itself is upon us.

Author Citations

4. Goldman Sachs, *Energy Weekly*, 11 August 1999.

5. EIA Annual Energy Outlook 2000 with Projections to 2020; current report available online at www.eia.doe.gov/oiaf/aeo/.

6. Blair made these comments on January 28, 2000, at Davos, Switzerland. See, for example, http://Singapore.emc/com/news/in_depth_archive/01032001_year_info.jsp.

7. Eric Haseltine, "Twenty Things That Will Be Obsolete in Twenty Years," *Discover*, Vol. 21, No. 10, October, 2000, p. 85.

8. William G. Phillips, "Are We Really Running Out of Oil?", *Popular Science*, May 2000, p. 56.

9. Hubbert was fortunate to deal with the US lower-48, where a simple bell-shaped curve could be derived from production statistics. Adding production data from Alaska changes the curve, revealing two cycles. Further, between 1960 and 1980 supply was almost never constrained by demand—because of mandatory quotas on oil imports instituted by Eisenhower in 1959. Without these quotas, US production would have been less since foreign oil was cheaper. Thus reduced demand for more expensive oil would have delayed the peak.

10. Kenneth S. Deffeyes, *Hubbert's Peak: The Impending World Oil Shortage* (Princeton University Press, 2001), pp. 134–49.

11. Kenneth S. Deffeyes, *Hubbert's Peak*, p. 135.

12. "Two Intellectual Systems: matter-energy and the Monetary Culture." Summary, by M. King Hubbert, of a seminar he taught at MIT Energy Laboratory, 30 September 1981, at www.hubbertpeak.com/hubbert/monetary.htm.

13. See www.hubbertpeak.com/hubbert/hubecon.htm.

14. See www.hubbertpeak.com/hubecon.htm.

15. See www.technocracy.com/articles/hubbert-econ.html.

24. From a personal communication with the author.

25. See www.bp.com/subsection.do?categoryId=95&contentId=2006480.

26. From a personal communication with the author.

27. See www.odac-info.org.

Discussion Questions

1. If only half of the world's oil reserves have been consumed when "peak oil" occurs, why is the peak a big deal?
2. Summarize the four methods for predicting peak oil.
3. In another chapter of *The Party's Over*, Heinberg discusses the concept of "Energy Returned over Energy Invested" (EROEI). This is essentially a measure of how "hard" it is to produce a fuel (find, extract, and process). If a fuel's EROEI is less than one, the fuel delivers less energy than was consumed in its production. Discuss peak oil in the context of EROEI.

 ## Supporting Activities

1. Find three independent predictions about when peak oil will occur. Record the year, the group or individual making the prediction, and, if possible, information about the methodology that was used to make the prediction.
2. Find one source that refutes the notion of peak oil. Record the source and summarize the argument made.
3. Heinberg describes the energy crisis of the 1970s as a "politically-based interruption in the delivery of crude." What are the causes of the oil crisis of the 2000s?
4. What does a barrel of crude oil sell for *today*? If possible, find out what this rate represents in 1960, 1970, or 1980 dollars.
5. What would you do if crude oil (and gasoline and natural gas) suddenly increased in price tenfold? How would your daily routine change, and how would you cope?

 ## Additional Resources

1. Richard Heinberg's Web site: www.richardheinberg.com.
2. Heinberg's sequel to *The Party's Over, Powerdown: Options and Actions for a Post-Carbon World* by Richard Heinberg (New Society Publishers, 2004) ISBN 0865715106, 9780865715103.
3. A great video introducing peak oil: *End of Suburbia* (endofsuburbia.com).
4. Web site of the Association for the Study of Peak Oil: www.peakoil.net, www.apso-usa.com.
5. Other peak oil sites: www.lifeaftertheoilcrash.net, www.peakoil.com.

Global Oil Production about to Peak? A Recurring Myth

Red Cavaney offers a counterpoint to the peak-oil theorists. He suggests that technology will allow oil supply to keep pace with demand for decades to come. And why not? Oil supply has, in fact, kept up with demand, which has grown on average 3 percent per year over the last 50 years.

Mr. Cavaney quotes oil supply projections from the Department of Energy's Energy Information Administration (EIA; www.eia.doe.gov), an acknowledged credible source for statistics (used extensively by these authors), but a dubious source of predictions. The EIA advertises a "business as usual" model, which by design predicts supply satisfying demand. Their models, therefore, cannot predict non-historic events (like Peak Oil). As a result, EIA predictions will typically project a continuation of the status quo. Both the United States Geological Survey (USGS) and the EIA are political bodies whose reports are required to be consistent with the "current administration," regardless of whom is in office.

Cavaney's statistics include what are called "unconventional" oil reserves, including oil shale and tar sands, both of which are indeed viable reserves. However, to imply that these resources can be harvested without acknowledging a significant increase in cost (economic and environmental) is irresponsible. The oil sands in Alberta, Canada provide a relevant case study. A 2006 report by the Canadian National Energy Board projects output from Alberta oil sands to reach between 2 and 5 million barrels per day (MBPD) by 2015.[5] Consistent with this projection, a $27B oil refinery project announced in 2007 will boost Canada's non-conventional oil refining capability to 3 MBPD.[6] To put these numbers in context, the U.S. currently consumes over 21 MBPD. Apparently, oil sands are not the silver bullet we might wish them to be in meeting a growing demand for oil.

Saying that we "cannot afford to leave the Age of Oil before realistic substitutes are fully in place" is like saying we "cannot afford $4/gallon gasoline." We may not like it, but there's not much we can do about it.

Red Cavaney has served as President and CEO of the American Petroleum Institute since 1997, prior to which he served as CEO of several other trade associations and as a senior member of the White House staffs of Presidents Nixon, Ford, and Reagan.

Global Oil Production about to Peak? A Recurring Myth

By Red Cavaney

Once again, we are hearing that world oil production is "peaking," and that we will face a steadily diminishing oil supply to fuel the global economy. These concerns have been expressed periodically over the years, but have always been at odds with energy and economic realities. Such is the case today.

Let's look at some history: In 1874, the chief geologist of Pennsylvania predicted we would run out of oil in four years—just using it for kerosene. Thirty years ago, groups such as the Club of Rome predicted an end of oil long before the current day. These forecasts were wrong because, nearly every year, we have found more oil than we have used, and oil reserves have continued to grow.

The world consumes approximately 80 million barrels of oil a day. By 2030, world oil demand is estimated to grow about 50 percent, to 121 million barrels a day, even allowing for sig-

Cavaney, R., "Global Oil Production About to Peak? A Recurring Myth," WorldWatch Institute, *World Watch, January/February, 2006,* www.worldwatch.org.

nificant improvements in energy efficiency. The International Energy Agency says there are sufficient oil resources to meet demand for at least the next 30 years.

The key factor here is technology. Revolutionary advances in technology in recent years have dramatically increased the ability of companies to find and extract oil—and, of particular importance, recover more oil from existing reservoirs. Rather than production peaking, existing fields are yielding markedly more oil than in the past. Advances in technology include the following:

DIRECTIONAL DRILLING. It used to be that wellbores were basically vertical holes. This made it necessary to drill virtually on top of a potential oil deposit. However, the advent of miniaturized computers and advanced sensors that can be attached to the drill bit now allows companies to drill directional holes with great accuracy because they can get real-time information on the

subsurface location throughout the drilling process.

HORIZONTAL DRILLING. Horizontal drilling is similar to directional drilling, but the well is designed to cut horizontally through the middle of the oil or natural gas deposit. Early horizontal wells penetrated only 500 to 800 feet of reservoir laterally, but technology advances recently allowed a North Slope operator to penetrate 8,000 feet of reservoir horizontally. Moreover, horizontal wells can operate up to 10 times more productively than conventional wells.

3-D SEISMIC TECHNOLOGY. Substantial enhancements in computing power during the past two decades have allowed the industry to gain a much clearer picture of what lies beneath the surface. The ability to process huge amounts of data to produce three-dimensional seismic images has significantly improved the drilling success rate of the industry.

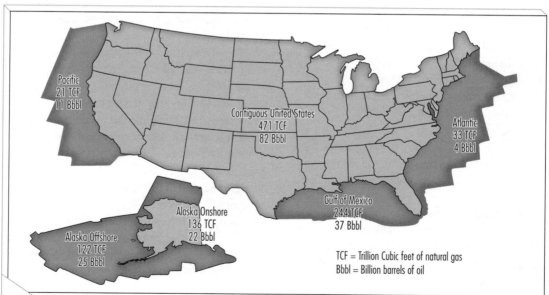

Total Undiscovered, Technically Recoverable, Natural Gas and Oil, United States.

Primarily due to these advances, the U.S. Geological Survey (USGS), in its 2000 *World Petroleum Assessment*, increased by 20 percent its estimate of undiscovered, technically recoverable oil. USGS noted that, since oil became a major energy source about 100 years ago, 539 billion barrels of oil have been produced outside the United States. USGS estimates there are 649 billion barrels of undiscovered, technically recoverable oil outside the United States. But, importantly, USGS also estimates that there will be an *additional* 612 billion barrels from "reserve growth"—nearly equaling the undiscovered resources. Reserve growth results from a variety of sources, including technological advancement in exploration and production, increases over initially conservative estimates of reserves, and economic changes.

The USGS estimates reflected several factors:

- As drilling and production within discovered fields progresses, new pools or reservoirs are found that were not previously known.
- Advances in exploration technology make it possible to identify new targets within existing fields.
- Advances in drilling technology make it possible to recover oil and gas not previously considered recoverable in the initial reserve estimates.
- Enhanced oil recovery techniques increase the recovery factor for oil and thereby increase the reserves within existing fields.

Here in the United States, rather than "running out of oil," potentially vast oil and natural gas reserves remain to be developed. According to the latest published government estimates, there are more than 131 billion barrels of oil and more than 1,000 trillion cubic feet of natural gas remaining to be discovered in the United States. However, 78 percent of this oil and 62 percent of this gas are expected to be found beneath federal lands—much of which are non-park and non-wilderness lands—and coastal waters. While there is plenty of oil in the ground, oil companies need to be allowed to make major investments to find and produce it.

The U.S. Energy Information Administration has projected that fossil fuels will continue to dominate U.S. energy consumption, with oil and natural gas providing almost two-thirds of that consumption in the year 2025, even though energy efficiency and renewables will grow faster than their historical rates. However, renewables in particular start from a very small base; and the major shares provided by oil, natural gas, and coal in 2025 are projected to be nearly identical to those in 2003.

Those who block oil and natural gas development here in the United States and elsewhere only make it much more difficult to meet the demand for oil, natural gas, and petroleum products. Indeed, it is not surprising that some of the end-of-oil advocates are the same people who oppose oil and natural gas development everywhere.

Failure to develop the potentially vast oil and natural gas resources that remain in the world will have a high economic cost. We must recognize that we live in a global economy, and that there is a strong link between energy and economic growth. If we are to continue to grow economically, here in the United States, in Europe, and the developing world, we must be cost-competitive in our use of energy. We need *all* sources of energy. We do not have the luxury of limiting ourselves to one source to the exclusion of others. Nor can we afford to write off our leading source of energy before we have found cost-competitive and readily available alternatives.

Consider how oil enhances our quality of life—fueling growth and jobs in industry and commerce, cooling and warming our homes, and getting us where we need to go. Here in the United States, oil provides about 97 percent of transportation fuels, which power nearly all of the cars and trucks traveling on our nation's highways. And plastics, medicines, fertilizers, and countless other products that extend and enhance our quality of life are derived from oil.

In considering our future energy needs, we also need to understand that gasoline-powered automobiles have been the dominant mode of transport for the past century—and the overwhelming preference of hundreds of millions of people throughout the world. Regardless of fuel, the automobile—likely to be configured far differently from today—will remain the consumer's choice for personal transport for decades to come. The freedom of mobility and the independence it affords consumers is highly valued.

The United States—and the world—cannot afford to leave the Age of Oil before realistic substitutes are fully in place. It is important to remember that man left the Stone Age not because he ran out of stones—and we will not leave the Age of Oil because we will run out. Yes, someday oil will be replaced, but clearly not until substitutes are found—substitutes that are proven more reliable, more versatile, and more cost-competitive than oil. We can rely on the energy marketplace to determine what the most efficient substitutes will be.

As we plan for our energy future, we also cannot afford to ignore the lessons of recent history. In the early 1970s, many energy policymakers were sure that oil and natural gas would soon be exhausted, and government policy was explicitly aimed at "guiding" the market in a smooth transition away from these fuels to new, more sustainable alternatives. Price controls, allocation schemes, limitations on natural gas, massive subsidies to synthetic fuels, and other measures were funded heavily and implemented.

Unfortunately, the key premises on which these programs were based, namely that oil was nearing exhaustion and that government guidance was desirable to safely transition to new energy sources, are now recognized as having been clearly wrong—and to have resulted in enormously expensive mistakes.

Looking into the distant future, there will be a day when oil is no longer the world's dominant energy source. We can only speculate as to when and how that day will come about. For example, there is an even bigger hydrocarbon resource that can be developed to provide nearly endless amounts of energy: methane hydrates (methane frozen in ice crystals). The deposits of methane hydrates are so vast that when we develop the technology to bring them to market, we will have clean-burning energy for 2,000 years. It's just one of the exciting scenarios we may see in the far-off future. But we won't be getting there anytime soon, and until we do, the Age of Oil will continue.

Discussion Questions

1. Evaluate Red Cavaney's statement "there are sufficient oil reserves to meet demand for at least the next 30 years" in the context of our earlier peak oil discussion.
2. How do you feel about drilling for oil and natural gas on federally owned land such as national forest land? National park land? Offshore?
3. If you were responsible for setting U.S. energy policy, what policies would you promote? Give a brief rationale for your choices.

 Supporting Activities

1. What is the current global estimated reserve of conventional oil? Of non-conventional reserve? What are some issues associated with non-conventional reserves?
2. What is the current global consumption of petroleum? U.S. consumption? What was global consumption 10 years ago? 20 years ago? Use the EIA's Web site. Based on EIA trends for the past 20 years, what level of consumption would you expect to see 20 years from now?
3. One commonly used indicator of future oil availability is to compare annual petroleum consumption to discoveries. Explain why this is an indicator, and find some data that shows this comparison over the past 10 or so years.
4. At the end of his article, Mr. Cavaney mentions methane hydrate (also called methane clathrate). Do some investigating. Does this fuel really exist? Is it a viable fuel? Are there any concerns?

 Additional Resources

1. Web site of the American Petroleum Institute: www.api.org.
2. An anti peak oil site: http://www.prisonplanet.com/archives/peak_oil/index.htm.

Powering the Future

If the mark of a good writer is becoming intimate with his subject, then Michael Parfit must be called a good writer. He lives off grid, and is therefore more qualified than most to write about alternatives to fossil fuels.

In this article, Parfit marches through the list of renewable and alternative energy sources: solar, wind, biofuels, nuclear fusion, and nuclear fission, and gives each one a balanced overview. Early on in the article, Mr. Parfit acknowledges that there is no "next great fuel." More specifically, he states that there is no *single* next great fuel. Consequences of fossil fuel consumption are summarized, but most of the article is spent examining the pros, cons, and prospects of each technology. Parfit examines the technical, social, environmental, and political challenges associated with each fuel in an unbiased way. His language is accessible and not jargon-filled.

Michael Parfit is a frequent contributor to *National Geographic* Magazine. He is the author of several books on environmental topics including water and coal, and has also written about his travels to Antarctica and across the U.S. in a small airplane.

Powering the Future

By Michael Parfit

Freedom!

I stand in a cluttered room surrounded by the debris of electrical enthusiasm: wire peelings, snippets of copper, yellow connectors, insulated pliers. For me these are the tools of freedom. I have just installed a dozen solar panels on my roof, and they work. A meter shows that 1,285 watts of power are blasting straight from the sun into my system, charging my batteries, cooling my refrigerator, humming through my computer, liberating my life.

The euphoria of energy freedom is addictive. Don't get me wrong; I love fossil fuels. I live on an island that happens to have no utilities, but otherwise my wife and I have a normal American life. We don't want propane refrigerators, kerosene lamps, or composting toilets. We want a lot of electrical outlets and a cappuccino maker. But when I turn on those panels, wow!

Maybe that's because for me, as for most Americans, one energy crisis or another has shadowed most of the past three decades. From the OPEC crunch of the 1970s to the skyrocketing cost of oil and gasoline today, the world's concern over energy has haunted presidential speeches, congressional campaigns, disaster books, and my own sense of well-being with the same kind of gnawing unease that characterized the Cold War.

As *National Geographic* reported in June 2004, oil, no longer cheap, may soon decline. Instability where most oil is found, from the Persian Gulf to Nigeria to Venezuela, makes this

From *National Geographic, 208(2), August 2005* by Michael Parfit. Copyright © 2005 by National Geographic Society. Reprinted by permission.

lifeline fragile. Natural gas can be hard to transport and is prone to shortages. We won't run out of coal anytime soon, or the largely untapped deposits of tar sands and oil shale. But it's clear that the carbon dioxide spewed by coal and other fossil fuels is warming the planet, as this magazine reported last September.

Cutting loose from that worry is enticing. With my new panels, nothing stands between me and limitless energy—no foreign nation, no power company, no carbon-emission guilt. I'm free!

Well, almost. Here comes a cloud.

Shade steals across my panels and over my heart. The meter shows only 120 watts. I'm going to have to start the generator and burn some more gasoline. This isn't going to be easy after all.

The trouble with energy freedom is that it's addictive; when you get a little, you want a lot. In microcosm I'm like people in government, industry, and private life all over the world, who have tasted a bit of this curious and compelling kind of liberty and are determined to find more.

Some experts think this pursuit is even more important than the war on terrorism. "Terrorism doesn't threaten the viability of the heart of our high-technology lifestyle," says Martin Hoffert, a professor of physics at New York University. "But energy really does."

Energy conservation can stave off the day of reckoning, but in the end you can't conserve what you don't have. So Hoffert and others have no doubt: It's time to step up the search for the next great fuel for the hungry engine of humankind.

Is there such a fuel? The short answer is no. Experts say it like a mantra: "There is no silver bullet." Though a few true believers claim that only vast conspiracies or lack of funds stand between us and endless energy from the vacuum of space or the core of the Earth, the truth is that there's no single great new fuel waiting in the heart of an equation or at the end of a drill bit.

Enthusiasm about hydrogen-fueled cars may give the wrong impression. Hydrogen is not a source of energy. It's found along with oxygen in plain old water, but it isn't there for the taking. Hydrogen has to be freed before it is useful, and that costs more energy than the hydrogen gives back. These days, this energy comes mostly from fossil fuels. No silver bullet there.

The long answer about our next fuel is not so grim, however. In fact, plenty of contenders for the energy crown now held by fossil fuels are already at hand: wind, solar, even nuclear, to name a few. But the successor will have to be a congress, not a king. Virtually every energy expert I met did something unexpected: He pushed not just his own specialty but everyone else's too.

"We're going to need everything we can get from biomass, everything we can get from solar, everything we can get from wind," says Michael Pacheco, director of the National Bioenergy Center, part of the National Renewable Energy Laboratories (NREL) in Golden, Colorado. "And still the question is, can we get enough?"

The big problem is big numbers. The world uses some 320 billion kilowatt-hours of energy a day. It's equal to about 22 bulbs burning nonstop for every person on the planet. No wonder the sparkle is seen from space. Hoffert's team estimates that within the next century humanity could use three times that much. Fossil fuels have met the growing demand because they pack millions of years of the sun's energy into a compact form, but we will not find their like again.

Fired up by my taste of energy freedom, I went looking for technologies that can address those numbers. "If you have a big problem, you must give a big answer," says a genial energy guru named Hermann Scheer, a member of the German parliament. "Otherwise people don't believe."

The answers are out there. But they all require one more thing of us humans who huddle around the fossil fuel fire: We're going to have to make a big leap—toward a different kind of world.

Solar: Free Energy, at a Price

On a cloudy day near the city of Leipzig in the former East Germany, I walked across a field of fresh grass, past a pond where wild swans fed. The field was also sown with 33,500 photovoltaic panels, planted in rows like silver flowers all turned sunward, undulating gently across the contours of the land. It's one of the largest solar arrays ever. When the sun emerges, the field produces up to five megawatts of power, and it averages enough for 1,800 homes.

Nearby are gaping pits where coal was mined for generations to feed power plants and factories. The skies used to be brown with smoke and acrid with sulfur. Now the mines are being turned into lakes, and power that once came from coal is made in a furnace 93 million miles (150 million kilometers) away.

Solar electric systems catch energy directly from the sun—no fire, no emissions. Some labs and companies are trying out the grown-up version of a child's magnifying glass: giant mirrored bowls or troughs to concentrate the sun's rays, producing heat that can drive a generator. But for now, sun power mostly means solar cells.

The idea is simple: Sunlight falling on a layer of semiconductor jostles electrons, creating a current. Yet the cost of the cells, once astronomical, is still high. My modest system cost over $15,000, about $10 a watt of capacity, including batteries to store power for when the sun doesn't shine.

Like most things electronic, solar power has been getting cheaper. "Thirty years ago it was cost-effective on satellites," says Daniel Shugar, president of PowerLight Corporation, a fast-growing California company that has built solar installations for clients including Toyota and Target. "Today it can be cost-effective for powering houses and businesses," at least where

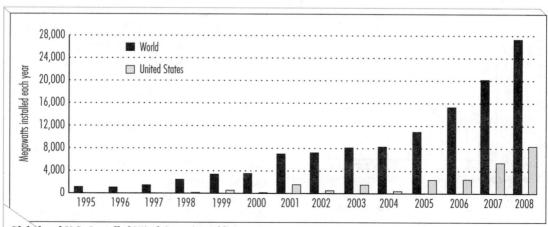

Global and U.S. Installed Wind Capacity Additions.
Art by Charles Floyd, NGM Art. Sources: European Wind Energy Association and American Wind Energy Association.

utility power is expensive or unavailable. Tomorrow, he says, it will make sense for almost everyone.

Martin Roscheisen, CEO of a company called Nanosolar, sees that future in a set of red-topped vials, filled with tiny particles of semiconductor. "I put some of that on my finger, and it disappeared right into my skin," he says. He won't say exactly what the particles are, but the "nano" in the company name is a hint: They are less than a hundred nanometers across—about the size of a virus, and so small they slip right through skin.

Roscheisen believes those particles promise a low-cost way to create solar cells. Instead of making the cells from slabs of silicon, his company will paint the particles onto a foil-like material, where they will self-assemble to create a semiconductor surface. The result: a flexible solar-cell material 50 times thinner than today's solar panels. Roscheisen hopes to sell it in sheets, for about 50 cents a watt.

"Fifty cents a watt is kind of the holy grail," says David Pearce, president and CEO of Mia-

solé, one of many other companies working on "thin-film" solar cells. At that price solar could compete with utilities and might take off. If prices continued to drop, solar cells might change the whole idea of energy by making it cheap and easy for individuals to gather for themselves. That's what techies call a "disruptive technology."

"Automobiles were disruptive to the horse and buggy business," Dan Shugar says. "PCs were disruptive to the typewriter industry. We believe solar electric systems will be disruptive to the energy industry."

Yet price isn't the only hurdle solar faces. There are the small matters of clouds and darkness, which call for better ways of storing energy than the bulky lead-acid batteries in my system. But even if those hurdles are overcome, can solar really make the big energy we need?

With solar now providing less than one percent of the world's energy, that would take "a massive (but not insurmountable) scale-up," NYU's Hoffert and his colleagues said in an article in *Science*. At present levels of efficiency, it would take about 10,000 square miles (30,000 square kilometers) of solar panels—an area bigger than Vermont—to satisfy all of the United States' electricity needs. But the land requirement sounds more daunting than it is: Open country wouldn't have to be covered. All those panels could fit on less than a quarter of the roof and pavement space in cities and suburbs.

Wind: Feast or Famine

Wind, ultimately driven by sun-warmed air, is just another way of collecting solar energy, but it works on cloudy days. One afternoon I stood in a field near Denmark's west coast under a sky so dark and heavy it would have put my own solar panels into a coma. But right above me clean power was being cranked out by the megawatt. A blade longer than an air-

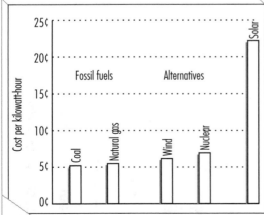

The Cost of a Kilowatt-Hour. Solar power will remain expensive for some time, as shown in a comparison of energy prices calculated for new plants coming online in 2013. But the cost of solar should fall as technology improves.

Source: U.S. Energy Information Administration.

plane wing turned slowly in a strong south breeze. It was a wind turbine.

The turbine's lazy sweep was misleading. Each time one of the three 130-foot (40-meter) blades swung past, it hissed as it sliced the air. Tip speed can be well over 100 miles (160 kilometers) an hour. This single tower was capable of producing two megawatts, almost half the entire output of the Leipzig solar farm.

In Denmark, turning blades are always on the horizon, in small or large groups, like spokes of wheels rolling toward a strange new world. Denmark's total installed wind power is now more than 3,000 megawatts—about 20 percent of the nation's electrical needs. All over Europe generous incentives designed to reduce carbon emissions and wean economies from oil and coal have led to a wind boom. The continent leads the world in wind power, with almost 35,000 megawatts, equivalent to 35 large coal-fired power plants. North America, even though it has huge potential for wind energy, remains a distant second, with just over 7,000 megawatts. With the exception of hydroelectric power—which has been driving machines for centuries but has little room to grow in developed countries—wind is currently the biggest success story in renewable energy.

"When I started in 1987, I spent a lot of time sitting in farmers' houses until midnight talking to the neighbors, just selling one turbine," says Hans Buus. He's director of project development for a Danish energy company called Elsam. "I would not have been able to imagine the level it is today."

He means not only the number of turbines but also their sheer size. In Germany I saw a fiberglass-and-steel prototype that stands 600 feet (200 meters) tall, has blades 200 feet (60 meters) long, and can generate five megawatts. It's not just a monument to engineering but also an effort to overcome some new obstacles to wind power development.

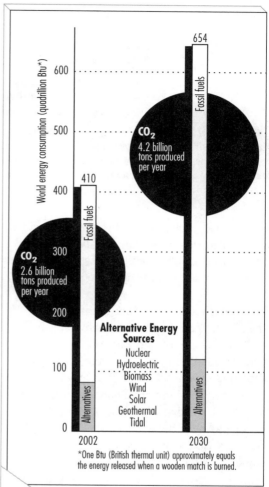

Power Breakdown. Without global changes, energy consumption from fossil fuels will leap, generating more climate-altering carbon dioxide (black circles). If today's trends continue, the use of alternative energy sources won't rise much (bottom of each bar). "We're running out of atmosphere faster than we're running out of fossil fuels," says energy scientist Dan Kammen. "The more we diversify our sources, the better." Source: International Energy Agency.

One is aesthetic. England's Lake District is a spectacular landscape of bracken-clad hills and secluded valleys, mostly protected as a national park. But on a ridge just outside the park, though not outside the magnificence, 27 towers

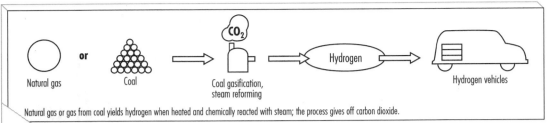

Natural gas or gas from coal yields hydrogen when heated and chemically reacted with steam; the process gives off carbon dioxide.

Conventional Technology. Hydrogen could power the nonpolluting cars of tomorrow, but the gas itself must be generated using other energy sources. As shown in this artists's interpretation, hydrogen would be only as eco-friendly as the original energy source. Current technology produces hydrogen from fossil fuel and releases carbon dioxide (CO_2) and other pollutants. Scaling up the process would add to global warming and its potential effects, such as intensified storms.

are planned, each as big as the two-megawatt machine in Denmark. Many locals are protesting. "This is a high-quality landscape," says one. "They shouldn't be putting those things in here."

Danes seem to like turbines more than the British, perhaps because many Danish turbines belong to cooperatives of local residents. It's harder to say "not in my backyard" if the thing in your backyard helps pay for your house. But environmental opposition is not the only trouble facing wind development. Across Europe many of the windiest sites are already occupied. So the five-megawatt German machine is designed to help take wind power away from the scenery and out to abundant new sites at sea.

Many coastlines have broad areas of shallow continental shelf where the wind blows more steadily than on land and where, as one wind expert puts it, "the seagulls don't vote." (Real voters, however, sometimes still object to the sight of towers on the horizon.) It costs more to build and maintain turbines offshore than on land, but an underwater foundation for a five-megawatt tower is cheaper per megawatt than a smaller foundation. Hence the German giant.

There are other challenges. Like sailboats, wind turbines can be becalmed for days. To keep the grid humming, other sources, such as coal-fired power plants, have to stand ready to take up the slack. But when a strong wind dumps power into the grid, the other generators have

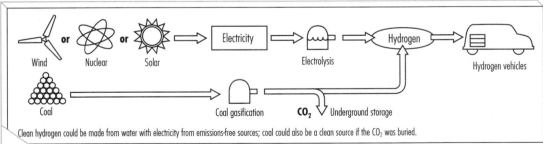

Clean hydrogen could be made from water with electricity from emissions-free sources; coal could also be a clean source if the CO_2 was buried.

Zero Emissions Technology. In a greener future, hydrogen would be produced with carbon dioxide-free energy, requiring a massive expansion of wind, solar, or nuclear power. The U.S. government is also studying the possibility of exploiting the country's vast coal reserves to make hydrogen but storing the carbon dioxide safely underground—a strategy that remains unproven. Other hurdles include developing practical hydrogen-powered cars.

to be turned down, and plants that burn fuel are not quickly adjustable. A wind-power bonanza can become a glut. Denmark, for example, is sometimes forced to unload power at uneconomic rates to neighbors like Norway and Germany.

What's needed for wind as well as solar is a way to store a large energy surplus. Technology already exists to turn it into fuels such as hydrogen or ethanol or harness it to compress air or spin flywheels, banking energy that can later churn out electricity. But most systems are still decades from becoming economically feasible.

On the plus side, both wind and solar can provide what's called distributed energy: They can make power on a small scale near the user. You can't have a private coal plant, but you can have your own windmill, with batteries for calm days. The more houses or communities make their own wind power, the smaller and cheaper central power plants and transmission lines can be.

In Europe's big push toward wind power, the turbines keep growing. But in Flagstaff, Arizona, Southwest Windpower makes turbines with blades you can pick up in one hand. The company has sold about 60,000 of the little turbines, most of them for off-grid homes, sailboats, and remote sites like lighthouses and weather stations. At 400 watts apiece they can't power more than a few lights.

But David Calley, Southwest's president, whose father built his first wind turbine out of washing machine parts, is testing a new product he calls an energy appliance. It will stand on a tower as tall as a telephone pole, produce up to two kilowatts in a moderate wind, and come with all the electronics needed to plug it into the house.

Many U.S. utilities are required to pay for power that individuals put back into the grid, so anyone in a relatively breezy place could pop up the energy appliance in the yard, use the power when it's needed, and feed it back into the grid when it's not. Except for the heavy loads of heating and air-conditioning, this setup could reduce a home's annual power bill to near zero. If, as Calley hopes, he can ultimately sell the energy appliance for under $3,000, it would pay for itself with energy savings within a few years.

Somewhere in this mix of the grand and the personal, there may be big numbers in wind too.

Biomass: Farming Your Fuel

In Germany, driving from the giant wind turbine near Hamburg to Berlin, I regularly got an odd whiff: the sort-of-appetizing scent of fast food. It was a puzzle until a tanker truck passed, emblazoned with the word "biodiesel." The scent was of burning vegetable oil. Germany uses about 450 million gallons (1,700 million liters) of biodiesel a year, about 3 percent of its total diesel consumption.

Biomass energy has ancient roots. The logs in your fire are biomass. But today biomass means ethanol, biogas, and biodiesel—fuels as easy to burn as oil or gas, but made from plants. These technologies are proven. Ethanol produced from corn goes into gasoline blends in the U.S.; ethanol from sugarcane provides 50 percent of automobile fuel in Brazil. In the U.S. and other nations, biodiesel from vegetable oil is burned, pure or mixed with regular diesel, in unmodified engines. "Biofuels are the easiest fuels to slot into the existing fuel system," says Michael Pacheco, the National Bioenergy Center director.

What limits biomass is land. Photosynthesis, the process that captures the sun's energy in plants, is far less efficient per square foot than solar panels, so catching energy in plants gobbles up even more land. Estimates suggest that powering all the world's vehicles with biofuels would mean doubling the amount of land devoted to farming.

At the National Bioenergy Center, scientists are trying to make fuel-farming more efficient. Today's biomass fuels are based on plant starches, oils, and sugars, but the center is testing organisms that can digest woody cellulose, abundant in plants, so that it too could yield liquid fuel. More productive fuel crops could help as well.

One is switchgrass, a plant native to North America's prairies that grows faster and needs less fertilizer than corn, the source of most ethanol fuel made in the U.S. It also thrives on land unfit for other crops and does double duty as a source of animal food, further reducing the pressure on farmland.

"Preliminary results look promising," says Thomas Foust, the center's technology manager. "If you increase automobile efficiency to the level of a hybrid and go with the switchgrass crop mix, you could meet two-thirds of the U.S. transportation fuel demand with no additional land."

But technically possible doesn't mean politically feasible. From corn to sugarcane, all crops have their own lobbyists. "We're looking down a lot of alleys," says Pacheco. "And every alley has its own vested interest group. Frankly, one of the biggest challenges with biomass is that there are so many options."

Nuclear: Still a Contender

Nuclear fission appeared to lead the race as an energy alternative decades ago, as countries began building reactors. Worldwide, about 440 plants now generate 16 percent of the planet's electric power, and some countries have gone heavily nuclear. France, for instance, gets 78 percent of its electricity from fission.

The allure is clear: abundant power, no carbon dioxide emissions, no blots on the land-scape except an occasional containment dome and cooling tower. But along with its familiar woes—the accidents at Three Mile Island and Chornobyl, poor economics compared with fossil fuel plants, and the challenge of radioactive waste disposal—nuclear power is far from renewable. The readily available uranium fuel won't last much more than 50 years.

Yet enthusiasm is reviving. China, facing a shortage of electric power, has started to build new reactors at a brisk pace—one or two a year. In the U.S., where some hydrogen-car boosters see nuclear plants as a good source of energy for making hydrogen from water, Vice President Dick Cheney has called for "a fresh look" at nuclear. And Japan, which lacks its own oil, gas, and coal, continues to encourage a fission program. Yumi Akimoto, a Japanese elder statesman of nuclear chemistry, saw the flash of the bomb at Hiroshima as a boy yet describes nuclear fission as "the pillar of the next century."

In the town of Rokkasho at the northernmost tip of Honshu Island, Japan is working to get around the limits of the uranium supply. Inside a new 20-billion-dollar complex, workers wear pale blue work suits and an air of patient haste. I looked in on cylindrical centrifuges for enriching uranium and a pool partly filled with rods of spent nuclear fuel, cooling. Spent fuel is rich in plutonium and leftover uranium—valuable nuclear material that the plant is designed to salvage. It will "reprocess" the spent fuel into a mixture of enriched uranium and plutonium called MOX, for mixed oxide fuel. MOX can be burned in some modern reactors and could stretch the fuel supply for decades or more.

Reprocessing plants in other countries also turn spent fuel into MOX. But those plants originally made plutonium for nuclear weapons, so the Japanese like to say that theirs, due to start up in 2007, is the first such plant built entirely for peaceful use. To assure the world that

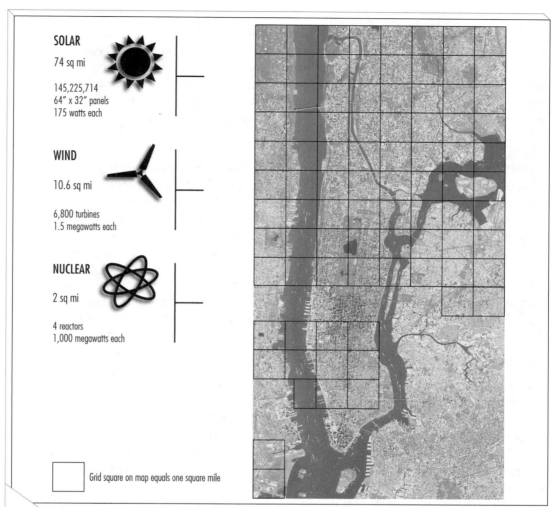

SOLAR

74 sq mi

145,225,714
64" x 32" panels
175 watts each

WIND

10.6 sq mi

6,800 turbines
1.5 megawatts each

NUCLEAR

2 sq mi

4 reactors
1,000 megawatts each

Grid square on map equals one square mile

A Greener Gotham: Imagining New York without Fossil Fuels. It takes a lot to make Broadway shine and Yankee Stadium glow—not to mention light the rest of New York City. Suppose the Big Apple were to set a big example by dumping dirty fuels for greener energy? The map on the right shows how much space would go to energy production if New Yorkers picked a single clean technology to generate 60 percent of their electricity—the amount now produced by coal and natural gas. Solar and wind need extra space to make up for the fact that they can't always produce at full capacity.

it will stay that way, the Rokkasho complex includes a building for inspectors from the International Atomic Energy Agency, the United Nations' nuclear watchdog, who will make certain that none of the plutonium is diverted for weapons.

That doesn't satisfy nuclear energy opponents. Opposition has mounted in Japan after fatal accidents at the country's nuclear plants, including one that killed two workers and exposed others to radiation. Shortly after my visit to Rokkasho, about a hundred protesters marched outside the plant in a blizzard.

A bigger controversy would greet what some nuclear proponents think is a crucial next step: a move to breeder reactors. Breeders can make more fuel than they consume, in the form of plutonium that can be extracted by reprocessing the spent fuel. But experimental breeder reactors have proved to be temperamental, and a full-scale breeder program could be an arms-control nightmare because of all the plutonium it would put in circulation.

Akimoto, for one, believes that society has to get comfortable with fuel reprocessing if it wants to count on nuclear energy. He spoke to me through an interpreter, but to emphasize this point he jumped into English: "If we are going to accept nuclear power, we have to accept the total system. Sometimes we want to get the first crop of fruit but forget how to grow the trees."

Fusion: The Fire Some Time

Fusion is the gaudiest of hopes, the fire of the stars in the human hearth. Produced when two atoms fuse into one, fusion energy could satisfy huge chunks of future demand. The fuel would last millennia. Fusion would produce no long-lived radioactive waste and nothing for terrorists or governments to turn into weapons. It also requires some of the most complex machinery on Earth.

A few scientists have claimed that cold fusion, which promises energy from a simple jar instead of a high-tech crucible, might work. The verdict so far: No such luck. Hot fusion is more likely to succeed, but it will be a decades-long quest costing billions of dollars.

Hot fusion is tough because the fuel—a kind of hydrogen—has to be heated to a hundred million degrees Celsius or so before the atoms start fusing. At those temperatures the hydrogen forms a roiling, unruly vapor of electrically charged particles, called plasma.

"Plasma is the most common state of matter in the universe," says one physicist, "but it's also the most chaotic and the least easily controlled." Creating and containing plasma is so challenging that no fusion experiment has yet returned more than 65 percent of the energy it took to start the reaction.

Now scientists in Europe, Japan, and the U.S. are refining the process, learning better ways to control plasma and trying to push up the energy output. They hope that a six-billion-dollar test reactor called ITER will get the fusion bonfire blazing—what physicists call "igniting the plasma." The next step would be a demonstration plant to actually generate power, followed by commercial plants in 50 years or so.

"I am 100 percent sure we can ignite the plasma," says Jerome Pamela, the project manager of a fusion machine called the Joint European Torus, or JET, at Britain's Culham Science Center. "The biggest challenge is the transition between the plasma and the outside world." He means finding the right materials for the lining of the ITER plasma chamber, where they will have to withstand a bombardment of neutrons and transfer heat to electric generators.

At Culham I saw an experiment in a tokamak, a device that cages plasma in a magnetic field shaped like a doughnut—the standard design for most fusion efforts, including ITER. The physicists sent a huge electrical charge into the gas-filled container, a scaled-down version of JET. It raised the temperature to about ten million degrees Celsius, not enough to start fusion but enough to create plasma.

The experiment lasted a quarter of a second. A video camera shooting 2,250 frames a second captured it. As it played back, a faint glow blossomed in the chamber, wavered, grew into a haze visible only on its cooling edges, and vanished.

It was—well, disappointing. I had expected the plasma to look like a movie shot of an exploding automobile. This was more like a ghost in an English paneled library.

But this phantom was energy incarnate: the universal but elusive magic that all our varied technologies—solar, wind, biomass, fission, fusion, and many others large or small, mainstream or crazy—seek to wrestle into our service.

Taming that ghost is not just a scientific challenge. The ITER project has been held up by a seemingly simple problem. Since 2003 the participating countries—including much of the developed world—have been deadlocked over where to build the machine. The choice has come down to two sites, one in France and one in Japan.

As all energy experts will tell you, this proves a well-established theory. There's only one force tougher to manage than plasma: politics.

Although some politicians believe the task of developing the new energy technologies should be left to market forces, many experts disagree. That's not just because it's expensive to get new technology started, but also because government can often take risks that private enterprise won't.

"Most of the modern technology that has been driving the U.S. economy did not come spontaneously from market forces," NYU's Martin Hoffert says, ticking off jet planes, satellite communications, integrated circuits, computers. "The Internet was supported for 20 years by the military and for 10 more years by the National Science Foundation before Wall Street found it."

Without a big push from government, he says, we may be condemned to rely on increasingly dirty fossil fuels as cleaner ones like oil and gas run out, with dire consequences for the climate. "If we don't have a proactive energy policy," he says, "we'll just wind up using coal, then shale, then tar sands, and it will be a continually diminishing return, and eventually our civilization will collapse. But it doesn't have to end that way. We have a choice."

It's a matter of self-interest, says Hermann Scheer, the German member of parliament. "I don't appeal to the people to change their conscience," he said in his Berlin office, where a small model of a wind turbine turned lazily in a window. "You can't go around like a priest." Instead, his message is that nurturing new forms of energy is necessary for an environmentally and economically sound future. "There is no alternative."

Already, change is rising from the grass roots. In the U.S., state and local governments are pushing alternative energies by offering subsidies and requiring that utility companies include renewable sources in their plans. And in Europe financial incentives for both wind and solar energy have broad support even though they raise electric bills.

Alternative energy is also catching on in parts of the developing world where it's a necessity, not a choice. Solar power, for example, is making inroads in African communities lacking power lines and generators. "If you want to overcome poverty, what do people need to focus on?" asks Germany's environment minister, Jürgen Trittin. "They need fresh water and they need energy. For filling the needs of remote villages, renewable energy is highly competitive."

In developed countries there's a sense that alternative energy—once seen as a quaint hippie enthusiasm—is no longer alternative culture. It's edging into the mainstream. The excitement of energy freedom seems contagious.

One afternoon last year, near a village north of Munich, a small group of townspeople and workers inaugurated a solar facility. It would soon surpass the Leipzig field as the largest in the world, with six megawatts of power.

About 15 people gathered on a little man-made hill beside the solar farm and planted four cherry trees on the summit. The mayor of the tidy nearby town brought out souvenir bottles of schnapps. Almost everyone had a swig, including the mayor.

Then he said he would sing to the project's construction supervisor and a landscape artist, both American women. The two women stood together, grinning, with the field of solar panels soaking up energy behind them. The German mayor straightened his dark suit, and the other men leaned on their shovels.

Fifty years ago, I thought, there were still bombed-out ruins in the cities of Europe. The Soviet Union was planning Sputnik. Texas oil was $2.82 a barrel. At the most, we have 50 years to make the world over again. But people change, adapt, and make crazy new stuff work. I thought about Dan Shugar talking about disruptive technologies. "There's a sense of excitement," he had said. "There's a sense of urgency. There's a sense that we cannot fail."

On the hilltop, the mayor took a deep breath. He sang, in a booming tenor, without missing a note or a word, the entire song "O Sole Mio." Everyone cheered.

Discussion Questions

1. In your opinion, how should renewable/alternative energies be included in U.S. energy policy? Specifically, what percentage of the federal energy budget should be invested in renewables/alternatives?
2. Based on what you have read, what renewable/alternative technologies should be aggressively pursued? Which shouldn't? Explain your answers.
3. Do you personally support nuclear power, and why?

 Supporting Activities

1. How much electricity did you and/or your family consume last month in your home? Get a copy of an electric bill and figure out the kWh consumption overall and on a per-person basis for your household.
2. Define "carbon tax" and "renewables portfolio standard" and explain how these policies can provide incentives for the adoption of renewable energy technologies. What are some other ways the government can promote renewables?
3. According to the EIA, what percentage of U.S. electricity comes from wind? From solar?
4. What country leads the world in installed solar capacity? Installed wind capacity?
5. What state leads the U.S. in installed solar capacity? Installed wind capacity?
6. Where is the nearest wind farm to your house? Where is the nearest nuclear plant?

 Additional Resources

1. American Solar Energy Society: www.ases.org.
2. International Solar Energy Society: www.ises.org.
3. American Wind Energy Association: www.ewea.org.
4. European Wind Energy Society: www.ewea.org.
5. Energy Information Administration: http://www.eia.doe.gov/fuelrenewable.html.
6. A magazine about residential-scale renewable energy oriented to the layperson: *Home Power Magazine*: www.homepower.com.

Endnotes

1. Pasternak, Alan D. 2000. *Global energy futures and human development: A framework for analysis.* U.S. Department of Energy, Lawrence Livermore National Laboratory. Available: www.llnl.gov/tid/lof/documents/pdf/239193.pdf.
2. U.S. Energy Information Administration. 2008. *U.S. product supplied.* Available: http://tonto.eia.doe.gov/dnav/pet/pet_cons_psup_dc_nus_mbblpd_a.htm.
3. U.S. Energy Information Administration. 2008. *Table 26. U.S. Coal Consumption by End Use Sector, by Census Division and State, 2007, 2006.* Available: http://www.eia.doe.gov/cneaf/coal/page/acr/table26.html.

4. U.S. Energy Information Administration. 2008. *World carbon dioxide emissions from the consumption and flaring of fossil fuels, 1980–2006.* Available: http://www.eia.doe.gov/pub/international/iealf/ tableh1co2.xls.

5. National Energy Board of Canada. (2006, June). *Canada's oil sands: Opportunities and challenges to 2015.* Available: http://www.neb-one.gc.ca/clf-nsi/rnrgynfmtn/nrgyrprt/lsnd/pprtntsndchllngs20152006/ pprtntsndchllngs20152006-eng.pdf.

6. Polaris Institute's Energy Program Tar Sands Watch. 2007. *Shell details $27B oilsands refinery; 8,000 workers to build plant near Edmonton.* Available: http://www.tarsandswatch.org/shell-details-27b-oilsands- refinery-8-000-workers-build-plant-near-edmonton.

Perspectives on Transportation Technologies

Perhaps the most dominant characteristic of American culture since the mid-twentieth century is personal mobility. Business trips are scheduled halfway around the world without a second thought; summer cross-country road trips are planned; consumer products are imported rather than manufactured domestically to save on labor costs; towns and cities are planned around the commuter; you unthinkingly transport 2,500 pounds of steel to the grocery store to pick up a gallon (around eight pounds) of milk. It has been said that if an alien being were to visit Planet Earth, it would conclude that the dominant life form is not *Homo sapiens*, but rather the automobile.

And why should it be otherwise? Personal mobility is, after all, the pinnacle of our technological achievements. The modern car is the result of 100 years of design, engineering, manufacturing, and marketing refinement—an inevitable consequence of accumulated wealth and prosperity. Science fiction movies consistently show 22nd Century families zipping around in futuristic personal hovercrafts as if it would be evolutionary backsliding for your great-grandkids to take the bus.

Why are Americans so obsessed with the automobile? It's easy to blame our fascination with technology, in addition to our wide-open spaces and our frontier heritage. Looking deeper, however, other contributing factors surface: the deliberate dismantling of urban light rail systems in the 1930s and 1940s by a General Motors, Standard Oil, and Firestone consortium; the creation of consumerism and the "American dream"; a seemingly infinite supply of cheap oil; and the subsidizing of suburbia; all of which were accompanied by a heavy dose of marketing. In any event, the question that framed this paragraph can be partially answered as follows: we really weren't given a choice.

Generations of subsidies for the infrastructure that supports private mobility have virtually eliminated the competition. In 2008, for example, the Federal Transit Administration, the division of the U.S. Department of Transportation responsible for public transport systems, received less than 25 percent of the funding allotted to the Federal Highway Administration (FHA).[1] It's not surprising, then, that the "energy intensity" of bus transit, the amount of energy expended per person-mile, declined from half that of a personal car in 1970 to 20 percent more than a car by 2006[2] as bus ridership steadily declined. Similarly, the Federal Railroad Administration received funding representing just 4 percent of that received by the FHA.[1] This imbalance in federal support seems economically misguided when one considers the personal costs associated with automobile ownership, which accounts for, on average, 17 percent of U.S. household income—as much as utilities and health care combined.[3]

Americans really do drive a lot. There are over 150 million vehicles in the U.S.—that's almost one vehicle for every two Americans (although the U.S. ranks 16th globally in vehicles per capita[4]). U.S. vehicle registration increased 162 percent from 1966 to 2006. Americans drove close to *3 trillion* miles last year, which is nearly 10,000 miles per capita, more than citizens of any other country. Perhaps more alarming is the increase in percentage of those miles driven by trucks, vans, and SUVs during the same time frame, from 10 percent to 37 percent.[5]

If personal mobility came at a reasonable cost—economically, politically, socially, and environmentally—then the automobile would have few critics. However, that's simply not the case. The Environmental Protection Agency (EPA) estimates lost U.S. productivity and wasted fuel costs due to highway congestion at $63 billion.[6] Dependence on unstable foreign countries to help satisfy our oil habit severely limits U.S. foreign policy options. The predicted peak in global oil production will certainly challenge policy makers. Emissions from U.S.

tailpipes contribute two billion tons of carbon to the atmosphere annually, representing 33 percent of total U.S. carbon output.[7]

In this unit, readings have been chosen to highlight the problems associated with the current, mainly American, concept of mobility (i.e., the automobile) and to offer possible alternatives, from reducing the need to drive to more attractive private automobile alternatives. It is hoped that the reader will learn to appreciate that an automobile-based society is not inevitable, but is rather the result of generations of public and private decisions, policies, and investments. Change will not come quickly or cheaply, but transitioning to a non-automobile-based society is possible and perhaps inevitable. While reading these articles, keep the following in mind:

- The automobile is but one option for personal mobility.
- There are pros and cons associated with a personal transportation-based society.
- The "need" for personal transportation is greatly affected by public policy, including zoning, tax policy, subsidies, and research expenditures.

Transportation's Perennial Problems

History is filled with examples of technological "fixes" whose unintended consequences proved more dire than the original problem. DDT and kudzu[8] come to mind, but should the automobile be included in that list? Are we as a society better off with cars than we would be without them? Clearly a car is faster, cleaner, and more reliable transportation than a horse, but have we erred in designing our communities around them? Henry Ford predicted that "we shall solve the city problems by leaving the city," but was Mr. Ford more interested in solving city problems or selling Model Ts? Many would argue that our cities are worse as a result of widespread automobile use.

In reading Gibbs' article, you may be wondering what the "perennial problem" is to which he refers. A technophile would say that many of the perceived problems associated with the automobile—pollution, resource consumption, congestion, cost, safety—can be "solved" through the application of technology. Technology can certainly provide us with efficient, smart electric cars that zip around on more and wider highways. However, if our towns and cities are widely dispersed, then there will always be a need for personal transportation, requiring large quantities of natural resources, more roads, congestion, and so on.

The "problem," it seems, is the *need* to travel. The only way to reduce the problems associated with the car is to reduce the need to drive. This will require systemic changes to our culture. Given viable alternatives, many people will choose to drive less or not to drive their car at all. For example, many European cities are characterized by their efficient and widely-used rail and bus systems, bike paths, and pedestrian-friendly neighborhoods. To be sure, the private automobile will be the dominant mode of transportation in the U.S. for years to come, but there is reason to believe that the days of the automobile as we know it are numbered.

The author, W. Wayt Gibbs, is a staff writer for *Scientific American*. He has written about genetics and computing, in addition to transportation.

Transportation's Perennial Problems

W. Wayt Gibbs

When the first issue of *Scientific American* hit the streets on August 28, 1845, its lead story excitedly touted "superbly splendid" new railroad cars able to "secure safety and convenience, and contribute ease and comfort to passengers, while flying at the rate of 30 or 40 miles per hour." Half a century later this journal devoted almost an entire issue to innovations in bicycles, ships and the new steam-, electric- and gas-powered automobiles. "If there are faults" with cars, the editors concluded, "only time is wanted to make them disappear. . . . There is no mechanism more inoffensive, no means of transport more sure and safe."

In hindsight, such blind faith that technology would solve the transportation woes of cities might seem quaint, even ironic. Now about half the travel on U.S. expressways slows to a crawl during the peak hours every day. Car crashes cause some three million injuries annually. According to the American Lung Association, roughly 100 million Americans live in cit-

From *Scientific American, 277(4), October 1997* by W. Gibbs. Reprinted with permission. Copyright © 1997 by Scientific American, Inc. All rights reserved.

ies where vehicle emissions regularly push ozone levels above federal standards. Hardly inoffensive, sure and safe.

But cars seemed a logical, progressive choice in 1899 because they helped to fulfill common human desires for mobility, space and status. They still do. For that reason, many developing nations are beginning to follow their rich peers down the asphalt path, with enormous consequences to their cities and environment. Also for that reason, attempts to reduce auto use have largely failed. Jane Holtz Kay argues in *Asphalt Nation* (Crown Publishers, 1997) that to solve the perennial problems of transportation "we must question why we travel at all. . . . We must alter our notions of mobility." Many urban planners agree but caution that such fundamental changes typically require generations. In the meantime, technological advances may offer the most realistic means to take us from here to there faster, more safely and more cleanly.

Man versus Machine

At least, technology is what worked in the past—if only for a time. Consider safety. "All through the 19th century there were spectacular train wrecks: boiler explosions, fires. Head-on collisions were not unusual," reports George M. Smerk, director of the Institute for Urban Transportation at Indiana University at Bloomington. To quell public outcry, rail and trolley lines installed steel cars, electric signals and air brakes. Accident rates fell. And then engineers responded by speeding up.

Drivers have shown the same tendency to adjust their behaviors to maintain a steady level of risk. Autos were initially safer than horses, says Clay McShane, a historian at Northeastern University: "Cars don't run away on their own, they don't bite, and they don't kick." In time,

of course, drivers more than compensated for the predictability of their vehicle by stepping on the gas.

More recently, seat belt use has jumped from 11 percent in the early 1980s to about 68 percent now; air bags are making similar inroads. Perhaps predictably, drivers have begun traveling faster and following more closely, so the 41,798 highway fatalities in 1995 were down only about 2,400 from 1983. On the other hand, they were up just 11,750 from the automotive death toll in 1931, despite a fivefold increase in the number of cars on the road.

Drivers seem less interested in cleaner vehicles than in safer ones: "A third of the cars today are larger than any auto on the road in the 1950s," McShane says. Yet here again, he recounts, "the auto looked initially like an enormous improvement to the environment." New York City in 1900 was buried under roughly four million pounds of manure every day. Horses had to be stabled away from their carriages, he states, "because their urine fumes were strong enough to blister paint. But the worst pollution problem was the air loaded with bacteria-carrying dust, through which respiratory diseases were transmitted." When autos displaced horses in the 1920s, he says; tuberculosis rates plummeted.

"Many argue that the current air-quality problem in urban America will be 'solved' with cleaner vehicles," notes Michael D. Meyer of the Georgia Institute of Technology. Indeed, hydrocarbon emissions fell 35 percent from 1984 to 1993, thanks to more efficient cars and cleaner gas. "However, the growth in vehicle miles traveled is expected to overwhelm any improvements that will likely occur in vehicle emissions," Meyer adds. Odometers will spin ever faster so long as cities continue to spread out.

"Jam Yesterday . . . Jam Tomorrow"

Like Alice at the Mad Hatter's tea party, highway planners are caught in a vicious cycle, says Martin Wachs of the University of California Transportation Center. "You can never build enough roads to keep up with congestion. Traffic always rises to exceed capacity."

Part of the problem, operations engineer Dietrich Braess showed in 1968, is that adding new routes often makes congestion worse, not better. That paradox seems to have vexed every age. "Rush hours have always been a mess," Smerk says. "Traffic jams were so bad in Rome 2,000 years ago that the city banned chariot riding during peak hours." In New York, McShane adds, "people complained about crowding on the horse cars 10 years after they began operation. Trolleys were overcrowded within five years of electrification. Mass automobility comes in 1907; by 1914 you have traffic jams. The U.S. built the first interstate highways in the early 1920s, and they were already jammed by the end of the decade."

More important than Braess's paradox is the fact that with increased mobility people move not just around but away. "The horse car allowed city dwellers to move out to single-family homes," McShane observes. "Then the laying of rails lowered fares to a nickel, allowing movement into the suburbs." By the time autos appeared, cities had already begun to sprawl along the main rail lines.

Cars—especially when abetted by government-subsidized housing loans after 1945—kindled that spark into explosive suburban growth. It continues today: about 86 percent of the population growth in the U.S. since 1970 happened in suburbs, Meyer reports. And for good reason, remarks Robert W. Burchell of the Center for Urban Policy Research at Rutgers University: "As you go farther out, your taxes fall, your housing generally costs less, your schools improve, you get increasing amounts of public recreation facilities, you are safer from crime, and you are more likely to be surrounded by people like yourself. Given its ability to deliver all that, it is no wonder the public loves sprawl."

Western European governments have showered fewer gifts and more auto taxes on their exurbanites. As a result, says John Pucher, an urban planner at Rutgers, their central cities typically have four times the population density of America's urban centers. Because stores and job sites are closer, Pucher adds, "Europeans make 40 to 50 percent of trips by walking or biking and about 10 percent by public transit. In contrast, 87 percent of trips in the U.S. are by car; only 3 percent involve transit."

Many urban planners in the U.S. now prescribe similar strictures to reduce traffic flows. Replace cur-de-sacs and parkways with old-fashioned street grids and rail stations, they suggest, and people will drive less. Put businesses closer to homes, and citizens should reduce their travel altogether [see "Why Go Anywhere?" by Robert Cervero; *Scientific American*, September 1995].

Forward to the Past?

The New Urbanism movement, as it is called, has noble goals. But it faces tremendous practical obstacles. Razing and rebuilding entire suburbs is not feasible, so most neotraditional communities have been, and will be, built on cities' outskirts. Unfortunately, "there is no cost-effective way to build a transit system that serves beltway locations," McShane argues. Boston has tried to do this, Harvard University professor Jose A. Gomez-Ibanez points out in a recent article, and as a result its transit agency has faced budget crises every decade or so since 1961. It is due for another soon.

A recent microeconomic analysis by Randall Crane of the University of California at Irvine concluded that neotraditional designs may be good ideas but will not necessarily curb traffic. Such towns tend to attract residents who already use public transit to get to work. Moreover, when Crane and his colleague Marlon G. Boarnet studied all 232 transit stations in southern California, they found that almost without exception, cities tend to put their stations near shopping centers and offices (which bring in jobs and taxes), not homes. "Transit-based housing will struggle," the two predicted, until cities begin chasing residents instead of businesses. "For the most part," they conclude, "that seems unlikely to happen."

In the interim, U.S. cities might find a different European strategy more effective: tolls. In 1931 Trondheim, Norway, Placed electronic tollbooths on all routes leading into the city, closing free access by road. It gave away radio tags; nearly all drivers now use them to pay without stopping at the gate. The city recouped its capital investment in six months, boasts Tore Hoven of the Trondheim Public Roads Administration. Tolls have since paid for new roads, sidewalks and buses. And because tolls rise during the morning rush hour; (a technique called congestion pricing), many drivers switched to trains, boosting transit ridership 7 percent in a single year. When Stuttgart tested a similar system in 1995, it found that congestion pricing cut rush-hour travel by 12 percent.

"Is the American public ready for full pricing? I don't think so," Meyer comments. But that may change; there is nothing inherently un-American about toils. Indeed, most of the first highways built in the U.S. were privately owned turnpikes. At least 2,000 companies maintained toll roads during the 19th century. The fashion may be returning; private highways have recently opened in Dulles, Va., and Orange County, California. Houston, Tex., is also considering congestion pricing on one of its interstates.

States will be increasingly forced to squeeze more out of existing roads, Burchell says, because "the consequences of sprawl are costly. We just did a study for South Carolina that calculated their infrastructure tab for the next 20 years as $57 billion. That is $1,000 a year for every person in the state for the rest of their lives. Increasing the gas tax by four cents would raise only $56 million. But just by living differently, by setting growth boundaries around cities, doubling the amount of development inside the circle and halving the amount outside, you could save $2.5 billion" in public infrastructure and services.

"Our best hope for easing sprawl" and the congestion it causes, Burchell contends, "is that we will run out of money. Sooner or later we will not be able to continue building so much infrastructure, because we can no longer afford to maintain it." Michigan and other states are already considering growth boundaries for that reason, he says.

On the other hand, McShane observes, "during a recession, highway building is a great way to inject money into the economy. If you had told me in 1988 that a city as environmentally conscious and transit-intensive as Boston would invest $10 billion in downtown highways, I would have laughed at you. It, happened."

The World Speeds Up

Recent work by Andreas Schafer of the Massachusetts Institute of Technology may help explain why, despite the well-known evils of automobiles, Americans—and, increasingly, Europeans—drive more miles year after year, often rearranging their communities to make that possible. Drawing on decades of travel surveys, Schafer found that city dwellers in the U.S., Europe, Russia, eastern Asia and even villages in Ghana share two important traits, which appear to have remained constant for at least 30 years. First, people in each location spend an average of 60 to 90 minutes traveling a day. And in every industrial country except Japan, people spend an average of 10 to 15 percent of their income doing it [see "The Past and Future of Global Mobility," by Andreas Schafer and David Victor, page 58].

As nations all over the world have grown richer, they have consistently used part of their wealth to buy speed. "Mobility is an underrated human right," Wachs declares. "You can never have enough of it."

If Schafer's trend holds true, it could have important implications for the developing world and those who share its atmosphere. Many Third World megacities already face huge transportation snarls. Cars in Manila average seven miles (11 kilometers) per hour, reports Ralph Gakenheimer of M.I.T. A typical auto in Bangkok is stopped in gridlock the equivalent of 44 days each year; the congestion eats 35 percent of the city's gross annual output. New Delhi already loses six citizens a day on its highways, and air pollution harms many more.

Yet as incomes rise in Asia, so will the number of motor vehicles. "Around the world, one of the first things people buy when they can is a car," Pucher says. Gakenheimer points to a Chinese government survey that found citizens typically willing to spend up to two years' income on an automobile. (The average American invests just six months earnings.) Schafer estimates that if India follows the example of other nations, it will have 267 million cars on its roads by 2050. Rising car ownership, Gakenheimer predicts, will overwhelm developing cities, causing explosive sprawl. And thus the cycle begins again.

Meanwhile auto-saturated countries such as the U.S. finding it difficult to eke more speed out of their cars, are taking increasingly to the air. That has already begun to spawn a host of new traffic, safety and pollution problems. Will it ever end—will we ever finally quench our thirst for mobility? Think warp drive.

Further Reading

Down The Asphalt Path: The Automobile and the American City. Clay McShane. Columbia University Press, 1994.

Urban Passenger Transport in the United States and Europe: A Comparative Analysis of Public Policies. J. Pucher in Transport Reviews, Vol. 15, No. 2, pages 99–117; 1995.

Big-City Transit Ridership, Deficits, and Politics: Avoiding Reality. In Boston. Jose A. Gomez-Ibanez in APA Journal, Vol. 62, No. 1, pages 30–50; Winter 1996.

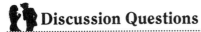 **Discussion Questions**

1. How many meaningful trips per week do you make by any mode of transportation *other than* a personal petroleum-fueled vehicle? Count the bus, but don't count a recreational bicycle ride. How many businesses that you regularly frequent are a reasonable walk from your apartment or house?
2. Consider the impacts that a transition from gasoline-powered personal automobiles to electric vehicles would have. What current problems would this transition help to solve? What problems would not be solved?
3. Respond to Martin Wach's statement that "Mobility is an underrated human right."
4. Estimate the daily savings in gasoline in million barrels per day if the average commuting distance of U.S. workers was cut in half. It's easy to find the necessary data (average commuting distance, number of workers, gallons per barrel of oil): try Googling the U.S. Census for starters. What percentage of total petroleum consumption would this savings represent?

 Supporting Activities

1. Surf to the Energy Information Administration's Web site and find the amount of petroleum consumed by the U.S. and world (in million barrels per day).
2. Use an online "commuting cost calculator" such as http://www.commuterpage.com/Userweb/CostCommuting/CostCommuting.htm, http://www.commutesolutions.com/howmuch.html, or http://www.costofcommuting.com to determine your own commuting costs.
3. Investigate recent public transit bonds that have been considered by voters in Massachusetts, California, New York, and Maine, among other states. What was the outcome of these votes? Briefly describe what projects were funded.
4. For one week, record the number of trips you make in your (or your friend's) car. For the next week, consciously try to reduce the number of trips. Record your data in a spreadsheet. How did you do?
5. For goodness' sake, walk somewhere!

 Additional Resources

1. A review of electric cars can be found at: Sperling, D. 1996. The case for electric vehicles. *Scientific American*, 54–59.
2. A review of hydrogen fuel cell powered cars can be found at: Burns, Lawrence D., McCormick, J. Byron, and Borroni-Bird, Christopher E. 2002. Vehicle of change. *Scientific American*, 64–73.
3. Joel K. Bourne's October 2007 *National Geographic* biofuels article is available online at: http://ngm.nationalgeographic.com/2007/10/biofuels/biofuels-text, along with a photo gallery and an interactive biofuels calculator.
4. For a look at what the next generation of private vehicles might look like, check out http://www.rmi.org/images/PDFs/Transportation/T04-01_HypercarH2AutoTrans.pdf. Or, for a lighter read, try http://www.rmi.org/sitepages/pid191.php.

5. A review of U.S. federal transportation policy can be found at: http://www.brookings.edu/reports/2003/12metropolitanpolicy_beimborn.aspx.
6. A great documentary about oil consumption is the video *The End of Suburbia: Oil Depletion and the Collapse of the American Dream* (2004).
7. A history of the growth and demise of rail in the U.S.: Goddard, Stephen B. 1994. *Getting There: The Epic Struggle between Road and Rail in the American Century*. University of Chicago Press.
8. A documentary about the end of light rail in the U.S. is the video *Taken for a Ride* by New Day Films.

Charter of the New Urbanism

Allow yourself, for a moment, to imagine a community in which the automobile is unnecessary; one that is designed from the ground up around people rather than around cars; a society in which the preferred modes of transportation are the foot, the bicycle, and the bus; where communities are pedestrian friendly. American society *could* very well have evolved in this way—Europe did, but it was not by accident.

There's a growing movement of people who would like to reinvent the American landscape. Led by architects including Peter Calthorpe and Robert Davis, the New Urbanism movement advocates thoughtful high-density, mixed-use zoning that places homes near where people want to be—schools, businesses, retail, and parks. The *Charter of the New Urbanism*, ratified by the Congress for the New Urbanism in 1996, offers a detailed blueprint for how such communities will look. A transition from suburban sprawl to New Urbanism won't come quickly or cheaply. It will require a radical change in the way planners think and politicians invest public capital.

The New Urbanist response to Henry Ford's vision for a car in every driveway would be "we don't need cars, we need better cities." Rather than providing the means to leave the city, as Ford did, the New Urbanists would remove the reasons to leave the city. Around the U.S., one can find isolated examples of communities, such as Seaside, Florida (see: http://www.theseasideinstitute.org/) that were planned from the ground up to adhere to New Urbanist principles.

The Congress for the New Urbanism is a San Francisco-based nonprofit organization founded in 1993 to promote walkable, neighborhood-based development as an alternative to suburban sprawl.

Charter of the New Urbanism

By Congress for the New Urbanism

The Congress for the New Urbanism views disinvestment in central cities, the spread of placeless sprawl, increasing separation by race and income, environmental deterioration, loss of agricultural lands and wilderness, and the erosion of society's built heritage as one interrelated community-building challenge.

We stand for the restoration of existing urban centers and towns within coherent metropolitan regions, the reconfiguration of sprawling suburbs into communities of real neighborhoods and diverse districts, the conservation of natural environments, and the preservation of our built legacy.

We recognize that physical solutions by themselves will not solve social and economic problems, but neither can economic vitality, community stability, and environmental health be sustained without a coherent and supportive physical framework.

We advocate the restructuring of public policy and development practices to support the following principles: neighborhoods should be diverse in use and population; communities should be designed for the pedestrian and transit as well as the car; cities and towns should be shaped by physically defined and universally accessible public spaces and community institu-

From *Congress for the New Urbanism*. Copyright © 1996 by Congress for the New Urbanism. Reprinted by permission.

tions; urban places should be framed by architecture and landscape design that celebrate local history, climate, ecology, and building practice.

We represent a broad-based citizenry, composed of public and private sector leaders, community activists, and multidisciplinary professionals. We are committed to reestablishing the relationship between the art of building and the making of community, through citizen-based participatory planning and design.

We dedicate ourselves to reclaiming our homes, blocks, streets, parks, neighborhoods, districts, towns, cities, regions, and environment.

We assert the following principles to guide public policy, development practice, urban planning, and design:

THE REGION: METROPOLIS, CITY, AND TOWN

1. Metropolitan regions are finite places with geographic boundaries derived from topography, watersheds, coastlines, farmlands, regional parks, and river basins. The metropolis is made of multiple centers that are cities, towns, and villages, each with its own identifiable center and edges.
2. The metropolitan region is a fundamental economic unit of the contemporary world. Governmental cooperation, public policy, physical planning, and economic strategies must reflect this new reality.
3. The metropolis has a necessary and fragile relationship to its agrarian hinterland and natural landscapes. The relationship is environmental, economic, and cultural. Farmland and nature are as important to the metropolis as the garden is to the house.
4. Development patterns should not blur or eradicate the edges of the metropolis. Infill development within existing urban areas conserves environmental resources, economic investment, and social fabric, while reclaiming marginal and abandoned areas. Metropolitan regions should develop strategies to encourage such infill development over peripheral expansion.
5. Where appropriate, new development contiguous to urban boundaries should be organized as neighborhoods and districts, and be integrated with the existing urban pattern. Noncontiguous development should be organized as towns and villages with their own urban edges, and planned for a jobs/housing balance, not as bedroom suburbs.
6. The development and redevelopment of towns and cities should respect historical patterns, precedents, and boundaries.
7. Cities and towns should bring into proximity a broad spectrum of public and private uses to support a regional economy that benefits people of all incomes. Affordable housing should be distributed throughout the region to match job opportunities and to avoid concentrations of poverty.
8. The physical organization of the region should be supported by a framework of transportation alternatives. Transit, pedestrian, and bicycle systems should maximize access and mobility throughout the region while reducing dependence upon the automobile.
9. Revenues and resources can be shared more cooperatively among the municipalities and centers within regions to avoid destructive competition for tax base and to promote rational coordination of transportation, recreation, public services, housing, and community institutions.

THE NEIGHBORHOOD, THE DISTRICT, AND THE CORRIDOR

1. The neighborhood, the district, and the corridor are the essential elements of development and redevelopment in the metropolis. They form identifiable areas that encourage citizens to take responsibility for their maintenance and evolution.
2. Neighborhoods should be compact, pedestrian-friendly, and mixed-use. Districts generally emphasize a special single use, and should follow the principles of neighborhood design when possible. Corridors are regional connectors of neighborhoods and districts; they range from boulevards and rail lines to rivers and parkways.
3. Many activities of daily living should occur within walking distance, allowing independence to those who do not drive, especially the elderly and the young. Interconnected networks of streets should be designed to encourage walking, reduce the number and length of automobile trips, and conserve energy.
4. Within neighborhoods, a broad range of housing types and price levels can bring people of diverse ages, races, and incomes into daily interaction, strengthening the personal and civic bonds essential to an authentic community.
5. Transit corridors, when properly planned and coordinated, can help organize metropolitan structure and revitalize urban centers. In contrast, highway corridors should not displace investment from existing centers.
6. Appropriate building densities and land uses should be within walking distance of transit stops, permitting public transit to become a viable alternative to the automobile.
7. Concentrations of civic, institutional, and commercial activity should be embedded in neighborhoods and districts, not isolated in remote, single-use complexes. Schools should be sized and located to enable children to walk or bicycle to them.
8. The economic health and harmonious evolution of neighborhoods, districts, and corridors can be improved through graphic urban design codes that serve as predictable guides for change.
9. A range of parks, from tot-lots and village greens to ballfields and community gardens, should be distributed within neighborhoods. Conservation areas and open lands should be used to define and connect different neighborhoods and districts.

THE BLOCK, THE STREET, AND THE BUILDING

1. A primary task of all urban architecture and landscape design is the physical definition of streets and public spaces as places of shared use.
2. Individual architectural projects should be seamlessly linked to their surroundings. This issue transcends style.
3. The revitalization of urban places depends on safety and security. The design of streets and buildings should reinforce safe environments, but not at the expense of accessibility and openness.
4. In the contemporary metropolis, development must adequately accommodate automobiles. It should do so in ways that respect the pedestrian and the form of public space.
5. Streets and squares should be safe, comfortable, and interesting to the pedestrian. Properly configured, they encourage walking and enable neighbors to know each other and protect their communities.

6. Architecture and landscape design should grow from local climate, topography, history, and building practice.

7. Civic buildings and public gathering places require important sites to reinforce community identity and the culture of democracy. They deserve distinctive form, because their role is different from that of other buildings and places that constitute the fabric of the city.

8. All buildings should provide their inhabitants with a clear sense of location, weather and time. Natural methods of heating and cooling can be more resource-efficient than mechanical systems.

9. Preservation and renewal of historic buildings, districts, and landscapes affirm the continuity and evolution of urban society.

Discussion Questions

1. Which of the Charter's guiding principles for the region, the neighborhood, and the block do you find most compelling? Explain your choices.
2. How "pedestrian friendly" is your town? Consider the availability of sidewalks, signage, busses, and bike racks. Also identify pedestrian *disincentives,* such as free parking.
3. List several pros and cons to living in a New Urbanist community. Would you choose living in such a community over a traditional suburban subdivision?
4. New Urbanism is sometimes criticized for being "utopian." In what ways might this be a valid criticism?

 Supporting Activities

1. Check out online some New Urbanist communities such as Seaside, Haile Village Center, and Celebration, Florida; Kentlands, Maryland; Addison Circle, Texas; Mashpee Commons, Massachusetts; Harbor Town, Tennessee; Orenco Station, Oregon; and Stapleton, Colorado. What features of these communities do you find most appealing? Least appealing?
2. Watch Jim Carrey's *The Truman Show.* It's a movie about a man living in a "constructed reality" that was filmed in Seaside, Florida.
3. For goodness' sake, take another walk!

 Additional Resources

1. Two examples of New Urbanist movement Web sites: http://www.newurbanism.org/ and http://www.cnu.org/.
2. A commentary on the car and urban planning: Kunstler, James H. 1994. *The Geography of Nowhere: The Rise and Decline of America's Man-Made Landscape.* Free Press.
3. A sampling of books on New Urbanism includes:
   - Katz, Peter. 1993. *The New Urbanism: Toward an Architecture of Community.* McGraw-Hill.
   - Haas, Tigan (Ed.). 2008. *New Urbanism and Beyond: Designing Cities for the Future.* Rizzoli.
   - Leinberger, Christopher B. 2007. *The Option of Urbanism: Investing in a New American Dream.* Island Press.
   - Hall, Kenneth B., and Porterfield, Gerald A. 2001. *Community by Design: New Urbanism for Suburbs and Small Communities.* McGraw-Hill Professional.

 Endnotes

1. U.S. Department of Transportation. 2008. *Crosswalk from discretionary budget authority to budgetary resources.* Available: http://www.dot.gov/bib2009/crosswalk.htm.
2. Davis, Stacy C., Diegel, Susan W., and Boundy, Robert G. 2008. *Transportation Energy Data Book, Edition 27* (Table 2.13: Energy intensities of highway passenger modes, 1970–2006). Available: http://cta.ornl.gov/data/chapter2.shtml.

3. Bureau of Labor Statistics. *Consumer Expenditure Survey: Shares of average annual expenditures and sources of income, 2004* (Table 47). Available: ftp://ftp.bls.gov/pub/special.requests/ce/share/2004/age.txt.

4. *The Economist*. 2008. *Highest Car Ownership* (Table). Available: http://www.economist.com/markets/rankings/pocketworldinfigures/displaystory.cfm?story_id=12796728.

5. Puentes, Robert, and Tomer, Adie. 2008. *The road . . . less traveled: An analysis of vehicle miles traveled trends in the U.S.* Brookings Metropolitan Policy Program. Available: http://www.brookings.edu/~/media/Files/rc/reports/2008/1216_transportation_tomer_puentes/vehicle_miles_traveled_report.pdf.

6. GreenBiz. 2006. *EPA Names "Best Workplaces for Commuters."* Available: http://www.greenbiz.com/news/2006/10/23/epa-names-best-workplaces-commuters.

7. Energy Information Administration. 2008. *Table 2: 2005 State Emissions by Sector (Million Metric Tons of Carbon Dioxide)*. Available: http://www.eia.doe.gov/oiaf/1605/ggrpt/excel/tbl_statesector.xls.

8. For more information about kudzu, a plant species introduced for erosion control that has become invasive in the southeastern United States, see: http://en.wikipedia.org/wiki/Kudzu.

Perspectives on Communication Technologies

Communication is the sharing and receiving of information. Access to information is critical in educational, business, research, and personal settings. Because information itself can represent a commodity that has value, it bestows a form of power on individuals with that access. Communication technologies—the tools that enhance our ability to communicate—have progressively developed in ways that allow us to communicate with more people, over greater distances, in shorter and shorter amounts of time. These technologies have inevitably shifted the balance of power.

We can identify at least three major milestones of communication technology in modern history. From a historical perspective it's difficult to associate any particular individual with these technological breakthroughs, since they almost always resulted from the cumulative contributions of many people. Yet each of these milestones was foundational in that it led to fundamental changes in the process of communication.

The first of these milestones was the development of the printing press or, more specifically, the advent of mass printing that was enabled through refinements in the technology of inks, paper, and printing machines. Beginning in the 15th Century, particularly in Europe, the growing availability of printed texts and subsequently of literacy shepherded in a new age of education and progress that came to be known as the Renaissance. From a societal standpoint, this access to books "democratized knowledge."[1] In addition to making classic texts (including the Bible) available to commoners, print technology gave a new forum for spreading news via the newsletter or newspaper. By the 19th Century, newspapers played a major role in the United States in shaping public opinion and helping citizens remain abreast of social and political events.

A second milestone in communication technology was the development of broadcast media; specifically, radio and television. The first commercial radio broadcasts occurred in the U.S. in the 1920s; the first television broadcasts occurred in the late 1930s and early 1940s. By the 1950s, television broadcasts were available in nearly every urban/suburban market in the country. Developments in recording technology meant that television no longer had to rely on live programming the way it did in the early days. Black and white television gave way to color TV, and the amount and type of programming expanded continually.[2] Through the 20th Century, radio and television became well established as important sources of news, for many people replacing the role that newspapers once played in helping them stay informed about current events.

A third milestone in communication technology was the development of affordable, powerful, personal computers, particularly in combination with the Internet. Computers provide functionality unlike any prior communication technology, because they allow us to access, manipulate, store, and disseminate vast amounts of information. Moreover, their ability to be networked allows for an interactivity not present with any other type of communication device, including telephones.

Some observations must be made with regard to the changes brought about with each of these advancements in communication technology. First, each development brought with it new technological capabilities that were simply not present before. For example, in the shift from a print to a broadcast tradition, information was enhanced by the use of sound and (with TV) moving images, allowing it to engage users in new ways. A second point is that the speed and thoroughness of adoption has been more rapid with each successive development in communication technology, making the associated cultural changes more rapid and more widespread. Finally, each development has allowed for a broadened reach in the ability of individuals to communicate. For example, the reach of broadcast media tended to be much broader than the more limited reach of local or regional newspapers. With the Internet, communication can happen globally almost instantaneously, and search engines and RSS feeds allow compatible individuals to find each other or particular kinds of information with unparalleled ease. One of the most famous commentators on the effects of media, Marshall McLuhan, wrote: "When technology extends one of our senses, a new translation of culture occurs as swiftly as the new technology is interiorized."[3] In other words, the impacts of new communication technologies extend beyond their mere ability to help us communicate; they also fundamentally change the ways we think and interact.

New communication technologies have given rise to a host of new privacy issues. Prominent among these issues is the way that personal information has been commodified, a development that has been enabled by the use of powerful databases and by the widespread use of the Internet. Data on how you use the Internet and the sites you visit is easily gathered and can be collected and sold to others. The ubiquity of information databases of all kinds—from what products you purchase at the grocery store to what organizations you belong to and much more—means that personal information about you is readily available to anyone who might seek it out for commercial or other purposes.

Access to personal information isn't necessarily a bad thing. For example, some parents might appreciate the fact that they can visit a government Web site showing the residences of all registered sex offenders in their town. Others like the fact that they can receive news feeds tailored to their individual tastes and interests. Organizations benefit from being able to locate like-minded individuals who might be inclined to donate to a worthy cause. Levels of concern about privacy can vary depending on the context. A useful way to categorize individual responses to privacy was developed by Dr. Alan Westin, known for his annual surveys on privacy and the Westin/Harris privacy segmentation index. *Privacy fundamentalists* are those who place a high value on maintaining individual privacy, and currently comprise about 35 percent of the adult population in the U.S. *Pri-*

vacy pragmatists, who make up approximately 55 percent of the adult population, are those who consider the trade-offs of access to personal information and weigh the relative benefits to the individual and to society. The *privacy unconcerned* make up about 10 percent of the adult population.[4]

Surveillance Nation

This article provides a good overview of some of the common uses of surveillance in the U.S. and abroad. These surveillance tools range from the seemingly helpful—things like "nanny-cams" so that anxious parents can monitor the child care their preschool children are receiving—to the more disturbing—such as monitors used in employee restrooms to prevent theft. As Farmer and Mann note, the world is fast becoming a place where "unmonitored public space will effectively cease to exist."

Why is the surveillance industry one of the fastest-growing areas of communication technology? Partly because the tools exist: cameras, monitors, electronic identification tags, and computer tools needed to monitor activity are affordable and easy to use. The uses to which surveillance tools have been put are surprisingly diverse and sometimes just downright surprising. For example, you can get a sub-dermal computer chip implanted in your dog so that, if he becomes lost, your contact information can be readily retrieved. Numerous products now have radio frequency identification (RFID) tags so that their progress through the supply chain can be tracked from manufacture to sale and beyond. In some cases these technologies have been adopted with little fanfare, so lots of people are not aware that their locations can be tracked via their cell phones; that chances are good that their employer is monitoring them electronically; or that their purchases at the local supermarket are being tracked. In some cases the surveillance tool was just a matter of built-in functionality that was deemed useful. If your instructor in this course uses a courseware program like Blackboard, for example, he or she can monitor when and for how long you access course materials on the site.

Charles C. Mann has written extensively on the intersection of science, technology, and commerce for publications such as *Science, Wired, The Atlantic Monthly*, and *Fortune*. The author of several books, his recent effort *1491* won the U.S. National Academy of Sciences' Keck Award for best book of the year in 2006. Dan Farmer is a software engineer and Web security expert known for creating the Security Administrator's Tool for Analyzing Networks (SATAN), which is a program for investigating the vulnerabilities of remote systems. He served as head of security at EarthLink and cofounded and served as chief technology officer at Elemental Security. Farmer coauthored the book *Forensic Discovery* (2005).

Surveillance Nation

By Dan Farmer and Charles C. Mann

Route 9 is an old two-lane highway that cuts across Massachusetts from Boston in the east to Pittsfield in the west. Near the small city of Northampton, the highway crosses the wide Connecticut River. The Calvin Coolidge Memorial Bridge, named after the president who once served as Northampton's mayor, is a major regional traffic link. When the state began a long-delayed and still ongoing reconstruction of the bridge in the summer of 2001, traffic jams stretched for kilometers into the bucolic New England countryside.

Used with permission of MIT Technology Review, from *Technology Review, Vol. 106, No. 3*, by D. Farmer & C. Mann, 2003; permission conveyed through Copyright Clearance Center, Inc.

In a project aimed at alleviating drivers' frustration, the University of Massachusetts Transportation Center, located in nearby Amherst, installed eight shoe-size digital surveillance cameras along the roads leading to the bridge. Six are mounted on utility poles and the roofs of local businesses. Made by Axis Communications in Sweden, they are connected to dial-up modems and transmit images of the roadway before them to a Web page, which commuters can check for congestion before tackling the road. According to Dan Dulaski, the system's technical manager, running the entire webcam system—power, phone, and Internet fees—costs just $600 a month.

The other two cameras in the Coolidge Bridge project are a little less routine. Built by Computer Recognition Systems in Wokingham, England, with high-quality lenses and fast shutter speeds (1/10,000 second), they are designed to photograph every car and truck that passes by. Located eight kilometers apart, at the ends of the zone of maximum traffic congestion, the two cameras send vehicle images to attached computers, which use special character-recognition software to decipher vehicle license plates. The license data go to a server at the company's U.S. office in Cambridge, MA, about 130 kilometers away. As each license plate passes the second camera, the server ascertains the time difference between the two readings. The average of the travel durations of all successfully matched vehicles defines the likely travel time for crossing the bridge at any given moment, and that information is posted on the traffic watch Web page.

To local residents, the traffic data are helpful, even vital: police use the information to plan emergency routes. But as the computers calculate traffic flow, they are also making a record of all cars that cross the bridge—when they do so, their average speed, and (depending on lighting and weather conditions) how many people are in each car.

Trying to avoid provoking privacy fears, Keith Fallon, a Computer Recognition Systems project engineer, says, "we're not saving any of the information we capture. Everything is deleted immediately." But the company could change its mind and start saving the data at any time. No one on the road would know.

The Coolidge Bridge is just one of thousands of locations around the planet where citizens are crossing—willingly, more often than not—into a world of networked, highly computerized surveillance. According to a January report by J.P. Freeman, a security market-research firm in Newtown, CT, 26 million surveillance cameras have already been installed worldwide, and more than 11 million of them are in the United States. In heavily monitored London, England, Hull University criminologist Clive Norris has estimated, the average person is filmed by more than 300 cameras each *day*.

The $150 million-a-year remote digital-surveillance-camera market will grow, according to Freeman, at an annual clip of 40 to 50 percent for the next 10 years. But astonishingly, other, nonvideo forms of monitoring will increase even faster. In a process that mirrors the unplanned growth of the Internet itself, thousands of personal, commercial, medical, police, and government databases and monitoring systems will intersect and entwine. Ultimately, surveillance will become so ubiquitous, networked, and searchable that unmonitored public space will effectively cease to exist.

This prospect—what science fiction writer David Brin calls "the transparent society"—may sound too distant to be worth thinking about. But even the farsighted Brin underestimated how quickly technological advances—more powerful microprocessors, faster network transmissions, larger hard drives, cheaper electronics, and more sophisticated and powerful software—would make universal surveillance possible.

It's not all about Big Brother or Big Business, either. Widespread electronic scrutiny is usually denounced as a creation of political tyranny or corporate greed. But the rise of omnipresent surveillance will be driven as much by ordinary citizens' understandable—even laudatory—desires for security, control, and comfort as by the imperatives of business and government. "Nanny cams," global-positioning locators, police and home security networks, traffic jam monitors, medical-device radio-frequency tags, small-business webcams: the list of monitoring devices employed by and for average Americans is already long, and it will only become longer. Extensive surveillance, in short, is coming into being because people like and want it.

"Almost all of the pieces for a surveillance society are already here," says Gene Spafford, director of Purdue University's Center for Education and Research in Information Assurance and Security. "It's just a matter of assembling them." Unfortunately, he says, ubiquitous surveillance faces intractable social and technological problems that could well reduce its usefulness or even make it dangerous. As a result, each type of monitoring may be beneficial in itself, at least for the people who put it in place, but the collective result could be calamitous.

To begin with, surveillance data from multiple sources are being combined into large databases. For example, businesses track employees' car, computer, and telephone use to evaluate their job performance; similarly, the U.S. Defense Department's experimental Total Information Awareness project has announced plans to sift through information about millions of people to find data that identify criminals and terrorists.

But many of these merged pools of data are less reliable than small-scale, localized monitoring efforts; big databases are harder to comb for bad entries, and their conclusions are far more difficult to verify. In addition, the inescapable nature of surveillance can itself create alarm, even among its beneficiaries. "Your little camera network may seem like a good idea to you," Spafford says. "Living with everyone else's could be a nightmare."

The Surveillance Ad-Hocracy

Last October deadly snipers terrorized Washington, DC, and the surrounding suburbs, killing 10 people. For three long weeks, law enforcement agents seemed helpless to stop the murderers, who struck at random and then vanished into the area's snarl of highways. Ultimately, two alleged killers were arrested, but only because their taunting messages to the authorities had inadvertently provided clues to their identification.

In the not-too-distant future, according to advocates of policing technologies, such unstoppable rampages may become next to impossible, at least in populous areas. By combining police cameras with private camera networks like that on Route 9, video coverage will become so complete that any snipers who waged an attack—and all the people near the crime scene—would be trackable from camera to camera until they could be stopped and interrogated.

The unquestionable usefulness and sheer affordability of these extensive video-surveillance systems suggest that they will propagate rapidly. But despite the relentlessly increasing capabilities of such systems, video monitoring is still but a tiny part—less than 1 percent—of surveillance overall, says Carl Botan, a Purdue center researcher who has studied this technology for 15 years.

Examples are legion. By 2006, for instance, law will require that every U.S. cell phone be designed to report its precise location during a 911 call; wireless carriers plan to use the same technology to offer 24-hour location-based services, including tracking of people and vehicles. To prevent children from wittingly or unwittingly calling up porn sites, the Seattle company N2H2 provides Web filtering and monitoring services for 2,500 schools serving 16 million students. More than a third of all large corporations electronically review the computer files used by their employees, according to a recent American Management Association survey. Seven of the 10 biggest supermarket chains use discount cards to monitor customers' shopping habits: tailoring product offerings to customers' wishes is key to survival in that brutally competitive business. And as part of a new, federally mandated tracking system, the three major U.S. automobile manufacturers plan to put special radio transponders known as radio frequency identification tags in every tire sold in the nation. Far exceeding congressional requirements, according to a leader of the Automotive Industry Action Group, an industry think tank, the tags can be read on vehicles going as fast as 160 kilometers per hour from a distance of 4.5 meters.

Many if not most of today's surveillance networks were set up by government and big business, but in years to come individuals and small organizations will set the pace of growth. Future sales of Net-enabled surveillance cameras, in the view of Fredrik Nilsson, Axis Communications' director of business development, will be driven by organizations that buy more than eight but fewer than 30 cameras—condo associations, church groups, convenience store owners, parent-teacher associations, and anyone else who might like to check what is happening in one place while he is sitting in another. A

dozen companies already help working parents monitor their children's nannies and day-care centers from the office; scores more let them watch backyards, school buses, playgrounds, and their own living rooms. Two new startups—Wherify Wireless in Redwood Shores, CA, and Peace of Mind at Light Speed in Westport, CT—are introducing bracelets and other portable devices that continuously beam locating signals to satellites so that worried moms and dads can always find their children.

As thousands of ordinary people buy monitoring devices and services, the unplanned result will be an immense, overlapping grid of surveillance systems, created unintentionally by the same ad-hocracy that caused the Internet to explode. Meanwhile, the computer networks on which monitoring data are stored and manipulated continue to grow faster, cheaper, smarter, and able to store information in greater volume for longer times. Ubiquitous digital surveillance will marry widespread computational power—with startling results.

The factors driving the growth of computing potential are well known. Moore's law—which roughly equates to the doubling of processor speed every 18 months—seems likely to continue its famous march. Hard drive capacity is rising even faster. It has doubled every year for more than a decade, and this should go on "as far as the eye can see," according to Robert M. Wise, director of product marketing for the desktop product group at Maxtor, a hard drive manufacturer. Similarly, according to a 2001 study by a pair of AT&T Labs researchers, network transmission capacity has more than doubled annually for the last dozen years, a tendency that should continue for at least another decade and will keep those powerful processors and hard drives well fed with fresh data.

Today a company or agency with a $10 million hardware budget can buy processing power equivalent to 2,000 workstations, two petabytes of hard drive space (two million gigabytes, or 50,000 standard 40-gigabyte hard drives like those found on today's PCs), and a two gigabit Internet connection (more than 2,000 times the capacity of a typical home broadband connection). If current trends continue, simple arithmetic predicts that in 20 years the same purchasing power will buy the processing capability of 10 million of today's workstations, 200 exabytes (200 million gigabytes) of storage capacity, and 200 exabits (200 million megabits) of bandwidth. Another way of saying this is that by 2023 large organizations will be able to devote the equivalent of a contemporary PC to monitoring every single one of the 330 million people who will then be living in the United States.

One of the first applications for this combination of surveillance and computational power, says Raghu Ramakrishnan, a database researcher at the University of Wisconsin-Madison, will be continuous intensive monitoring of buildings, offices, and stores: the spaces where middle-class people spend most of their lives. Surveillance in the workplace is common now: in 2001, according to the American Management Association survey, 77.7 percent of major U.S. corporations electronically monitored their employees, and that statistic had more than doubled since 1997 (see "Eye on Employees," p. 194). But much more is on the way. Companies like Johnson Controls and Siemens, Ramakrishnan says, are already "doing simplistic kinds of 'asset tracking,' as they call it." They use radio frequency identification tags to monitor the locations of people as well as inventory. In January, Gillette began attaching such tags to 500 million of its Mach 3 Turbo razors. Special "smart shelves" at Wal-Mart stores will record the removal of razors by shoppers, thereby alerting stock clerks whenever shelves need to be refilled—and effectively transforming Gillette customers into walking radio beacons. In

the future, such tags will be used by hospitals to ensure that patients and staff maintain quarantines, by law offices to keep visitors from straying into rooms containing clients' confidential papers, and in kindergartens to track toddlers.

By employing multiple, overlapping types of monitoring, Ramakrishnan says, managers will be able to "keep track of people, objects, and environmental levels throughout a whole complex." Initially, these networks will be installed for "such mundane things as trying to figure out when to replace the carpets or which areas of lawn get the most traffic so you need to spread some grass seed preventively." But as computers and monitoring equipment become cheaper and more powerful, managers will use surveillance data to construct complex, multidimensional records of how spaces are used. The models will be analyzed to improve efficiency and security—and they will be sold to other businesses or governments. Over time, the thousands of individual monitoring schemes inevitably will merge together and feed their data into large commercial and state-owned networks. When surveillance databases can describe or depict what every individual is doing at a particular time, Ramakrishnan says, they will be providing humankind with the digital equivalent of an ancient dream: being "present, in effect, almost anywhere and anytime."

Garbage In, Gragbea Otu

In 1974 Francis Ford Coppola wrote and directed *The Conversation*, which starred Gene Hackman as Harry Caul, a socially maladroit surveillance expert. In this remarkably prescient movie, a mysterious organization hires Caul to record a quiet discussion that will take place in the middle of a crowd in San Francisco's Union Square. Caul deploys three microphones: one in a bag carried by a confederate and two directional mikes installed on buildings overlooking the area. Afterward Caul discovers that each of the three recordings is plagued by background noise and distortions, but by combining the different sources, he is able to piece together the conversation. Or, rather, he thinks he has pieced it together. Later, to his horror, Caul learns that he misinterpreted a crucial line, a discovery that leads directly to the movie's chilling denouement.

The Conversation illustrates a central dilemma for tomorrow's surveillance society. Although much of the explosive growth in monitoring is being driven by consumer demand, that growth has not yet been accompanied by solutions to the classic difficulties computer systems have integrating disparate sources of information and arriving at valid conclusions. Data quality problems that cause little inconvenience on a local scale—when Wal-Mart's smart shelves misread a razor's radio frequency identification tag—have much larger consequences when organizations assemble big databases from many sources and attempt to draw conclusions about, say, someone's capacity for criminal action. Such problems, in the long run, will play a large role in determining both the technical and social impact of surveillance.

The experimental and controversial Total Information Awareness program of the Defense Advanced Research Projects Agency exemplifies these issues. By merging records from corporate, medical, retail, educational, travel, telephone, and even veterinary sources, as well as such "biometric" data as fingerprints, iris and retina scans, DNA tests, and facial-characteristic measurements, the program is intended to create an unprecedented repository of information about both U.S. citizens and foreigners with U.S. contacts. Program director John M. Poindexter has explained that analysts will use custom data-mining techniques to sift through the mass of information, attempting to "detect, classify, and identify foreign terrorists" in order

to "preempt and defeat terrorist acts"—a virtual Eye of Sauron, in critics' view, constructed from telephone bills and shopping preference cards.

In February Congress required the Pentagon to obtain its specific approval before implementing Total Information Awareness in the United States (though certain actions are allowed on foreign soil). But President George W. Bush had already announced that he was creating an apparently similar effort, the Terrorist Threat Integration Center, to be led by the Central Intelligence Agency. Regardless of the fate of these two programs, other equally sweeping attempts to pool monitoring data are proceeding apace. Among these initiatives is Regulatory DataCorp, a for-profit consortium of 19 top financial institutions worldwide. The consortium, which was formed last July, combines members' customer data in an effort to combat "money laundering, fraud, terrorist financing, organized crime, and corruption." By constantly poring through more than 20,000 sources of public information about potential wrongdoings—from newspaper articles and Interpol warrants to disciplinary actions by the U.S. Securities and Exchange Commission—the consortium's Global Regulatory Information Database will, according to its owner, help clients "know their customers."

Equally important in the long run are the databases that will be created by the nearly spontaneous aggregation of scores or hundreds of smaller databases. "What seem to be small-scale, discrete systems end up being combined into large databases," says Marc Rotenberg, executive director of the Electronic Privacy Information Center, a nonprofit research organization in Washington, DC. He points to the recent, voluntary efforts of merchants in Washington's affluent Georgetown district. They are integrating their in-store closed-circuit television networks and making the combined results available to city police. In Rotenberg's view, the

Eye on Employees

Percentage of major U.S. employers that record and review their workers' activities

Surveillance Activity	1997	1998	1999	2000	2001
Recording telephone conversations	10.4	11.2	10.6	11.5	11.9
Monitoring telephone usage	34.4	40.2	38.6	44.0	43.3
Storing and reviewing voice mail	5.3	5.3	5.8	6.8	7.8
Storing and reviewing computer files	13.7	19.6	21.4	30.8	36.1
Storing and reviewing e-mail	14.9	20.2	27.0	38.1	46.5
Monitoring Internet connections	NA[1]	NA[1]	NA[1]	54.1	62.8
Clocking overall computer use	16.1	15.9	15.2	19.4	18.9
Video recording of employee performance	15.7	15.6	16.1	14.6	15.2
Video surveillance for security	33.7	32.7	32.8	35.3	37.7
Any active electronic monitoring	35.3	42.7	45.1	73.5[2]	77.7[2]

[1] Not available.
[2] Includes Internet monitoring, which was not measured prior to 2000

collection and consolidation of individual surveillance networks into big government and industry programs "is a strange mix of public and private, and it's not something that the legal system has encountered much before."

Managing the sheer size of these aggregate surveillance databases, surprisingly, will not pose insurmountable technical difficulties. Most personal data are either very compact or easily compressible. Financial, medical, and shopping records can be represented as strings of text that are easily stored and transmitted; as a general rule, the records do not grow substantially over time.

Even biometric records are no strain on computing systems. To identify people, genetic-testing firms typically need stretches of DNA that can be represented in just one kilobyte—the size of a short email message. Fingerprints, iris scans, and other types of biometric data consume little more. Other forms of data can be preprocessed in much the way that the cameras on Route 9 transform multimegabyte images of cars into short strings of text with license plate numbers and times. (For investigators, having a video of suspects driving down a road usually is not as important as simply knowing that they were there at a given time.) To create a digital dossier for every individual in the United States—as programs like Total Information Awareness would require—only "a couple terabytes of well-defined information" would be needed, says Jeffrey Ullman, a former Stanford University database researcher. "I don't think that's really stressing the capacity of [even today's] databases."

Instead, argues Rajeev Motwani, another member of Stanford's database group, the real challenge for large surveillance databases will be the seemingly simple task of gathering valid data. Computer scientists use the term GIGO—garbage in, garbage out—to describe situations in which erroneous input creates erroneous output. Whether people are building bombs or buying bagels, governments and corporations try to predict their behavior by integrating data from sources as disparate as electronic toll-collection sensors, library records, restaurant credit-card receipts, and grocery store customer cards—to say nothing of the Internet, surely the world's largest repository of personal information.

Unfortunately, all these sources are full of errors, as are financial and medical records. Names are misspelled and digits transposed; address and e-mail records become outdated when people move and switch Internet service providers; and formatting differences among databases cause information loss and distortion when they are merged. "It is routine to find in large customer databases defective records—records with at least one major error or omission—at rates of at least 20 to 35 percent," says Larry English of Information Impact, a database consulting company in Brentwood, TN.

Unfortunately, says Motwani, "data cleaning is a major open problem in the research community. We are still struggling to get a formal technical definition of the problem." Even when the original data are correct, he argues, merging them can introduce errors where none had existed before. Worse, none of these worries about the garbage going into the system even begin to address the still larger problems with the garbage going out.

The Dissolution of Privacy

Almost every computer-science student takes a course in algorithms. Algorithms are sets of specified, repeatable rules or procedures for accomplishing tasks such as sorting numbers; they are, so to speak, the engines that make programs run. Unfortunately, innovations in algorithms are not subject to Moore's law, and progress in the field is notoriously sporadic. "There are certain areas in algorithms we basically can't do better and others where creative work will have to be done," Ullman says. Sifting through large surveillance databases for information, he says, will essentially be "a problem in research in algorithms. We need to exploit some of the stuff that's been done in the data-mining community recently and do it much, much better."

Working with databases requires users to have two mental models. One is a model of the data. Teasing out answers to questions from the popular search engine Google, for example, is easier if users grasp the varieties and types of data on the Internet—Web pages with words and pictures, whole documents in a multiplicity of formats, downloadable software and media files—and how they are stored. In exactly the same way, extracting information from surveillance databases will depend on a user's knowledge of the system. "It's a chess game," Ullman says. "An unusually smart analyst will get things that a not-so-smart one will not."

Second, and more important according to Spafford, effective use of big surveillance databases will depend on having a model of what one is looking for. This factor is especially crucial, he says, when trying to predict the future, a goal of many commercial and government projects. For this reason, what might be called *reactive* searches that scan recorded data for specific patterns are generally much more likely to obtain useful answers than *proactive* searches that seek to get ahead of things. If, for instance, police in the Washington sniper investigation had been able to tap into a pervasive network of surveillance cameras, they could have tracked people seen near the crime scenes until they could be stopped and questioned: a reactive process. But it is unlikely that police would have been helped by proactively asking surveillance databases for the names of people in the Washington area with the requisite characteristics (family difficulties, perhaps, or military training and a recent penchant for drinking) to become snipers.

In many cases, invalid answers are harmless. If Victoria's Secret mistakenly mails 1 percent of its spring catalogs to people with no interest in lingerie, the price paid by all parties is small. But if a national terrorist-tracking system has the same 1 percent error rate, it will produce millions of false alarms, wasting huge amounts of investigators' time and, worse, labeling many innocent U.S. citizens as suspects. "A 99 percent hit rate is great for advertising," Spafford says, "but terrible for spotting terrorism."

Because no system can have a success rate of 100 percent, analysts can try to decrease the likelihood that surveillance databases will identify blameless people as possible terrorists. By making the criteria for flagging suspects more stringent, officials can raise the bar, and fewer ordinary citizens will be wrongly fingered. Inevitably, however, that will mean also that the "borderline" terrorists—those who don't match all the search criteria but still have lethal intentions—might be overlooked as well. For both types of error, the potential consequences are alarming.

Yet none of these concerns will stop the growth of surveillance, says Ben Shneiderman, a computer scientist at the University of Maryland. Its potential benefits are simply too large. An example is what Shneiderman, in his recent book *Leonardo's Laptop: Human Needs and the New Computing Technologies*, calls the World Wide Med: a global, unified database that makes every patient's complete medical history instantly available to doctors through the Internet, replacing today's scattered sheaves of paper records (see "Paperless Medicine" in *TR*, April 2003, p. 58). "The idea," he says, "is that if you're brought to an ER anywhere in the world, your medical records pop up in 30 seconds." Similar programs are already coming into existence. Backed by the Centers for Disease Control and Prevention, a team based at Harvard Medical School is planning to monitor the records of 20 million walk-in hospital patients throughout the United States for clusters of symptoms asso-

ciated with bioterror agents. Given the huge number of lost or confused medical records, the benefits of such plans are clear. But because doctors would be continually adding information to medical histories, the system would be monitoring patients' most intimate personal data. The network, therefore, threatens to violate patient confidentiality on a global scale.

In Shneiderman's view, such tradeoffs are inherent to surveillance. The collective by-product of thousands of unexceptional, even praiseworthy efforts to gather data could be something nobody wants: the demise of privacy. "These networks are growing much faster than people realize," he says. "We need to pay attention to what we're doing right now."

In *The Conversation*, surveillance expert Harry Caul is forced to confront the trade-offs of his profession directly. The conversation in Union Square provides information that he uses to try to stop a murder. Unfortunately, his faulty interpretation of its meaning prevents him from averting tragedy. Worse still, we see in scene after scene that even the expert snoop is unable to avoid being monitored and recorded. At the movie's intense, almost wordless climax, Caul rips his home apart in a futile effort to find the electronic bugs that are hounding him.

The Conversation foreshadowed a view now taken by many experts: surveillance cannot be stopped. There is no possibility of "opting out." The question instead is how to use technology, policy, and shared societal values to guide the spread of surveillance—by the government, by corporations, and perhaps most of all by our own unwitting and enthusiastic participation—while limiting its downside.

Discussion Questions

1. Which of the examples provided in the article by Farmer and Mann do you believe represent useful and appropriate uses of surveillance technology? Which do not? Support your opinion with reasoning.

2. Events such as the terrorist attacks on the World Trade Towers and the Pentagon in 2001 are often used as a justification for expanded use of surveillance. Do you believe that this expanded surveillance achieves the goal of making us safer as a society? Are there reasons why, or situations when, we should resist expanded uses of surveillance?

3. An important issue that emerges in the field of surveillance is the "garbage in/garbage out" syndrome. What does this mean, in this context? Why is it a major concern with regard to surveillance?

4. The authors suggest that it's not possible to "opt out" of the surveillance society. Do you think this is true? Why or why not? Under what conditions do you think it might be possible to opt out?

 Supporting Activities

1. Watch and discuss (or write a review of) the movies *Gattica* or *Minority Report*, both of which imagine a science-fiction world of the future in which biometric identifiers are used to track the movement of individuals.

2. Find a surveillance camera in your community that provides real-time video footage of a public space. Can you locate information about why the camera was installed? For example, you can view streaming video of Times Square (NY) from any of a number of different video cameras at: http://www.earthcam.com/usa/newyork/timessquare/.

3. As a group, try to compile a listing of all of the ways that your activity is monitored on a day-to-day basis. Which of these do you think is useful or appropriate? Which, if any, do you object to?

 Additional Resources

1. A summary of HR 3162, the USA PATRIOT Act, developed by the Congressional Research Service of the Library of Congress, can be found at: http://www.fas.org/irp/crs/RS21203.pdf. The full text of the bill can be read on the Electronic Privacy Information Center (EPIC) site: http://epic.org/privacy/terrorism/hr3162.html.

2. The American Civil Liberties Union (ACLU) is an organization devoted to protecting civil rights. See what they have to say about privacy and surveillance at: http://www.aclu.org/privacy/spying/index.html.

3. For a very readable description of how RFID tags work, visit the How Stuff Works site: http://electronics.howstuffworks.com/rfid.htm.

4. View the materials on the National Geographic site about the so-called War on Terror. Go to: http://www.nationalgeographic.com/ and use the search function to find the "high tech war on terror" page, which includes photos and video.

Television Addiction Is No Mere Metaphor

The social effect of television viewing is a subject that has been studied intensively for many years.[5] Alternatively seen as a powerful educational tool, as a relatively cheap form of entertainment for the masses, and as a contributor to a variety of social ills, of one thing there is no doubt: television is ubiquitous. The statistics on television viewing, to quote the authors, are "astonishing." In the United States, individuals spend *on average* three hours per day watching television, and in most American homes the television is on (although not necessarily watched) for much longer periods of time. Television ownership in the United States expanded rapidly—from 9 percent of households in 1950 to over 64 percent in 1955—and has reached almost total saturation (98.9 percent of American households in 2008), and according to Nielsen data the average American household in 2008 had over three television sets.[6] Television viewing statistics worldwide are surprisingly similar, even in many developing countries, making television a truly "universal medium."[7]

For those interested in the subject, selective reading of the literally thousands of studies on the effects of television is encouraged. This article by Kubey and Csikszentmihalyi highlights research of a somewhat different nature by focusing on the *physiological* effects of television viewing. Their work helps to explain why television viewing is an activity that many of us engage in more than any other activity besides sleeping and working.

Robert Kubey is Professor of Journalism and Media Studies and is Director of the Center for Media Studies at Rutgers University. Kubey has been an Annenberg Scholar at the University of Pennsylvania, co-edits a series of research volumes on media literacy for Lawrence Erlbaum Associates, and has published widely on media-related topics. Mihaly Csikszentmihalyi is Distinguished Professor of Psychology at Claremont Graduate University and is Director of the Quality of Life Research Center, a nonprofit research institute that focuses on human characteristics such as optimism, creativity, and motivation. He is widely known for his series of books on what he calls "flow," which includes *Flow: They Psychology of Optimal Experience* (1990), *Creativity: Flow and the Psychology of Discovery and Invention* (1996), and *Good Business: Flow, Leadership and the Making of Meaning* (2003).

Television Addiction Is No Mere Metaphor

By Robert Kubey and Mihaly Csikszentmihalyi

Perhaps the most ironic aspect of the struggle for survival is how easily organisms can be harmed by that which they desire. The trout is caught by the fisherman's lure, the mouse by cheese. But at least those creatures have the excuse that bait and cheese look like sustenance. Humans seldom have that consolation. The temptations that can disrupt their lives are often pure indulgences. No one has to drink alcohol, for example. Realizing when a diversion has gotten out of control is one of the great challenges of life.

Excessive cravings do not necessarily involve physical substances. Gambling can become compulsive; sex can become obsessive. One activity, however, stands out for its prominence and ubiquity—the world's most popular leisure pastime, television. Most people admit to

From *Scientific American, 286(2), February 2002* by R. Kubey & M. Csikszentmihalyi. Reprinted with permission. Copyright © 2002 by Scientific American, Inc. All rights reserved.

having a love-hate relationship with it. They complain about the "boob tube" and "couch potatoes," then they settle into their sofas and grab the remote control. Parents commonly fret about their children's viewing (if not their own). Even researchers who study TV for a living marvel at the medium's hold on them personally. Percy Tannenbaum of the University of California at Berkeley has written: "Among life's more embarrassing moments have been countless occasions when I am engaged in conversation in a room while a TV set is on, and I cannot for the life of me stop from periodically glancing over to the screen. This occurs not only during dull conversations but during reasonably interesting ones just as well."

Scientists have been studying the effects of television for decades, generally focusing on whether watching violence on TV correlates with being violent in real life [see "The Effects of Observing Violence," by Leonard Berkowitz; *Scientific American*, February 1964; and "Communication and Social Environment," by George Gerbner; September 1972]. Less attention has been paid to the basic allure of the small screen—the medium, as opposed to the message.

The term "TV addiction" is imprecise and laden with value judgments, but it captures the essence of a very real phenomenon. Psychologists and psychiatrists formally define substance dependence as a disorder characterized by criteria that include spending a great deal of time using the substance; using it more often than one intends; thinking about reducing use or making repeated unsuccessful efforts to reduce use; giving up important social, family or occupational activities to use it; and reporting withdrawal symptoms when one stops using it.

All these criteria can apply to people who watch a lot of television. That does not mean that watching television, per se, is problematic. Television can teach and amuse; it can reach

aesthetic heights; it can provide much needed distraction and escape. The difficulty arises when people strongly sense that they ought not to watch as much as they do and yet find themselves strangely unable to reduce their viewing. Some knowledge of how the medium exerts its pull may help heavy viewers gain better control over their lives.

A Body at Rest Tends to Stay at Rest

The amount of time people spend watching television is astonishing. On average, individuals in the industrialized world devote three hours a day to the pursuit—fully half of their leisure time, and more than on any single activity save work and sleep. At this rate, someone who lives to 75 would spend nine years in front of the tube. To some commentators, this devotion means simply that people enjoy TV and make a conscious decision to watch it. But if that is the whole story, why do so many people experience misgivings about how much they view? In Gallup polls in 1992 and 1999, two out of five adult respondents and seven out of 10 teenagers said they spent too much time watching TV. Other surveys have consistently shown that roughly 10 percent of adults call themselves TV addicts.

To study people's reactions to TV, researchers have undertaken laboratory experiments in which they have monitored the brain waves (using an electroencephalograph, or EEG), skin resistance or heart rate of people watching television. To track behavior and emotion in the normal course of life, as opposed to the artificial conditions of the lab, we have used the Experience Sampling Method (ESM). Participants carried a beeper, and we signaled them six to eight times a day, at random, over the period of a week; whenever they heard the beep, they wrote down what they were doing and how they were feeling using a standardized scorecard.

As one might expect, people who were watching TV when we beeped them reported feeling relaxed and passive. The EEG studies similarly show less mental stimulation, as measured by alpha brain-wave production, during viewing than during reading.

What is more surprising is that the sense of relaxation ends when the set is turned off, but the feelings of passivity and lowered alertness continue. Survey participants commonly reflect that television has somehow absorbed or sucked out their energy, leaving them depleted. They say they have more difficulty concentrating after viewing than before. In contrast, they rarely indicate such difficulty after reading. After playing sports or engaging in hobbies, people report improvements in mood. After watching TV, people's moods are about the same or worse than before.

Within moments of sitting or lying down and pushing the "power" button, viewers report feeling more relaxed. Because the relaxation occurs quickly, people are conditioned to associate viewing with rest and lack of tension. The association is positively reinforced because viewers remain relaxed throughout viewing, and it is negatively reinforced via the stress and dysphoric rumination that occurs once the screen goes blank again.

Habit-forming drugs work in similar ways. A tranquilizer that leaves the body rapidly is much more likely to cause dependence than one that leaves the body slowly, precisely because the user is more aware that the drug's effects are wearing off. Similarly, viewers' vague learned sense that they will feel less relaxed if they stop viewing may be a significant factor in not turning the set off. Viewing begets more viewing.

Thus, the irony of TV: people watch a great deal longer than they plan to, even though prolonged viewing is less rewarding. In our ESM studies the longer people sat in front of the set, the less satisfaction they said they derived from it. When signaled, heavy viewers (those who consistently watch more than four hours a day) tended to report on their ESM sheets that they enjoy TV less than light viewers did (less than two hours a day). For some, a twinge of unease or guilt that they aren't doing something more productive may also accompany and depreciate the enjoyment of prolonged viewing. Researchers in Japan, the U.K. and the U.S. have found that this guilt occurs much more among middle-class viewers than among less affluent ones.

Grabbing Your Attention

What is it about TV that has such a hold on us? In part, the attraction seems to spring from our biological "orienting response." First described by Ivan Pavlov in 1927, the orienting response is our instinctive visual or auditory reaction to any sudden or novel stimulus. It is part of our evolutionary heritage, a built-in sensitivity to movement and potential predatory threats. Typical orienting reactions include dilation of the blood vessels to the brain, slowing of the heart, and constriction of blood vessels to major muscle groups. Alpha waves are blocked for a few seconds before returning to their baseline level, which is determined by the general level of mental arousal. The brain focuses its attention on gathering more information while the rest of the body quiets.

In 1986 Byron Reeves of Stanford University, Esther Thorson of the University of Missouri and their colleagues began to study whether the simple formal features of television—cuts, edits, zooms, pans, sudden noises—activate the orienting response, thereby keeping attention on the screen. By watching how brain waves were affected by formal features, the researchers concluded that these stylistic tricks can indeed trigger involuntary responses and "derive their attentional value through the evolutionary significance of detecting movement. . . . It is the form, not the content, of television that is unique."

The orienting response may partly explain common viewer remarks such as: "If a television is on, I just can't keep my eyes off it," "I don't want to watch as much as I do, but I can't help it," and "I feel hypnotized when I watch television." In the years since Reeves and Thorson published their pioneering work, researchers have delved deeper. Annie Lang's research team at Indiana University has shown that heart rate decreases for four to six seconds after an orienting stimulus. In ads, action sequences and music videos, formal features frequently come at a rate of one per second, thus activating the orienting response continuously.

Lang and her colleagues have also investigated whether formal features affect people's memory of what they have seen. In one of their studies, participants watched a program and then filled out a score sheet. Increasing the frequency of edits—defined here as a change from one camera angle to another in the same visual scene—improved memory recognition, presumably because it focused attention on the screen. Increasing the frequency of cuts—changes to a new visual scene—had a similar effect but only up to a point. If the number of cuts exceeded 10 in two minutes, recognition dropped off sharply.

Producers of educational television for children have found that formal features can help learning. But increasing the rate of cuts and edits eventually overloads the brain. Music videos and commercials that use rapid intercutting of unrelated scenes are designed to hold attention more than they are to convey information. People may remember the name of the product or band, but the details of the ad itself float in

one ear and out the other. The orienting response is overworked. Viewers still attend to the screen, but they feel tired and worn out, with little compensating psychological reward. Our ESM findings show much the same thing.

Sometimes the memory of the product is very subtle. Many ads today are deliberately oblique: they have an engaging story line, but it is hard to tell what they are trying to sell. Afterward you may not remember the product consciously. Yet advertisers believe that if they have gotten your attention, when you later go to the store you will feel better or more comfortable with a given product because you have a vague recollection of having heard of it.

The natural attraction to television's sound and light starts very early in life. Dafna Lemish of Tel Aviv University has described babies at six to eight weeks attending to television. We have observed slightly older infants who, when lying on their backs on the floor, crane their necks around 180 degrees to catch what light through yonder window breaks. This inclination suggests how deeply rooted the orienting response is.

"TV Is Part of Them"

That said, we need to be careful about overreacting. Little evidence suggests that adults or children should stop watching TV altogether. The problems come from heavy or prolonged viewing.

The Experience Sampling Method permitted us to look closely at most every domain of everyday life: working, eating, reading, talking to friends, playing a sport, and so on. We wondered whether heavy viewers might experience life differently than light viewers do. Do they dislike being with people more? Are they more alienated from work? What we found nearly leaped off the page at us. Heavy viewers report feeling significantly more anxious and less happy than light viewers do in unstructured situations, such as doing nothing, daydreaming or waiting in line. The difference widens when the viewer is alone.

Subsequently, Robert D. McIlwraith of the University of Manitoba extensively studied those who called themselves TV addicts on surveys. On a measure called the Short Imaginal Processes Inventory (SIPI), he found that the self-described addicts are more easily bored and distracted and have poorer attentional control than the nonaddicts. The addicts said they used TV to distract themselves from unpleasant thoughts and to fill time. Other studies over the years have shown that heavy viewers are less likely to participate in community activities and sports and are more likely to be obese than moderate viewers or nonviewers.

The question that naturally arises is: In which direction does the correlation go? Do people turn to TV because of boredom and loneliness, or does TV viewing make people more susceptible to boredom and loneliness? We and most other researchers argue that the former is generally the case, but it is not a simple case of either/or. Jerome L. and Dorothy Singer of Yale University, among others, have suggested that more viewing may contribute to a shorter attention span, diminished self-restraint and less patience with the normal delays of daily life. More than 25 years ago psychologist Tannis M. Mac-Beth Williams of the University of British Columbia studied a mountain community that had no television until cable finally arrived. Over time, both adults and children in the town became less creative in problem solving, less able to persevere at tasks, and less tolerant of unstructured time.

To some researchers, the most convincing parallel between TV and addictive drugs is that people experience withdrawal symptoms when they cut back on viewing. Nearly 40 years ago

Gary A. Steiner of the University of Chicago collected fascinating individual accounts of families whose set had broken—this back in the days when households generally had only one set: "The family walked around like a chicken without a head." "It was terrible. We did nothing—my husband and I talked." "Screamed constantly. Children bothered me, and my nerves were on edge. Tried to interest them in games, but impossible. TV is part of them."

In experiments, families have volunteered or been paid to stop viewing, typically for a week or a month. Many could not complete the period of abstinence. Some fought, verbally and physically. Anecdotal reports from some families that have tried the annual "TV turn-off" week in the U.S. tell a similar story.

If a family has been spending the lion's share of its free time watching television, reconfiguring itself around a new set of activities is no easy task. Of course, that does not mean it cannot be done or that all families implode when deprived of their set. In a review of these cold-turkey studies, Charles Winick of the City University of New York concluded: "The first three or four days for most persons were the worst, even in many homes where viewing was minimal and where there were other ongoing activities. In over half of all the households, during these first few days of loss, the regular routines were disrupted, family members had difficulties in dealing with the newly available time, anxiety and aggressions were expressed. . . . People living alone tended to be bored and irritated. . . . By the second week, a move toward adaptation to the situation was common." Unfortunately, researchers have yet to flesh out these anecdotes; no one has systematically gathered statistics on the prevalence of these withdrawal symptoms.

Even though TV does seem to meet the criteria for substance dependence, not all researchers would go so far as to call TV addictive. McIlwraith said in 1998 that "displacement of other activities by television may be socially significant but still fall short of the clinical requirement of significant impairment." He argued that a new category of "TV addiction" may not be necessary if heavy viewing stems from conditions such as depression and social phobia. Nevertheless, whether or not we formally diagnose someone as TV-dependent, millions of people sense that they cannot readily control the amount of television they watch.

Slave to the Computer Screen

Although much less research has been done on video games and computer use, the same principles often apply. The games offer escape and distraction; players quickly learn that they feel better when playing; and so a kind of reinforcement loop develops. The obvious difference from television, however, is the interactivity. Many video and computer games minutely increase in difficulty along with the increasing ability of the player. One can search for months to find another tennis or chess player of comparable ability, but programmed games can immediately provide a near-perfect match of challenge to skill. They offer the psychic pleasure—what one of us (Csikszentmihalyi) has called "flow"—that accompanies increased mastery of most any human endeavor. On the other hand, prolonged activation of the orienting response can wear players out. Kids report feeling tired, dizzy and nauseated after long sessions.

In 1997, in the most extreme medium-effects case on record, 700 Japanese children were rushed to the hospital, many suffering from "optically stimulated epileptic seizures" caused by viewing bright flashing lights in a Pokemon video game broadcast on Japanese TV. Seizures and other untoward effects of video games are significant enough that software companies and platform manufacturers now

routinely include warnings in their instruction booklets. Parents have reported to us that rapid movement on the screen has caused motion sickness in their young children after just 15 minutes of play. Many youngsters, lacking self-control and experience (and often supervision), continue to play despite these symptoms.

Lang and Shyam Sundar of Pennsylvania State University have been studying how people respond to Web sites. Sundar has shown people multiple versions of the same Web page, identical except for the number of links. Users reported that more links conferred a greater sense of control and engagement. At some point, however, the number of links reached saturation, and adding more of them simply turned people off. As with video games, the ability of Web sites to hold the user's attention seems to depend less on formal features than on interactivity.

For growing numbers of people, the life they lead online may often seem more important, more immediate and more intense than the life they lead face-to-face. Maintaining control over one's media habits is more of a challenge today than it has ever been. TV sets and computers are everywhere. But the small screen and the Internet need not interfere with the quality of the rest of one's life. In its easy provision of relaxation and escape, television can be beneficial in limited doses. Yet when the habit interferes with the ability to grow, to learn new things, to lead an active life, then it does constitute a kind of dependence and should be taken seriously.

Further Information

Television and the Quality of Life: How Viewing Shapes Everyday Experience. Robert Kubey and Mihaly Csikszentmihalyi. Lawrence Erlbaum Associates, 1990.

Television Dependence, Diagnosis, and Prevention. Robert W. Kubey in *Tuning in to Young Viewers: Social Science Perspectives on Television*. Edited by Tannis M. MacBeth. Sage, 1995.

"I'm Addicted to Television": The Personality, Imagination, and TV Watching Patterns of Self-Identified TV Addicts. Robert D. McIlwraith in *Journal of Broadcasting and Electronic Media*, Vol. 42, No. 3, pages 371–386; Summer 1998.

The Limited Capacity Model of Mediated Message Processing. Annie Lang in *Journal of Communication*, Vol. 50, No. 1, pages 46–70; March 2000.

Internet Use and Collegiate Academic Performance Decrements: Early Findings. Robert Kubey, Michael J. Lavin and John R. Barrows in *Journal of Communication*, Vol. 51, No. 2, pages 366–382; June 2001.

Discussion Questions

1. If it's true that communication technologies go beyond just helping us to communicate to actually changing the ways that we think and interact, in what ways do you think television has changed us? Do you see this change as positive or negative? Have computers and the Internet changed us in ways that are different from the changes imposed by television?
2. Kubey and Csikszentmihalyi state that "millions of people sense that they cannot readily control the amount of television they watch." Is this, or has this ever been, true of your viewing habits? Do you watch more or less television today than you did when you were younger? What factors affect how much television you watch on a given day?
3. In the study reported, researchers demonstrated that television viewing has addictive qualities. How would you summarize the results of their findings and the conclusions they have drawn?

 Supporting Activities

1. In a small group, determine what your average television viewing per day is (or, alternatively, calculate the average number of hours per week per individual). Among members of your group, what are the most popular programs?
2. Read the article "The Man Who Counts the Killings" about media researcher George Gerbner, whose in-depth study of television and movie content over three decades led to some influential conclusions: http://www.theatlantic.com/issues/97may/gerbner.htm.
3. Watch the movie *The Killing Screens* (1994; Media Education Foundation), which describes the work done by George Gerbner and colleagues at the Annenberg School for Communication at the University of Pennsylvania.
4. Take the "TV Addiction Quiz" online at: http://www.trashyourtv.com/survey. Is your score too high? Do a search for tips on how to break your TV addiction—you'll find lots of advice.

 Additional Resources

1. Learn more about the Nielsen rating service, which compiles the most authoritative data on television viewing, at their Web site: http://www.nielsenmedia.com/nc/portal/site/Public/.
2. For fun, watch the movie *The Truman Show*, a comedy and commentary on reality television. A movie with a similar theme is *EdTV*.
3. Read the book *Children and Television: Fifty Years of Research* (2007), edited by Norma Pecora, John P. Murray, and Ellen Ann Wartella. Mahwah, NJ: Lawrence Erlbaum Associates, Inc.

Get Me Rewrite!

In 2008, the Internet overtook newspapers as a leading source of news, second only to television. According to the Pew Research Center, 40 percent of adults cited the Internet as their primary source, and the percentage of Americans under 30 who did so was even higher (60 percent). These figures compare with television (70 percent, down slightly since 2000) and newspaper (35 percent, down from a high of 50 percent in 2003)[8] as sources of news. Author Michael Hirschorn provides a brief analysis of what this shift means for the newspaper industry, as well as for the rest of us. The rise of the Internet provides a classic case study of an existing technology (in this case, print media) being replaced and perhaps made obsolete by a new technology (think DVD versus VHS, for example).

Hirschorn uses the phrase "dead-tree media" to refer to newspapers, implying that the Internet is a more environmentally friendly medium than print. Yet the relative merits of the Internet are not so clear-cut. The server farms that store and route all of the terabytes of data traveling along the Internet are huge energy users; according to a report released by the EPA in 2007, server farms in the U.S. used about 61 billion kilowatt-hours of electricity each year, or about 1.5 percent of the nation's total electricity consumption—enough electricity to feed nearly 6 million households.[9] And the amount of energy used is growing.

Michael Hirschorn served as the Executive Vice President for Original Programming at VH1, and is a contributing editor at *The Atlantic Monthly*.

Get Me Rewrite!

by Michael Hirschorn

A modest proposal for reinventing newspapers for the digital age

If the twenty-first-century news business has a Zapruder film, it's an eight-minute Flash-based movie called *EPIC 2014*. For reasons that will soon become obvious, it has not received a lot of attention in the mainstream media (MSM in "Web-ese"), but has propagated quietly among news geeks since it was released online in late 2004. I first saw it last year at a "Whither the News" klatch at the Museum of Television and Radio in New York, where glum top editors from the major dailies and news networks gathered with sallow, unmistakably smug representatives of the digital world.

EPIC, which is composed almost entirely of simple text, graphics, and narration, launched the proceedings, and I think it would be fair to say that it rocked the world of the MSM mandarins. This was because, speaking from the prospective perch of 2014, it mapped out in calm detail exactly how the MSM would meet its doom. Eighteen months, and hundreds of millenarian prophesies later, *EPIC 2014* (and its updated version, *EPIC 2015*, released in 2005) already seems quaint, even a bit absurd. And its camp retro-futurism (Toffler by way of Epcot) is much funnier now that I'm watching it on my

Used with permission of The Atlantic Monthly, from *The Atlantic Monthly, Vol. 298, No. 5, 2006*; permission conveyed through Copyright Clearance Center, Inc.

computer and not with ashen-faced news execs. The movie, ostensibly a product of the fictional Museum of Media History, begins:

> In the year 2014, people have access to a breadth and depth of information unimaginable in an earlier age. Everyone contributes in some way. Everyone participates to create a living, breathing mediascape. However, the press, as you know it, has ceased to exist. The Fourth Estate's fortunes have waned. Twentieth-century news organizations are an afterthought, a lonely remnant of a not-too-distant past.

In 2008, we learn, Amazon and Google merged to form Googlezon, which allowed this most excellently named new conglomerate to use its "detailed knowledge of every user's social network, demographics, consumption habits, and interests to provide total customization of content and advertising." Six years later, Googlezon has launched the ultimate killer app: EPIC, or "Evolving Personalized Information Construct," a "system by which our sprawling, chaotic mediascape is filtered, ordered, and delivered." Under EPIC, anyone can create news, the users subscribe to independent editors based on their interests, and everyone is paid from the billions in advertising Googlezon sells across this vast mediaverse. The film ends with an Orwellian prediction—"EPIC is what we wanted, it is what we chose, and its commercial success preempted any discussions of media and democracy or journalistic ethics"—and a joke:

> Today in 2014, The New York Times has gone offline, in feeble protest to Googlezon's hegemony. The Times has become a print-only newsletter for the elite and the elderly.

As a piece of pop futurism, EPIC 2014 is both brilliant and brilliantly self-subverting (at once inevitable and preposterous). But what's remarkable is how many of its ten-years-out

predictions have already come true—if not materially, then de facto: the mass migration of everything to the Web, the explosion of blogging, the near-instant embrace of social media (see YouTube, MySpace, Facebook, Wikipedia), the growing sophistication of Google's AdWords and AdSense (the latter soon to be extended to user-customized RSS file format and other feeds), the TiVo-ization of television, and on and on. Instead of buying Amazon, Google bought YouTube, an Evolving Personalized Information Construct that didn't exist in 2004—GoogleTube instead of Googlezon. Thus does two-year-old futurism already seem hopelessly recherché.

The Times Company hasn't thrown in the towel, but it is inarguably *in extremis*. It plans to cut more than 1,000 jobs in the next two years, and its profits continue to fall along with its stock price; only the most purblind of optimists could deny that this is a harbinger of further miseries. A study released in late October by the Audit Bureau of Circulations showed that daily newspaper circulation had dropped about 2.8 percent over the previous year, while Sunday circ dropped 3.4 percent. More worrisome, the Project for Excellence in Journalism noted in its annual report on newspaper audiences, this slide is both persistent and accelerating:

> In 2004, the newspaper circulation losses that had been building slowly over 15 years began to accelerate. In 2005 things got roughly three times worse.

This would seem like the moment to get on my high horse and defend the daily newspaper, with its omnibus approach to everything from your town to the world, its high/low pastiche, its editorial ordering function that allows readers to weigh and sort multitudinous news inputs into a coherent worldview. But this is what I would call, to borrow a Wall Street term, *sell-side* logic. It flatters the people who have a vested interest in preserving the gatekeeper function and the economic margins provided by dead-tree media, or who see newspapers as a cultural bulwark against the barbarians. The barbarians, on the other hand, don't seem to care; they'd rather get the news they want, not the news the mandarins say is good for them.

And while it's true that fewer and fewer people are purchasing news*papers*, it's also almost certainly true that more and more people are reading *news*. This thanks to portals, newspaper Web sites, search engines, syndication feeds, and millions of blogs—a goodly percentage built on the hard labor of professional journalists, whose work the bloggers link to, praise, mock, and recombine with the hard labor of other professional journalists. Meanwhile, many of these blogs, produced on the cheap, have become profitable businesses that generate virtually no revenue for the journos who provide the constantly updated fodder. Feasting on the rotting corpse, if you will, while making polite chitchat.

For all the many things blogs do, their most disruptive application has been to provide an alternate portal into news, bypassing, or "disintermediating," the sorting traditionally done by newspaper editors and TV news producers. Drudge, Huffington, and their tens of thousands of less-popular competitors effectively offer alternate front pages targeted to audiences grouped by similar interests and affections. And because most newspapers (and their dot-coms) have so far been too proud to integrate the work of other publications, the smartest blogs can provide deeper and wider-ranging news experiences than any individual newspaper does. John Vinocur writes a great weekly column for the *International Herald Tribune*, but anyone who cares about Europe can tap hundreds of other sources in a matter of minutes.

Meanwhile, top reporters and columnists at major newspapers are realizing (or will realize

soon) that their fates are not necessarily tied to those of their employers. As portals and search engines and blogs increasingly allow readers to consume media without context or much branding, writers like Thomas Friedman will increasingly wonder what is the benefit of working for a newspaper—especially when the newspaper is burying his article behind a subscriber wall. It will require only a slight shift in the economic model for the Friedmans of the world to realize that they don't need the newspapers they work for; that they can go off and blog on their own, or form United Artists—like cooperatives to financially support their independent efforts.

So what should newspapers do? They could stop printing. It may happen eventually, or perhaps newsprint *will* find a financially sustainable market among the elite and elderly (or perhaps it will have a nostalgic vogue not unlike that of, say, heirloom tomatoes), but that's not what I'm getting at. The current Web-publishing model that newspapers are using isn't likely to become financially viable anytime soon. With few exceptions, the media businesses thriving on the Web either are low-cost blog-like efforts or follow a many-to-many model, in which communities create, share, and consume content. Publishing an article on the Web gets you one click; getting your users to write the article for you gets you a thousand clicks, and costs less to boot. In other words, turning your users into contributors increases their engagement with your site—each click is, after all, also an "ad impression"—while simultaneously generating more content that you in turn can sell to advertisers.

That, I'd venture, is how you start rethinking the newspaper business. Not only do you allow your reporters to blog; you make them the hubs of their own social networks, the maestros of their own wikis, the masters of their own many-to-many realms. To take but one example, Kelefa Sanneh is the pop-music critic for *The New York Times*. He is very likely the best music critic in the country, and certainly the best new *Times* music writer in years. Let's say that Sanneh creates his own community around the music he likes. Or *The Washington Post*'s Dana Priest creates an interactive online universe around her intelligence reportage. With editorial oversight only for libel and factual accuracy, Sanneh or Priest are allowed to do whatever they want on their sites (while their mother ships pour their resources into marketing them). In Sanneh's case, allow other people to write music reviews under the *Times*/Sanneh "brand." In Priest's case, turn the site into a clearinghouse for global intelligence information, rumors, conspiracy theories, and so forth (obligatory disclaimer: "The views of posters do not necessarily represent those of the Washington Post Company"). Go even further: incentivize the critics and reporters by allowing them to profit based on the popularity of their sites; make it worth their while to stick around.

Gaming this out in the most baldly capitalistic fashion, the papers then stand a chance of transforming one Sanneh review (one impression) into the organic back-and-forth of social media (1,000 impressions). This, in turn, would allow *The Times* (or *The Post*) to start achieving the scale, and the cost efficiency, that make online publishing profitable. In fact, there's a rough model for this emerging already: it's called About.com, a desperately unglamorous site that features hundreds of freelancers who can tailor their part of the site to the needs and desires of their users. *The Times* bought it last year for $410 million, and it is currently the company's primary growth area.

Playing this logic out, the next task would be uniting the Sanneh or Priest site to the *Times* or *Post* whole. You could essentially self-syndicate, sending your regular *Times* or *Post*

headlines to Sanneh's and Priest's sites, luring readers back to the mother ship while increasing the number of times each story is read. Indeed, the logic could be (and in some circles already is being) played out even further. What if you essentially exploded the central function of the newspaper and "microchunked" (to borrow a current term) the content, syndicating all of it to bloggers or other news sites in return for a share of any advertising revenue each site generates? The Associated Press has made this the centerpiece of its digital-age strategy: it recently signed a potentially breakthrough deal with Google, in which Google will pay the AP for access to its stories; and the AP has launched a broadband player that Web sites can use to access AP video content. Its content goes where the readers are, and the AP gets paid, no matter what. Remarkably, this most old-school of services is a lone bright spot in the MSM landscape. The AP's revenues have increased from more than $593 million in 2003 to more than $654 million in 2005; its digital revenue grew at a rate of 66 percent from 2004 to 2006. Of course, the AP has always been a syndicator, so no conceptual leap of faith (indeed no leap whatsoever) was required to move the business from analog to digital.

The Times, in particular, seems increasingly aware of the gargantuan leap of faith it will need to make to avoid the curse of *EPIC 2014*. If you go to the *Times* site, you can find a button on the top navigation bar for something called "My Times." The paper is promising "a new service that lets you create a personalized page with what you like best in *The New York Times* and your favorite sites and blogs from all over the Web." (If it works, I still intend to take credit.)

So what does this mean for newsprint? Counterintuitively, I'd argue that this disaggregation strategy could provide a renewed logic to the printed product. As news itself becomes more of an instantly available commodity, readers will crave an oasis of coherence and analysis (which is also why books, and magazines like *The Atlantic* and *The New Yorker*, are potentially brilliant counterprogramming for ADD'ed info burnouts). Online news, microchunked, consumed on the fly, is fast food; the newspaper, fed by its newly invigorated journalist-brands, is the sit-down meal. In this marginally more optimistic future history, the roles of print and digital are inverted. Original news—in the form of stories, postings, and community—begins online, while print offers an intelligent digest/redaction that readers—and not only the elite and elderly—can peruse at their leisure. You could even call it *Reader's Digest*.

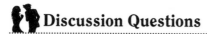

Discussion Questions

1. Where do you turn most regularly to get your news? Which source(s) do you trust the most, and why?
2. The use of blogs and other user-generated content on the Internet is a fast-growing development. What are the implications of this trend?
3. Increasingly, sites offer "customization of content" so that busy readers can see only the news and content that is of interest. What are the larger societal implications of this trend?
4. What, in summary, does Hirschorn see as a likely future role for print news?

Supporting Activities

1. Select a current event of national or international significance and find information about it from three different sources (make sure they are not all from the same news service such as the Associated Press). How does the reporting compare?
2. Watch and discuss the short video *EPIC 2014*, available on YouTube.
3. Read about the history of Wikipedia, arguably the most popular of user-generated information sites. Where to find it? Where else—on Wikipedia! http://en.wikipedia.org/wiki/History_of_Wikipedia.

Additional Resources

1. Visit the Pew Research Center's Project for Excellence in Journalism, which includes the annual "State of the News Media" report: http://www.journalism.org/.
2. For an interesting look at the intersection between news and surveillance, read the article "Having Won a Pulitzer for Exposing Data Mining, *Times* Now Eager to Do Its Own Data Mining" by Keach Hagey, available on *The Village Voice* (http://www.villagevoice.com/). Once at the site, type in the search phrase "data mining."

Endnotes

1. Burke, James. 1978. *Connections*. Boston: Little, Brown and Company. p. 105.
2. Abramson, Albert. 2003. *The History of Television, 1942–2000*. Jefferson, NC: McFarland.
3. McLuhan, Marshall. 1962. *The Gutenburg Galaxy: The Making of Typographic Man*. University of Toronto Press. p. 40.
4. Joinson, Adam N., and Paine, Carina B. 2007. Self disclosure, privacy and the Internet. In *The Oxford Handbook of Internet Psychology*. Oxford University Press. Chapter 16; pp. 237–251.
5. See, for example, the sampling of studies on the effects of media that have been sponsored by the Kaiser Family Foundation in recent years: http://www.kff.org/entmedia/tv.cfm.
6. Television Bureau of Advertising. 2009. *Media Trends Track*. Available: http://www.tvb.org/nav/build_frameset.asp?url=/rcentral/index.asp.
7. Comstock, George, and Scharrer, Erica. 2002. The use of television and other film related media. In Dorothy G. Singer and Jerome L. Singer (Eds.), *Handbook of Children and the Media*. Sage Publications. pp. 47–72.

8. Pew Research Center for People and the Press. 2008. *Internet overtakes newspapers as news outlet*. Available: http://people-press.org/report/479/internet-overtakes-newspapers-as-news-source.
9. Garber, Kent. 2009. Powering the information age. *U.S. News & World Report*. 146 (3): 46–48.

Perspectives on Biological and Medical Technologies

It is in the field of medical technologies, perhaps more than any other area of technological change, where we can readily agree that the tools and processes developed have been predominantly beneficial to humankind. Medicines such as antibiotics, pain relievers, and drug therapies; diagnostic tools such as MRIs, ultrasound, and even the lowly stethoscope; and life-extending machines such as oxygen tanks, life-support equipment, and kidney dialysis—all of these technologies and scientific breakthroughs have allowed humans to live longer and to survive accidents or illnesses that at one time would have meant certain death. Furthermore, emerging fields such as genetic therapy and advanced neuroscience mean that even intractable illnesses or infirmities may become a thing of the past.

Why, then, would anyone raise concerns about advances in medical technology? Because, as with every other category of technological development, we can identify both positive and negative outcomes. In other words, the effects of medical technologies, although substantially positive, have also created dilemmas related to costs, access, and the ways that medicine is practiced.

The debate about access to health care that has been waged in the U.S. for many years centers around one essential issue: a growing number of Americans cannot afford private health insurance and do not qualify for public assistance for medical care. As health-care costs continue to rise,[1] this means that millions of Americans simply cannot afford health care, preventative or otherwise.[2] Developments in new medical technologies have contributed greatly to the rising cost of health care, yet their availability has not necessarily translated into better overall care. Because health care spending represents one of the single biggest categories of spending in the U.S., we must come to terms with the need for a cost-benefit analysis of those expenditures.

In addition to access issues, some new medical technologies have fundamentally challenged our concept of what is meant by "health care." Should some things be ethically off limits? For example, should cloning technology be pursued to provide replacement organs, knowing that cloning can also potentially provide replacement people? Should a couple know the genetic particulars of their unborn child, perhaps causing them to face the difficult decision to abort? Even more controversial, should embryos harvested for in vitro fertilization be "graded" and the parents be allowed to choose the "best" one? These questions, by definition, cannot be resolved through technology, but rather must be answered by members of a society who are both technologically literate and ethically engaged.

Most medical procedures carry some risks. Generally speaking, the more intrusive the procedure, the greater the likelihood of complications, which in some cases turn out to be more damaging than the original condition. The statistics on iatrogenic (treatment-induced) illness and death are sobering. Estimates are that they account for up to 12 percent of office or hospital visits; for somewhere between 44,000 and 98,000 deaths annually in the U.S.; and that the total cost of medical errors of all types is between $37 billion and $50 billion annually.[3] Children and the elderly are at particular risk. This problem is not confined to the U.S. alone, and is certainly not always a result of high-tech medical care. Nevertheless, medical consumers are cautioned to actively oversee their health care, and to question the necessity of prescribed medicines and procedures.[4]

Another key point regarding the cultural effects of medical technologies is the way this approach to health care has influenced our relationships with our own health. There is less incentive to follow good judgment with regard to exposure to illness, nutrition, exercise, and adequate rest when we believe that there will be treatments for whatever ill health may result. For example, six in ten Americans are estimated to be overweight or obese, and as a nation we spend tens of billions of dollars annually on weight loss products and services. Much of this money is spent on a "never-ending quest for easy solutions" to the problem of being overweight.[5] A technological approach to medical care also may make us less likely to seek out and/or accept traditional or alternative treatments, some of which may be superior to riskier or more costly modern approaches.[6]

The Ideology of Machines: Medical Technology

Neil Postman provides a historical background to help explain the dominant philosophy of medical practice in the United States, which he characterizes as "aggressive" and much more interventionist than the health care typically provided in other developed nations.

There are two central impacts of medical technology on health care that are highlighted in this excerpt. First is that the focus of medical attention has shifted to the condition and away from the patient. Second, physicians have come to rely more on the information they receive from the medical technologies than they do on the patients themselves. These may seem like subtle points, but an examination of their effects can reveal fundamental changes in how we approach health care and, in fact, how we think about *health* in general. The important question that emerges, then, is whether we are better off from a quality of life standpoint. Does a highly technologized form of health care delivery lead to better overall health? Is this form of care more cost effective than other strategies? Finally, how can the system of health care delivery be improved to achieve greater levels of overall health, at sustainable levels of spending, for all citizens?

Neil Postman, who died in 2003, was a professor of media, culture, and communication, and was the author of numerous essays and books, including *Technopoly: The Surrender of Culture to Technology* (1993), *The Disappearance of Childhood* (1994), *Teaching as a Subversive Activity* (1971), and *Building a Bridge to the 18th Century: How the Past Can Improve Our Future* (2000).

The Ideology of Machines: Medical Technology

By Neil Postman

A few years ago, an enterprising company made available a machine called HAGOTH, of which it might be said, this was Technopoly's most ambitious hour. The machine cost $1,500, the bargain of the century, for it was able to reveal to its owner whether someone talking on the telephone was telling the truth. It did this by measuring the "stress content" of a human voice as indicated by its oscillations. You connected HAGOTH to your telephone and, in the course of conversation, asked your caller some key question, such as "Where did you go last Saturday night?" HAGOTH had sixteen lights—eight green and eight red—and when the caller replied, HAGOTH went to work. Red lights went on when there was much stress in the voice, green lights when there was little. As an advertisement for HAGOTH said, "Green indicates no stress, hence truthfulness." In other words, according to HAGOTH, it is not possible to speak the truth in a quivering voice or to lie in a steady one—an idea that would doubtless amuse Richard Nixon. At the very least, we must say that HAGOTH's definition of truthfulness was peculiar, but so precise and exquisitely technical as to command any bureaucrat's admiration. The same may be said of the definition of intelligence as expressed in a standard-brand intelligence test. In fact, an intelligence test works exactly like HAGOTH. You connect a pencil to the fingers of a young per-

From *Technopoly* by Neil Postman, copyright © 1992 by Neil Postman. Used by permission of Alfred A. Knopf, a division of Random House, Inc.

son and address some key questions to him or her; from the replies a computer can calculate exactly how much intelligence exists in the young person's brain.[1]

HAGOTH has mercifully disappeared from the market, for what reason I do not know. Perhaps it was sexist or culturally biased or, worse, could not measure oscillations accurately enough. When it comes to machinery, what Technopoly insists upon most is accuracy. The idea embedded in the machine is largely ignored, no matter how peculiar.

Though HAGOTH has disappeared, its idea survives—for example, in the machines called "lie detectors." In America, these are taken very seriously by police officers, lawyers, and corporate executives who ever more frequently insist that their employees be subjected to lie-detector tests. As for intelligence tests, they not only survive but flourish, and have been supplemented by vocational aptitude tests, creativity tests, mental-health tests, sexual-attraction tests, and even marital-compatibility tests. One would think that two people who have lived together for a number of years would have noticed for themselves whether they get along or not. But in Technopoly, these subjective forms of knowledge have no official status, and must be confirmed by tests administered by experts. Individual judgments, after all, are notoriously unreliable, filled with ambiguity and plagued by doubt, as Frederick W. Taylor warned. Tests and machines are not. Philosophers may agonize over the questions "What is truth?" "What is intelligence?" "What is the good life?" But in Technopoly there is no need for such intellectual struggle. Machines eliminate complexity, doubt, and ambiguity. They work swiftly, they are standardized, and they provide us with numbers that you can see and calculate with. They tell us that when eight green lights go on someone is speaking the truth. That is all there is to it. They tell us that a score of 136 means more

brains than a score of 104. This is Technopoly's version of magic.

What is significant about magic is that it directs our attention to the wrong place. And by doing so, evokes in us a sense of wonder rather than understanding. In Technopoly, we are surrounded by the wondrous effects of machines and are encouraged to ignore the ideas embedded in them. Which means we become blind to the ideological meaning of our technologies. In this chapter and the next, I should like to provide examples of how technology directs us to construe the world.

In considering here the ideological biases of medical technology, let us begin with a few relevant facts. Although the U.S. and England have equivalent life-expectancy rates, American doctors perform six times as many cardiac bypass operations per capita as English doctors do. American doctors perform more diagnostic tests than doctors do in France, Germany, or England. An American woman has two to three times the chance of having a hysterectomy as her counterpart in Europe; 60 percent of the hysterectomies performed in America are done on women under the age of forty-four. American doctors do more prostate surgery per capita than do doctors anywhere in Europe, and the United States leads the industrialized world in the rate of cesarean-section operations—50 to 200 percent higher than in most other countries. When American doctors decide to forgo surgery in favor of treatment by drugs, they give higher dosages than doctors elsewhere. They prescribe about twice as many antibiotics as do doctors in the United Kingdom and commonly prescribe antibiotics when bacteria are likely to be present, whereas European doctors tend to prescribe antibiotics only if they know that the infection is caused by bacteria *and* is also serious.[2] American doctors use far more X-rays per patient than do doctors in other countries. In one review of the extent of X-ray use, a radiologist discovered cases in which fifty to one hundred X-rays had been taken of a single patient when five would have been sufficient. Other surveys have shown that, for almost one-third of the patients, the X-ray could have been omitted or deferred on the basis of available clinical data.[3]

The rest of this chapter could easily be filled with similar statistics and findings. Perhaps American medical practice is best summarized by the following warning, given by Dr. David E. Rogers in a presidential address to the Association of American Physicians:

> As our interventions have become more searching, they have also become more costly and more hazardous. Thus, today it is not unusual to find a fragile elder who walked into the hospital, [and became] slightly confused, dehydrated, and somewhat the worse for wear on the third hospital day because his first 48 hours in the hospital were spent undergoing a staggering series of exhausting diagnostic studies in various laboratories or in the radiology suite.[4]

None of this is surprising to anyone familiar with American medicine, which is notorious for its characteristic "aggressiveness." The question is, why? There are three interrelated reasons, all relevant to the imposition of machinery. The first has to do with the American character, which I have previously discussed as being so congenial to the sovereignty of technology. In *Medicine and Culture*, Lynn Payer describes it in the following way:

> The once seemingly limitless lands gave rise to a spirit that anything was possible if only the natural environment . . . could be conquered. Disease could also be conquered, but only by aggressively ferreting it out diagnostically and just as aggressively treating it, preferably by taking something out rather than adding something to increase the resistance.[5]

To add substance to this claim, Ms. Payer quotes Oliver Wendell Holmes as saying, with his customary sarcasm:

> How could a people which has a revolution once in four years, which has contrived the Bowie Knife and the revolver . . . which insists in sending out yachts and horses and boys to outsail, outrun, outfight and checkmate all the rest of creation; how could such a people be content with any but "heroic" practice? What wonder that the stars and stripes wave over doses of ninety grams of sulphate of quinine and that the American eagle screams with delight to see three drachms [180 grains] of calomel given at a single mouthful?[26]

The spirit of attack mocked here by Holmes was given impetus even before the American Revolution by Dr. Benjamin Rush, perhaps the most influential medical man of his age. Rush believed that medicine had been hindered by doctors placing "undue reliance upon the powers of nature in curing disease," and specifically blamed Hippocrates and his tradition for this lapse. Rush had considerable success in curing patients of yellow fever by prescribing large quantities of mercury and performing purges and bloodletting. (His success was probably due to the fact that the patients either had mild cases of yellow fever or didn't have it at all.) In any event, Rush was particularly enthusiastic about bleeding patients, perhaps because he believed that the body contained about twenty-five pints of blood, which is more than twice the average actual amount. He advised other doctors to continue bleeding a patient until four-fifths of the body's blood was removed. Although Rush was not in attendance during George Washington's final days, Washington was bled seven times on the night he died, which, no doubt, had something to do with why he died. All of this occurred, mind you, 153 years after Harvey discovered that blood circulates throughout the body.

Putting aside the question of the available medical knowledge of the day, Rush was a powerful advocate of action—indeed, gave additional evidence of his aggressive nature by being one of the signers of the Declaration of Independence. He persuaded both doctors and patients that American diseases were tougher than European diseases and required tougher treatment. "Desperate diseases require desperate remedies" was a phrase repeated many times in American medical journals in the nineteenth century. The Americans, who considered European methods to be mild and passive—one might even say effeminate—met the challenge by eagerly succumbing to the influence of Rush: they accepted the imperatives to intervene, to mistrust nature, to use the most aggressive therapies available. The idea, as Ms. Payer suggests, was to conquer both a continent and the diseases its weather and poisonous flora and fauna inflicted.

So, from the outset, American medicine was attracted to new technologies. Far from being "neutral," technology was to be the weapon with which disease and illness would be vanquished. The weapons were not long in coming. The most significant of the early medical technologies was the stethoscope, invented (one might almost say discovered) by the French physician René-Théophile-Hyacinthe Laënnec in 1816. The circumstances surrounding the invention are worth mentioning.

Working at the Necker Hospital in Paris, Laënnec was examining a young woman with a puzzling heart disorder. He tried to use percussion and palpation (pressing the hand upon the body in hope of detecting internal abnormalities), but the patient's obesity made this ineffective. He next considered auscultation (placing his ear on the patient's chest to hear the heart beat), but the patient's youth and sex discouraged him. Laënnec then remembered that sound traveling through solid bodies is amplified. He rolled some sheets of paper into a cylin-

der, placed one end on the patient's chest and the other to his ear. *Voilà!* The sounds he heard were clear and distinct. "From this moment," he later wrote, "I imagined that the circumstance might furnish means for enabling us to ascertain the character, not only of the action of the heart, but of every species of sound produced by the motion of all the thoracic viscera." Laënnec worked to improve the instrument, eventually using a rounded piece of wood, and called it a "stethoscope," from the Greek words for "chest" and "I view."[7]

For all its simplicity, Laënnec's invention proved extraordinarily useful, particularly in the accuracy with which it helped to diagnose lung diseases like tuberculosis. Chest diseases of many kinds were no longer concealed: the physician with a stethoscope could, as it were, conduct an autopsy on the patient while the patient was still alive.

But it should not be supposed that all doctors or patients were enthusiastic about the instrument. Patients were often frightened at the sight of a stethoscope, assuming that its presence implied imminent surgery, since, at the time, only surgeons used instruments, not physicians. Doctors had several objections, ranging from the trivial to the significant. Among the trivial was the inconvenience of carrying the stethoscope, a problem some doctors solved by carrying it, crosswise, inside their top hats. This was not without its occasional embarrassments—an Edinburgh medical student was accused of possessing a dangerous weapon when his stethoscope fell out of his hat during a snowball fight. A somewhat less trivial objection raised by doctors was that if they used an instrument they would be mistaken for surgeons, who were then considered mere craftsmen. The distinction between physicians and surgeons was unmistakable then, and entirely favorable to physicians, whose intellect, knowledge, and insight were profoundly admired. It is perhaps to be expected that Oliver Wendell Holmes, professor of anatomy at Harvard and always a skeptic about aggressiveness in medicine, raised objections about the overzealous use of the stethoscope; he did so, in characteristic fashion, by writing a comic ballad, "The Stethoscope Song," in which a physician makes several false diagnoses because insects have nested in his stethoscope.

But a serious objection raised by physicians, and one which has resonated throughout the centuries of technological development in medicine, is that interposing an instrument between patient and doctor would transform the practice of medicine; the traditional methods of questioning patients, taking their reports seriously, and making careful observations of exterior symptoms would become increasingly irrelevant. Doctors would lose their ability to conduct skillful examinations and rely more on machinery than on their own experience and insight. In his detailed book *Medicine and the Reign of Technology*, Stanley Joel Reiser compares the effects of the stethoscope to the effects of the printing press on Western culture. The printed book, he argues, helped to create the detached and objective thinker. Similarly, the stethoscope

> *helped to create the objective physician, who could move away from involvement with the patient's experiences and sensations, to a more detached relation, less with the patient but more with the sounds from within the body. Undistracted by the motives and beliefs of the patient, the auscultator [another term for the stethoscope] could make a diagnosis from sounds that he alone heard emanating from body organs, sounds that he believed to be objective, bias-free representations of the disease process.[8]*

Here we have expressed two of the key *ideas* promoted by the stethoscope: Medicine is about

disease, not the patient. And, what the patient knows is untrustworthy; what the machine knows is reliable.

The stethoscope could not by itself have made such ideas stick, especially because of the resistance to them, even in America, by doctors whose training and relationship to their patients led them to oppose mechanical interpositions. But the ideas were amplified with each new instrument added to the doctor's arsenal: the ophthalmoscope (invented by Hermann von Helmholtz in 1850), which allowed doctors to see into the eye; the laryngoscope (designed by Johann Czermak, a Polish professor of physiology, in 1857), which allowed doctors to inspect the larynx and other parts of the throat, as well as the nose; and, of course, the X-ray (developed by Wilhelm Roentgen in 1895), which could penetrate most substances but not bones. "If the hand be held before the fluorescent screen," Roentgen wrote, "the shadow shows the bones darkly with only faint outlines of the surrounding tissues." Roentgen was able to reproduce this effect on photographic plates and make the first X-ray of a human being, his wife's hand.

By the turn of the century, medicine was well on its way to almost total reliance on technology, especially after the development of diagnostic laboratories and the discovery and use of antibiotics in the 1940s. Medical practice had entered a new stage. The first had been characterized by direct communication with the patient's experiences based on the patient's reports, and the doctor's questions and observations. The second was characterized by direct communication with patients' bodies through physical examination, including the use of carefully selected technologies. The stage we are now in is characterized by indirect communication with the patient's experience and body through technical machinery. In this stage, we see the emergence of specialists—for example, pathologists and radiologists—who interpret the meaning of technical information and have no connection whatsoever with the patient, only with tissue and photographs. It is to be expected that, as medical practice moved from one stage to another, doctors tended to lose the skills and insights that predominated in the previous stage. Reiser sums up what this means:

> So, without realizing what has happened, the physician in the last two centuries has gradually relinquished his unsatisfactory attachment to subjective evidence—what the patient says—only to substitute a devotion to technological evidence—what the machine says. He has thus exchanged one partial view of disease for another. As the physician makes greater use of the technology of diagnosis, he perceives his patient more and more indirectly through a screen of machines and specialists; he also relinquishes control over more and more of the diagnostic process. These circumstances tend to estrange him from his patient and from his own judgment.[9]

There is still another reason why the modern physician is estranged from his own judgment. To put it in the words of a doctor who remains skilled in examining his patients and in evaluating their histories: "Everyone who has a headache wants and expects a CAT scan." He went on to say that roughly six out of every ten CAT scans he orders are unnecessary, with no basis in the clinical evidence and the patient's reported experience and sensations. Why are they done? As a protection against malpractice suits. Which is to say, as medical practice has moved into the stage of total reliance on machine-generated information, so have the patients. Put simply, if a patient does not obtain relief from a doctor who has failed to use all the available technological resources, including drugs, the doctor is deemed vulnerable to the charge of incompetence. The situation is compounded by the fact that the personal relationship between doctor and patient now, in contrast to a century ago, has become so arid that the patient is not restrained by intimacy or empathy from appealing to the courts. Moreover, doctors are reimbursed by medical-insurance agencies on the basis of what they *do,* not on the amount of time they spend with patients. Nontechnological medicine is time-consuming. It is more profitable to do a CAT scan on a patient with a headache than to spend time getting information about his or her experiences and sensations.

What all this means is that even restrained and selective technological medicine becomes very difficult to do, economically undesirable, and possibly professionally catastrophic. The culture itself—its courts, its bureaucracies, its insurance system, the training of doctors, patients' expectations—is organized to support technological treatments. There are no longer methods of treating illness; there is only one method—the technological one. Medical competence is now defined by the quantity and variety of machinery brought to bear on disease.

As I remarked, three interrelated reasons converged to create this situation. The American character was biased toward an aggressive approach and was well prepared to accommodate medical technology; the nineteenth-century technocracies, obsessed with invention and imbued with the idea of progress, initiated a series of remarkable and wondrous inventions; and the culture reoriented itself to ensure that technological aggressiveness became the basis of medical practice. The ideas promoted by this domination of technology can be summed up as follows: Nature is an implacable enemy that can be subdued only by technical means; the problems created by technological solutions (doctors call these "side effects") can be solved only by the further application of technology (we all know the joke about an amazing new drug that cures nothing but has interesting side effects); medical practice must focus on disease, not on the patient (which is why it is possible to say that the operation or therapy was successful but the patient died); and information coming from the patient cannot be taken as seriously as information coming from a machine, from which it follows that a doctor's judgment, based on insight and experience, is less worthwhile than the calculations of his machinery.

Do these ideas lead to better medicine? In some respects, yes; in some respects, no. The answer tends to be "yes" when one considers how doctors now use lasers to remove cataracts quickly, painlessly, and safely; or how they can remove a gall-bladder by using a small television camera (a laparoscope) inserted through an equally small puncture in the abdomen to guide the surgeon's instruments to the diseased organ through still another small puncture, thus making it unnecessary to cut open the abdomen. Of course, those who are inclined to answer "no" to the question will ask how many laparoscopic cholecystectomies are performed *because* of the existence of the technology. This is a crucial point.

Consider the case of cesarean sections. Close to one out of every four Americans is now born by C-section. Through modern technology, American doctors can deliver babies who would have died otherwise. As Dr. Laurence Horowitz notes in *Taking Charge of Your Medical Fate,* ". . . the proper goal of C-sections is to improve the chances of babies at risk, and that goal has been achieved."[10] But C-sections are a surgical procedure, and when they are done routinely as an elective option, there is considerable and unnecessary danger; the chances of a woman's dying during a C-section delivery are two to four times greater than during a normal vaginal delivery. In other words, C-sections can and do save the lives of babies at risk, but when they are done for other reasons—for example, for the convenience of doctor or mother—they pose an unnecessary threat to health, and even life.

To take another example: a surgical procedure known as carotid endarterectomy is used to clean out clogged arteries, thus reducing the likelihood of stroke. In 1987, more than one hundred thousand Americans had this operation. It is now established that the risks involved in such surgery outweigh the risks of suffering a stroke. Horowitz again: "In other words, for certain categories of patients, the operation may actually kill more people than it saves."[11] To take still another example: about seventy-eight thousand people every year get cancer from medical and dental X-rays. In a single generation, it is estimated, radiation will induce 2.34 million cancers.[12]

Examples of this kind can be given with appalling ease. But in the interests of fairness the question about the value of technology in medicine is better phrased in the following way: Would American medicine be better were it not so totally reliant on the technological imperative? Here the answer is clearly, yes. We know, for example, from a Harvard Medical School study which focused on the year 1984 (no Orwellian reference intended), that in New York State alone there were thirty-six thousand cases of medical negligence, including seven thousand deaths related in some way to negligence. Although the study does not give figures on what kinds of negligence were found, the example is provided of doctors prescribing penicillin without asking the patients whether they were hypersensitive to the drug. We can assume that many of the deaths resulted not only from careless prescriptions and the doctors' ignorance of their patients' histories but also from unnecessary surgery. In other words, iatrogenics (treatment-induced illness) is now a major concern for the profession, and an even greater concern for the patient. Doctors themselves feel restricted and dominated by the requirement to use all available technology. And patients may be justifiably worried by reports that quite possibly close to 40 percent of the operations performed in America are not necessary. In *Health Shock,* Martin Weitz cites the calculations of Professor John McKinlay that more deaths are caused by surgery each year in the United States than the annual number of deaths during the wars in Korea and Vietnam. As early as 1974, a Senate investigation into unnecessary surgery reported that American doctors had performed 2.4 million unnecessary operations, causing 11,900 deaths and costing about $3.9 billion.[13] We also know that, in spite of advanced technology (quite possibly because of it), the infant-survival rate in the United States ranks only fourteenth in the world, and it is no exaggeration to say that American hospitals are commonly regarded as among the most dangerous places in the nation. It is also well documented that, wherever doctor strikes have occurred, the mortality rate declines.

There are, one may be sure, very few doctors who are satisfied with technology's stranglehold on medical practice. And there are far too many patients who have been its serious victims. What conclusions may we draw? First, technology is not a neutral element in the practice of medicine: doctors do not merely use technologies but are used by them. Second, technology creates its own imperatives and, at the same time, creates a wide-ranging social system to reinforce its imperatives. And third, technology changes the practice of medicine by redefining what doctors are, redirecting where they focus their attention, and reconceptualizing how they view their patients and illness.

Like some well-known diseases, the problems that have arisen as a result of the reign of technology came slowly and were barely perceptible at the start. As technology grew, so did the influence of drug companies and the manufacturers of medical instruments. As the training of doctors changed, so did the expectations of patients. As the increase in surgical procedures multiplied, so did the diagnoses which made them seem necessary. Through it all, the question of what was being *undone* had a low priority if it was asked at all. The Zeitgeist of the age placed such a question in a range somewhere between peevishness and irrelevance. In a growing Technopoly, there is no time or inclination to speak of technological debits.

Author Citations

1. I am not sure whether the company still exists, but by way of proving that it at least once did, here is the address of the HAGOTH Corporation as I once knew it: 85 NW Alder Place, Department C, Issaquah, Washington 98027.
2. All these facts and more may be found in: Payer, L. *Medicine and Culture: Varieties of Treatment in the United States, England, West Germany, and France.* New York: Penguin Books, 1988; or in: Inlander, C.B.; Levin, L.S.; and Weiner, E. *Medicine on Trial: The Appalling Story of Medical Ineptitude and the Arrogance that Overlooks It.* New York: Pantheon Books, 1988.
3. Reiser, S.J. *Medicine and the Reign of Technology.* Cambridge University Press, 1978, (p. 160).
4. Ibid., p. 161.
5. Payer, p. 127.
6. Quoted in ibid.
7. For a fascinating account of Laënnec's invention, see Reiser.
8. Ibid., p. 38.
9. Ibid., p. 230.
10. Horowitz, L.C., M.D. *Taking Charge of Your Medical Fate.* New York: Random House, 1988, (p. 31).
11. Ibid., p. 80.
12. Cited in Inlander et al., p. 106.
13. Cited in ibid., p. 113.

Discussion Questions

1. Postman writes that "technology is not a neutral element in the practice of medicine: doctors do not merely use technologies but are used by them." What does he mean by this? Do you agree or disagree with this statement? Provide specific examples to support your point of view.
2. Postman has characterized the way that medicine is practiced in the U.S. as being "aggressive." To what factors does he attribute this?
3. The author Stanley Joel Reiser, who compared the effects of the stethoscope to those of the printing press, is quoted in this excerpt. Although the two technologies are quite different, nevertheless the comparison is apt for the point this author wishes to make. What is his point?
4. The "reign of technology" in medicine, according to Postman, has led to systemic changes in the health care industry, including changes that have in essence provided incentives for doctors to make use of all of the medical technologies at their disposal. Identify two of these incentives.

 Supporting Activities

1. Compare U.S. health care statistics with those of other industrialized nations. Your search could include statistics such as total health care spending, infant mortality rates, incidence of specific surgical procedures per 1,000 people, and so on. If differences are observed (as they are likely to), to what do you think these differences can be attributed?
2. Read and discuss the article "The cost conundrum: What a Texas town can teach us about health care" by Atul Gawande in the June 1, 2009 issue of *The New Yorker* (available online at: http://www.newyorker.com/reporting/2009/06/01/090601fa_fact_gawande?yrail).
3. Visit "WebMD" (http://www.webmd.com/) and look up a condition that you or a close friend or family member has had in the past few years. Compare the information provided there with the information you were given by your physician or caregiver. Pay particular attention to the diagnostic tests recommended for the condition. Are Web-based information sites like this one helpful? Potentially dangerous? Support your response.

 Additional Resources

1. Learn more about Neil Postman, whose body of work presented a comprehensive critique of technological development and its cultural impacts. His biography and links to print, audio, and video resources can be found at: http://www.neilpostman.org/.
2. Visit the Human Genome Research Institute Web site (http://www.genome.gov/) to learn more about genome research and the future of DNA testing and therapy. See also the work that has been done on genomics through the U.S. Department of Energy (http://genomics.energy.gov/).
3. Learn how the U.S. National Institutes of Health treats "alternative" medicines at the National Center for Complementary and Alternative Medicine Web site (http://www.nccam.nih.gov/).

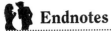 **Endnotes**

1.   According to the National Coalition on Health Care, "in 2008, total national health expenditures were expected to rise 6.9 percent—two times the rate of inflation. Total spending was $2.4 trillion in 2007, or $7900 per person. Total health care spending represented 17 percent of the gross domestic product (GDP). . . . U.S. health care spending is expected to increase at similar levels for the next decade, reaching $4.3 trillion in 2017, or 20 percent of GDP." (From *Health Insurance Costs*: http://www.nchc.org/facts/cost.shtml.)

2.   According to the Centers for Disease Control (CDC), over 43 million Americans were without any form of health insurance in 2006, and for more than half of these individuals cost was the primary factor (see: http://www.cdc.gov/Features/Uninsured/).

3.   Cook, Dawn M. 2001. Iatrogenic illness: A primer for nurses. *MedSurge Nursing.* 10 (3): 139–146.

4.   Moser, Marvin. The Patient as a Consumer. In Barry L. Zaret, Marvin Moser, and Lawrence S. Cohen (Eds.), *Yale University School of Medicine Heart Book*. New York: William Morrow and Company, Inc. pp. 359–362.

5.   Federal Trade Commission. 2002. *Weight loss advertising: An analysis of current trends*. Available: http://www.ftc.gov/bcp/reports/weightloss.pdf.

6.   See, for example, the World Health Organization's overview of traditional medicine at: http://www.who.int/topics/traditional_medicine/en/.

Perspectives on Military and Security Technologies

Military research and development has throughout history been a driver of technological change, representing what Alex Roland has called "the dark side of innovation."[1] The mandate of war (gaining the upper hand on one's enemy) has spurred the development of new and more sophisticated tools and strategies, at times resulting in diffusion and adoption of those technologies by the larger society. The Internet is a classic modern example of this phenomenon; it started as the Advanced Research Projects Agency Network (ARPANET), which enabled computer file sharing between agencies funded by the Department of Defense through the use of the world's first packet switching network, a technique that allows information packets to detour around damaged (in war, for example) lines of communication. The 20th Century saw the systematic expansion of military capability through the use of advanced materials, control systems, and transport mechanisms.

Military superiority comes at a high cost. U.S. spending on defense is more than the 45 next highest-spending countries in the world combined, and accounts for 48% of total military spending worldwide.[2] The total allocation for the Department of Defense for FY 2009 is estimated at over $651 billion,[3] not including supplemental budget requests. According to the American Association for the Advancement of

Science, total U.S. funding for defense-related R&D from all federal sources for FY 2009 is over $80 billion.[4] In a world of finite resources, financial and otherwise, money spent on the development of the tools of war is money not available to address other needs. Given the large percentage of the federal discretionary budget allocated to defense, a thorough examination of how that money is being spent is warranted.

The tools of war might be organized into two categories: those that are aimed at direct engagement (e.g., guns, bombs, tanks) and those that are aimed at gaining intelligence (e.g., tools of surveillance). Use of these tools is not necessarily confined to fighting the "enemy." When the definition of war changes, as it conspicuously has with the emergence of the 21st Century's War on Terror, the ways in which military tools are applied can cross boundaries into the civilian sphere. In addition to concerns about privacy due to expanded authority for surveillance as codified in the USA-PATRIOT Act and concerns about human rights related to civilian deaths in Afghanistan and Iraq and to the use of torture, there is cause for unease about the emergence of what Zbigniew Brzezinski has called "terror entrepreneurs." Brzezinski, former national security adviser to President Jimmy Carter, wrote a hard-hitting editorial in *The Washington Post* claiming that we have been "terrorized by the War on Terror,"

225

and stating that the culture of fear that has resulted from the war on terror has been reinforced by "security entrepreneurs [who are] . . . engaged in competition to justify their existence."[5] In other words, development of military technologies is just plain old good business for some members of the military industrial complex.[6]

If the larger goal of war is greater security, it could well be argued that the resources that are poured into tools whose sole purpose is warfare or surveillance would be better applied toward the infrastructure that supports society. This includes things like power plants, roads, bridges, schools, hospitals, and communication networks. Ensuring the reliability and *resilience* (resistance to failure) of these components of the national infrastructure might ultimately be the best defensive posture a country can take.

Technology Studies for Terrorists: A Short Course

In this excerpt, Langdon Winner applies to the subject of terrorism a theme that he has expressed in various ways over the past three decades. This theme, which was introduced in Section One, can be briefly summarized by saying that our technologies are inextricably linked with our social and political structures. The embodied design of any particular technology is reflective of the socio-political landscape from which it emerged, and in turn it influences the thoughts and actions of humans within that landscape.

Winner does little to hide his political leanings in this excerpt. Regardless of whether one agrees with his politics, the message sent by Winner is one that should not be ignored. Probably more than any social critic alive today, Winner has helped to shape the discourse about the impacts of technology. He has always challenged claims that technology is neutral, instead insisting that technologies can enable and, indeed, even create new ways of thinking about the world and new value systems. By extension, he also advocates for new approaches in which we design our technological systems to reflect the social and political outcomes we desire.

To that end, Winner examines the U.S. response to the attacks of September 11, 2001, and suggests that the responses we have chosen may have in reality done very little to deflect future terrorist attacks. He applies theories about complex technological systems to identify what may be a more effective response for the long term, and one that is more consistent with our democratic ideals. In essence, this approach would focus on identifying our areas of greatest vulnerability—technological systems like transportation or energy production and transmission—and re-engineering them in such a way that any disruptions would not be catastrophic (i.e., would not shut the entire system down).

Langdon Winner is the Thomas Phelan Chair of Humanities and Social Sciences at Rensselaer Polytechnic Institute, where he teaches in the Department of Science and Technology Studies. He is also Director of Rensselaer's Center for Cultural Design. Winner, who has written widely on the social and political issues surrounding technology, is perhaps best known for his books *Autonomous Technology: Technics Out-of-Control as a Theme in Political Thought* (1977) and *The Whale and the Reactor: A Search for Limits in an Age of High Technology* (1986).

Technology Studies for Terrorists
A Short Course

By Langdon Winner

During the weeks that followed the terrorist attacks of September 11, 2001, I devoured dozens of newspapers, magazines, and online documents trying to gain a better understanding of the origins and significance of those awful events. From the stack of material, one item leaped out. An essay by political scientist Thomas Homer-Dixon in *Foreign Policy* noted, "Langdon Winner, a theorist of politics and technology, provides the first rule of modern terrorism: 'Find the critical but non-redundant parts of the system and sabotage . . . them according to your purposes.'"[1]

Used with permission of Taylor & Francis, LLC, from *Surveillance and Security: Technological Politics and Power in Everyday Life* by Langdon Winner, 2006; permission conveyed through Copyright Clearance Center, Inc.

Oh wonderful, I thought to myself, this is just what I need—to be known as the person who formulated the first rule of modern terrorism. I imagined the FBI knocking at my door: "Mr. Winner, we'd like you to come down the office to answer a few questions." The musings about sabotage that Homer-Dixon had unearthed came from a chapter I'd written thirty years earlier, a contribution to a book on an apparently drab theme—organized social complexity.[2] As I worked on the piece back then, it occurred to me that knowledge about inner workings of technological systems could, perversely, be used by system wreckers. The context was America in the early 1970s, when a rash of bombings spread across the United States, blasts targeted at banks and other public buildings in twisted protest of the war in Vietnam. My thoughts about sabotage occurred as I was moving from a background in classical political theory to ponder the social theories of technology. Both bodies of thought emphasize the building and maintenance of frameworks of order in human affairs. But, I wondered, couldn't the same understandings be applied to projects of destruction? Over the years I'd forgotten that the question had ever crossed my mind.

Following Homer-Dixon's prompt, the topic reemerged while I struggled with my misgivings about the nation's response to 9/11. As someone who lives just two hours from the site of the World Trade Center and who spends a good amount of time in New York City, I experienced the catastrophe with feelings of shock, outrage, and sadness shared by millions around the globe. During the hours and days that followed, politicians and pundits gravely intoned, "This is the day everything changed." But what exactly was it that had changed? For the nation's political leaders and much of the American populace as well, there seemed to be but one answer. September 11, 2001, was as a day of infamy equivalent to Pearl Harbor, a provocation that propelled the nation into a life-and-death struggle called "the war on terror." Required now was a massive military campaign to punish the perpetrators wherever they could be found, thus defending the nation from any further terrorist threat.

The metaphor of "war" has gained currency in American public discourse in a wide range of contexts during the past forty years. In the 1960s President Lyndon Johnson declared "war on poverty." In the 1970s President Nixon boldly declared "war on crime." Nixon and subsequent presidents moved on to declare an aggressive "war on drugs." Not to be outdone, President Jimmy Carter argued that the energy crisis of the 1970s required the nation to eliminate its dependence on foreign sources of oil, an initiative that Carter called "the moral equivalent of war."

Among these so-called wars is a crucial similarity. They have all been lost or at least not decided in a way that even remotely resembles victory. Poverty and crime still loom as chronic problems in American life, with scant signs of victory over their sources or the damage they cause. Although it is extremely violent and costly, the war on drugs has not significantly reduced drug use in the country or the social decay that accompanies it. Despite much political hand-wringing and well-meaning research programs on renewable energy, the nation's dependency on foreign oil is now greater than in the late 1970s. By now these incessant calls to war reflect the torpor of our political speech. But even to address that fact would probably require yet another declaration of war: "My fellow Americans, the crisis before us demands a bold and decisive response—the war on metaphorical exhaustion!"

It is true that the 9/11 attacks by al Qaeda were acts of war in the most direct, compelling sense. Yet I wondered then, as I do now, if conceiving our situation post-9/11 as a state of war with all that implies is the most appropriate and productive response. Could it be that our leaders have launched yet another ambiguously defined "war" clouded with uncertainty and motivated by the quest for domestic political advantage?

America's lockstep march into the "war on terror" has been extremely costly, especially as it involves the conquest and occupation of Iraq. Hundreds of billions of tax dollars squandered, thousands of American soldiers killed and wounded, mounting evidence of torture in U.S. detention centers in Iraq and elsewhere, rampant corruption among contractors and quislings in Iraq, and a sharp decline in the reputation of the country as a force for peace, international law, and human rights around the globe all stem from the hasty, ill-conceived consensus that formed after 9/11. It seems altogether likely that the nation's bellicose response has spawned many more terrorists than had existed previously, a fact that could vex the United States, Europe, and other countries for decades to come. Even more disturbing (but seldom emphasized) are the tens of thousands of deaths and injuries of innocent Iraqi civilians in this conflict, casualties that are not simply "collateral damage" but more accurately war crimes committed in pursuit of a hasty, vengeful, ill-considered policy.

Among the costs at home are ones directly related to the theme of this book, increasing surveillance in social life. Justified by the supposed need to discover and eliminate covert terrorist plots such as those hatched by Mohammed Atta and his associates, new varieties of police power have been devised and implemented. Antiterrorist legislation and the use of technologies to monitor the activities of citizens have vastly expanded possibilities for the government to shadow people's daily comings and goings while diminishing legal and practical

resistance to such spying. Among the casualties of the ongoing "war" in this setting are some of our cherished rights and liberties.

At this writing, four years after the attacks, it is increasingly clear that opportunism has been a crucial feature of post-9/11 politics. The neoconservative clique around President George W. Bush quickly adapted the fears and passions of the moment to justify their long-standing plans for renewed militarization at home and bellicose policies abroad, all in the name of asserting the United States as the world's "lone superpower." This has resulted in an extraordinary reallocation of public funds toward the Pentagon and projects in "homeland security" while starving public spending on social needs. Yet so powerful has been the metaphor, that even months after 9/11 there was essentially no debate about whether the crisis confronting the nation was best, or even adequately, defined as another war. There has been little or no discussion about possible alternate conceptions and strategies. Our elected officials, journalists, and media pundits, as well as our scientists and scholars in universities and think tanks, have been notably silent on the matter. Is the cause a mistaken sense of patriotism, a desperate hope for national unity, an abject failure of imagination, or something else? Whatever the case, few Americans were prepared to ask the following questions: What is our predicament really? Which strategies now make sense? And shouldn't there be widespread public deliberation about what should be done?

Given the heavy costs, foreign and domestic, incurred in the "war on terror," it seems imperative to reconsider our situation and renew the search for alternatives. The article that fingered me as the author of the "first rule of modern terrorism" gave rise to a question: Is there anything in my field of research and teaching—the field of technology studies (broadly construed)—that might contribute a fresh understanding of the terrible problems that loom before us? Upon reflection, there are several themes in social and political studies of technology that could be usefully brought to bear on problems of terrorism. I briefly comment on four of them here: the interweaving of technology and society, the phenomenon of technological style, the dynamics of risky technology and "normal accidents," and the social construction of technological systems.

Interweaving

A common insight has emerged from the historians, sociologists, anthropologists, political scientists, and philosophers who have studied the social dimensions of technology in recent years. There is growing awareness that technological devices, systems, and routines are thoroughly interwoven with the structures and processes of social and political life. Conceptions of this kind have largely replaced the view in earlier scholarship that one could identify a clear, obvious boundary between technology on one hand and society on the other.[3]

From my own standpoint, this insight is crucial for understanding modern political society. As people design technologies, negotiate their features, and introduce them into the broader realm of human affairs, they are engaged in something far more profound than improving material well-being, for technological devices and systems reflect and, indeed, materially and institutionally embody forms of social and political life. Technical things bear responsibilities, express commitments, and assume roles as agents in the realm of human relationships. In an era in which computerized devices have become important intermediaries in many parts of everyday life, an awareness of the social and political qualities of technical objects has become increasingly common.

Studies of interweaving of this kind are often directed at the effects of new technological developments within political culture. For example, in the United States in recent years we have seen the rise of interconnected patterns in architecture, transportation, information, and communications packaged as "gated communities." People live in clusters of buildings, behind walls, using electronic passkeys to enter and leave, driving to work and back, watching endless hours of video on elaborate home entertainment systems. These costly structures respond to concerns for personal security that are rife in America today. But this rapidly spreading sociotechnical pattern has been criticized as an unfortunate development in America, for it realizes a return of segregation and the dismantling of community as a living, face-to-face experience (see Blakely and Snyder 1997).

By the same token, we can employ lessons about interweaving to identify materially embodied social reforms that merit praise for their political effects. For example, during the past thirty years, an array of changes in technology and architecture have made it possible for millions of people with disabilities—including paraplegics and quadriplegics—to enter domains of social life where they had previously been excluded, an overwhelmingly positive, democratic development (Shapiro 1993).

From this vantage point the horrifying events of 9/11 present phenomena of interweaving and new challenges for political society. The acts of terrorism caused a rupture within the complex interconnection of technical systems and political culture, for the consequences of the attacks were not merely in the lives lost, people injured, and material structures destroyed; they soon extended crucially and directly to ramifications in the country's social and political order. Indeed, the institutional responses to 9/11 have caused far more damage than the initial attack did. Many of these responses involved the kinds of surveillance mentioned earlier, passage of several draconian laws, and the creation of a wide range of antiterrorist policies and practices. Most notorious of these is a law passed shortly after the 9/11 attack: "Uniting and Strengthening America by Providing Appropriate Tools Required to Intercept and Obstruct Terrorism," or USA PATRIOT Act in its acronym. Federal initiatives of this kind are echoed in a host of antiterrorist laws passed at the state level, all of which extend government mechanisms for the routine monitoring of everyday life in airports, schools, offices, libraries, banks, online communications, and the like. Not to be outdone, the Pentagon has expanded its secretive Counter-intelligence Field Activity, using "leading edge information technologies and data harvesting" to determine who within the U.S. population is a security threat (Pincus 2005).

Groups concerned about the erosion of rights and liberties—the American Civil Liberties Union, the Electronic Privacy Information Center, and the American Library Association, among others—fear that government snooping far exceeds any legitimate concern to prevent criminal, terrorist conspiracies. One concern centers on the 30,000 "national security letters" issued by the FBI in recent years to obtain a wide range of information about citizens whose innocuous communications make them suspect, triggering a comprehensive, clandestine search. As reported in the *Washington Post*:

> *Senior FBI officials acknowledged in interviews that the proliferation of national security letters results primarily from the bureau's new authority to collect intimate facts about people who are not suspected of any wrongdoing. Criticized for failure to detect the Sept. 11 plot, the bureau now casts a much wider net, using national security letters to generate leads as well as to pursue them. Casual or unwitting contact*

> *with a suspect—a single telephone call, for example—may attract the attention of investigators and subject a person to scrutiny about which he never learns. (Gellman 2005)*

Amid the smoking wreckage of the World Trade Center one finds other debris, including significant parts of the U.S. Constitution, including the fourth and sixth amendments of the Bill of Rights. Traditional protections of civil liberties have been badly weakened by Congressional legislation, overshadowed by the expanding powers of the executive branch and undermined by the virtually unlimited scope of information technologies used for surveillance. Within the new security apparatus of "homeland security," individuals are defined not as citizens but as suspects.

Developments of this kind suggest an updated version of Winner's first rule of modern terrorism: find the nonredundant parts of the system that also have great symbolic significance and strike there. This will not only bring the greatest damage to material infrastructures but produce generalized damage to the country's political order as well. In this light, what the response to 9/11 revealed, unfortunately, is an astonishing *lack of resilience* in the fundamental techno-political institutions of American society. Scholars in the field of technology studies could well have predicted this. Among other results, the thorough, complex interweaving of large-scale technical systems and political society leaves us vulnerable, not only in a physical sense but in cultural and political ways as well.

Technological Style

Another idea in contemporary technology studies relevant to our predicament is the theme of technological style. Historians of technology have tried to explain how it is that societies in different historical periods prefer different technical forms (see Staudenmaier 1985; T.P. Hughes 1983). It appears that making and using technology sometimes reflect an overall pattern or style in contrast to other technical possibilities available in principle. In his cultural history of technology *Leonardo to the Internet,* Tom Misa argues that political conditions often determine which technological style is chosen in a particular historical setting. As illustration he shows how some of the most prominent technical accomplishments of fifteenth- and sixteenth-century Europe expressed a distinctive conception of power and authority, one that favored the grandeur of the patron over the prosperity of the general populace. "Characteristically," he observes, "Leonardo and his fellow Renaissance-era technologists had surprisingly little to do with improving industry or making money in the way we typically think of technology today. Instead, Renaissance-era courts commissioned them for numerous technical projects of city-building, courtly entertainment, and dynastic display, and for the means of war" (Misa 2004: 3).

From this vantage point we can ask the following question: What aspects of contemporary technological style are called into question by prospects of terrorism? One element that seems especially significant is the style of openness and trust expressed in many of the technological systems on which modern life depends. In democratic societies where freedom and equality are key ideals, a long-standing, largely unstated assumption has been that the linkages that hold together systems in energy, communications, transportation, water supply, food supply, and the like could be left essentially open and unprotected. People trust crucial technical systems of this kind to operate efficiently; in turn, ordinary people are trusted not to interfere with or damage the apparatus. Thus, even the structures of relatively hazardous techno-

logical systems, plants that process toxic chemicals, for example, have long presupposed qualities of openness that could make them susceptible to attack. We generally assume that no one would be so malicious or foolish to destroy technologies on which their well-being depends.[4]

For the September 11 terrorists, the American technological style based on openness and trust provided a golden opportunity. For example, in retrospect the airport gate checks were far too trusting; no one tried to confiscate the box cutters that Atta and his men carried as weapons. For a time even after the planes had been hijacked, the trust among the passengers continued. The terrorists reassured the passengers that, as in hijackings of the past, they would eventually land and be set free.

Recognition that sociotechnical arrangements based on trust are also sources of insecurity bought a widespread, highly costly refurbishing of many technological devices and systems. This is clearly visible at airports, where the gate check has become a time-consuming, intrusive exercise orchestrated by guards who guide passengers through a variety of electronic and electromechanical stages. In countless sociotechnical settings, as fear has replaced trust, institutions have retooled in ways that replace openness with closure. What used to be readily available information about the structure and workings of large-scale systems—water systems, transit systems, energy systems, and the like—is now restricted or secret. More and more of infrastructure and public architecture are placed behind fences and concrete barriers. The new technological style seems to be, "You can't be too careful."

The creation of an increasingly closed technological style in post-9/11 sociotechnical arrangements also has ramifications for habits of mind in society at large. An obsession with security fuels the rising popularity of what are called "conservative" ways of thinking—fear and loathing expressed in a variety of socially divisive ways, including suspicion of immigrants, protests against teaching the theory of evolution in the schools, and open contempt of unconventional political ideas, for example, gay rights. Where democratic, live-and-let-live tolerance once prevailed, there is often a bellicose insistence in traditional cultural norms as the identifying signs of public virtue. Whether the al Qaeda terrorists intended to achieve these effects, a clear consequence of 9/11 has been an abrupt closure of intellectual horizons and policy perspectives common in American public life. In a thoroughly interwoven sociotechnical world, a shift in technological style involves profound changes in the ways people think about social life in general.

Risky Technologies

Of all the topics explored in the literature of technology studies, the one with most obvious relevance for understanding terrorist attacks is the large body of research on risk and risky technologies. Scholars in psychology, philosophy, sociology, management, political science, and engineering have all contributed to our knowledge here, focusing on recurring risks associated with technology in everyday life but also on accidents in large-scale systems.[5] What has been learned from research on risk that might be useful in this context?

One might begin by rejecting the war metaphor and equivalent terms altogether. Rather than define the possibility of terrorist attack as something that would immediately require a military response, one might think about it as a particular category of risk that challenges us to study which human-machine systems harbor dangerous malfunctions and what might be done to prevent them from being realized as catastrophes. One could study these possibili-

ties, analyze their dynamics, and propose serviceable remedies.

A common finding in studies of risk that might be helpful is that people find it very difficult to judge the likelihood of the real dangers they face and how such dangers arise. The hazards we imagine to be most likely and consequential are often not ones that square with statistical probabilities of the dangers that await us. For example, in the United States about 40,000 people die in car accidents each year, but cars are still manufactured and driven in ways that are remarkably unsafe. By comparison, 3,011 people died in the 9/11 attack. We now agonize endlessly about the 3,011 but take the 40,000 for granted.

Yes, it is unseemly to compare levels of death. One death is always too many. But it may be that looking at terrorist attacks from the standpoint of technological risk would be more reasonable and more fruitful than defining terror as an ill-defined, perpetual war waged in numerous locations around the globe. Social analysis of risk, a well-developed field of research, could make it possible to distinguish between possibilities for terrorism that are greatly worrisome and those that are less so. It might help us compare and judge remedies for terrorism that focus on truly urgent yet manageable problems as compared to measures that are of little use and may even make matters worse.

Thus, how can we judge the level of risk presented by Muslim and Middle Eastern immigrants studying and working in the United States—the kinds of people we are now deporting by the hundreds? Many immigrants of this description are peaceful, productive persons, not dangerous in the least. Why are they identified as especially dangerous? Is religion or country of national origin a good predictor of harmful intentions? By comparison, the dangers contained within technological systems crucial to our way of life—the international containerized cargo system, for example—seem to pose a much greater threat. Why we are we more vigilant about supposedly dangerous immigrant groups than we are with familiar, possibly vulnerable, complex systems? The literature on risk assessment (Mary Douglas's *Purity and Danger* is a classic in this genre) notes that cultural meanings inform our sense of who or what is dangerous, judgments that are sometimes far from reasonable (Douglas 1966). At a time in which the presence of immigrants is a gnawing issue in the United States, it is perhaps not surprising to find ideas about dangers from terrorism centered on them rather than on the refinery down the road that processes tons of toxic substances each week using outdated equipment.

The same kinds of questions can be asked about other conceptions and measures now applied in antiterrorist surveillance. In the United States, one option government officials can employ is to obtain records of what persons are reading from libraries and bookshops. Librarians must release the list of books a patron has checked out if the FBI requests it; they break the law if they refuse or if they tell anyone about the search. As in the McCarthy period of the 1950s, special danger is now attributed to the strange ideas and information Americans get from the books they read. But compared to other possible dangers in the age of terrorism, how significant are library books? If someone checks out a copy of the Qur'an, will he or she be flagged as suspicious?

The body of research on risky technology that may be most relevant to understanding possibilities of terrorism concerns the operation of large-scale technical systems. Of special relevance is the research of sociologist Charles Perrow on what he terms "normal accidents." Looking at a variety of cases—marine collisions, airline traffic control, accidents in chemical and nuclear plants, and others—Perrow identifies

patterns of events that often lead to system failures, the worst of which become catastrophes with significant loss of life and property. Typically what happens is that two or more failures occur with results that interact in surprising ways. For example, a failure in a key technical component is compounded by operator error, amplified by a breakdown in communications. He explains:

> *Occasionally . . . two or more failures, none of them devastating in themselves in isolation, come together in unexpected ways and defeat the safety devices—the definition of a "normal accident" or system accident. If the system is also tightly coupled, these failures can cascade faster than any safety device or operator can cope with them, or they can even be incomprehensible to those responsible for doing the coping. If the accident brings down a significant part of the system, and the system has catastrophic potential, we will have a catastrophe.* (Perrow 1999: 356–57)

Although Perrow's studies do not pay much attention to catastrophes caused by acts of terrorism, his analysis and recommendations can easily be applied in this context. The initial cause of calamity is no longer a component failure or operator error but a deliberate, malicious act. Nevertheless, the chain of events may proceed in ways his theory anticipates. Much of the 9/11 Commission Report released in the summer of 2004 reads like an extended description of a normal accident in terrorist mode. The ability of the hijackers to get through security screening, the communications mix-ups among federal agencies, and the failure of U.S. air defense to intercept the aircraft all follow the typical pattern of a Perrowian calamity. In one passage of this kind, the report observes, "Existing protocols on 9/11 were unsuited in every respect for an attack in which hijacked planes were used as weapons. . . . A shootdown authorization was not communicated to the NORAD air defense sector until 28 minutes after United 93 has crashed in Pennsylvania. Planes were scrambled, but ineffectively, as they did not know where to go or what targets they were to intercept."[6]

The commission's account of what happened after the planes hit the World Trade Center also corresponds closely to what happens in catastrophic "normal accidents." Firemen and police could not communicate adequately for a variety of reasons, including channel overload. A repeater system in the World Trade Center that could have greatly improved communications had two buttons; someone switched on one of them but not the other. First responders on the scene had a less accurate overview of their predicament than people watching the disaster on CNN.

Terrorists could learn a great deal reading the literature on large-scale technical systems and the 9/11 report, namely, how it is possible to out-maneuver, disrupt, and destroy highly costly, highly sophisticated systems of contemporary technology by using clever planning and simple tools. It is likely that the more studious of them know much of this already. By the same token, it is possible to read such studies with the purpose of finding ways to anticipate and prevent similar calamities in the future. Decades of research and analysis on risky technologies have much to offer our understanding of the circumstances in which acts of terrorism could occur. Who among serious students of these situations will pass the final exam—wrongdoers seeking to achieve maximum damage or those people hoping to frustrate any such malign intentions?

Social Construction

The final range of topics in contemporary technology studies I want to emphasize is the social construction of technology. Constructivist research is especially good at mapping the complex negotiations that go into the creation of technical artifacts and systems. Donald MacKenzie's *Inventing Accuracy* offers an excellent case study of this kind, following an extensive collection of individuals, groups, and institutions involved in deciding which guidance system would control the flight of U.S. ballistic missiles (MacKenzie 1990). Rather than identify one inventor or handful of innovators, we should chart the contributions of numerous actors involved in shaping technical outcomes.

In this vein, the sports utility vehicle, the wildly popular but highly problematic vehicle, emerged not as a simple response to market pressure but within a complex set of initiatives and negotiations lasting several decades, ones that involved dozens of groups with seemingly different interests—manufacturers, government officials, labor unions, trade associations, environmentalists, and consumers among the most prominent. The design of the sports utility vehicle was not a single, isolated accomplishment. It was the product of complex deliberations, deals, and compromises (Bradsher 2002).

As applied to social processes of technological design, there are often a variety of constituent groups that influence the eventual outcome. Although it may seem odd, from today's perspective terrorists can be seen as one among many constituencies with needs and problems that are somehow communicated and fed into the mix of social construction. Of course, it may be difficult to determine in advance of their "use" of technological systems exactly what their input entails. They don't (as far as we know) come to focus group meetings or attend design charrettes to make their preferences known. Nevertheless, terrorist influence on the processes of social construction can be formidable. Especially after 9/11, their silent presence must be taken into account by those who hope to derail their murderous interventions.

A chapter in terrorist social construction of technology surfaced in preparations to build the Freedom Tower in New York, a 1,776-foot-tall symbolic skyscraper designed by architect Daniel Liebeskind as a replacement for the World Trade Center and tribute to the 9/11 victims. In May 2005, very late in the process, someone in the New York City police department called attention to the fact that in its existing design, the edifice was open to a blast from a truck bomb parked on the city's West Side highway.[7] Heeding the warning, planners delayed construction of the building while the blueprints were modified to prevent an attack from that angle. Thus, as silent, shadow participants, imaginary terrorists had a substantial influence on the design of a monumental work of architecture, in fact the very tower meant to defy terrorist schemes in perpetuity.

How could one make such unseen terrorist presence a continuing contribution to technology shaping in the post-9/11 world? What kinds of research, development, and testing are suited to the challenge? One ingenious approach surfaced in October 2003, when Nathaniel Heatwole, a student at Guilford College in Greensboro, North Carolina, revealed that over a period of months, he had carried box cutters and other dangerous devices onto commercial airliners. His aim, he explained later, was to show the inadequacies of newly installed airline security systems. In the end, Heatwole left some of his implements on two airplanes and sent the authorities an e-mail indicating where the items could be found. He was promptly arrested and charged with several felonies.[8] It is fortunate for Heatwole that the judge in the case recognized that he was not a dangerous criminal and sentenced him to a $500 fine and 100 hours of community service.[9]

Following Heatwole's example, one might propose funding groups of covert surrogate terrorists whose work it would be to find ways to breach security arrangements and disrupt large-scale technological systems, going just far enough to demonstrate conclusively what is possible in principle and then stopping any further penetration. Rather than throw them in jail, one could award them graduate fellowships and support them in novel dissertation projects. If nothing else, this could give a new surge of energy to research on the social construction of technology, a field that, for all its virtues, has become a little dull and repetitive in its range of application.

Conclusion

This brief exploration suggests some ways in which social studies of technology might be applied to the realm of terrorism and counterterrorism. My comments about the interweaving of society and technology, technological style, the analysis of risk technologies, and the social construction and deconstruction of technology may even point to more fruitful strategies than those commonly employed in today's "war" on terror. It is possible to achieve a broader and deeper understanding of the specific circumstances of our vulnerability and to map more sensible and productive paths of actions. This idea is not new with me or even especially radical. An emphasis of this kind has emerged within a series of studies by think tanks and blue ribbon panels, most notably the 9/11 Commission, that have noted how ill prepared the United States remains in confronting the real prospects of terrorist attacks on its own soil.[10] Evidently, President George W. Bush and his administration have been so fixed on the strategy of "taking the battle to the enemy" overseas that more urgent locations of vulnerability, including ones that are obviously the most crucial—badly controlled stockpiles of nuclear materials in the former Soviet Union and elsewhere—have been woefully neglected. As the

Harvard Project on Managing the Atom concluded in May 2005, "Unfortunately, the on-the-ground progress in securing, consolidating and eliminating nuclear stockpiles in the last year remained slow, when compared to the urgency of the threat" (Brunn and Wier 2005: v).

Closer to home, the nation has been notoriously slow and ineffective in its response to the vulnerability of containerized cargo systems. Each month millions of crates are brought in, which are poorly scanned for hazardous materials, including nuclear bombs and dirty bombs—crates that are loosely monitored in their movement from origin to destination. The same can be said of the vulnerability of the nation's 15,000 chemical plants, built under now dubious assumptions of openness and trust.

As we own up to the nation's lax, ill-focused, wildly bellicose response to the real problems unearthed by 9/11, the literature of technology studies offers a wealth of concepts, theories, and case studies that could be applied to research on possibilities for terrorist attacks and reasonable strategies for preventing them. An interesting conclusion in Charles Perrow's work, for example, is that it is actually rather difficult to bring about catastrophe in large-scale systems either by accident or by malicious intention. Exactly the right arrangement of causes and effects, of failures and blunders have to be in place. Research findings of that kind should be reassuring to us. Perrow suggests a variety of reforms to diminish the odds of disaster, ones that involve strategies for loose coupling of components in technical systems so that one diminishes the chance of cascading failures. He argues for greater flexibility in the communications and behaviors of the people who work in and around large-scale systems. Yes, there is a cost to such measures, a loss in efficiency, speed, and volume of throughput in the hazardous systems of modern life. To achieve much greater security, we would have to give up a measure of the productivity and convenience Americans and Europeans have gotten used to. However, if one is willing to live with these costs, the likelihood of catastrophic normal accidents and, by implication, catastrophic consequences from terrorist strikes can be substantially reduced.

Specific detailed proposals about ways to reduce vulnerability through reform in the design and management of key technological systems are the focus of Stephen Flynn's book *America the Vulnerable*. Although Flynn buys much of the bombastic, misleading rhetoric of the war on terror, he draws on his experience as a commissioned officer in the Coast Guard and subsequent academic research on risky technologies to identify areas of blindness in America's response to 9/11 and to outline paths of improvement. Containerized cargo crates could be redesigned to include sensors, global positioning systems, and communications devices. The global system of containerized cargo could be rearranged to include a limited number of institutional gateways where safe practices could be installed. Flynn upholds the total reorganization of material and social frameworks at Boston Logan Airport after 9/11 as a model of reform. What he finds there are well-rehearsed practices that emphasize open not closed communication and flexibility in the choices made available to employees (Flynn 2004).

In writings like these—technology studies broadly interpreted—one finds useful ideas in the quest to create more resilient and reliable institutions in our sociotechnical landscape. The path to a safer, more secure society involves projects in the reengineering of systems that loom as targets for catastrophic attack. In this mode one identifies vulnerabilities and fixes them, using the best social wisdom and technological ingenuity available. One continually monitors the workings of such systems to make sure that the worst possibilities for damage are anticipated and prevented. Rigorous, intellectually responsible studies of the broader horizons of terrorism suggest that remedies of this kind are the best focus for our efforts and money.

An important implication of this insight is that the destructive focus of the "war on terror" in its domestic setting—the making of systems for thoroughgoing surveillance of civilians—actually has little relevance to the nation's safety and security. Yes, it makes sense of be vigilant against criminal conspiracies, watchful of purchases of explosives and other devices that could be used in terrorist plots. But it is likely that, following the Oklahoma City bombing of 1996 and the attacks of 9/11, local and federal police are already well prepared to uncover and intercept insidious plots that involve mass destruction on American soil. Beyond that, the greatest threats to domestic security are ones that involve the structure and operation of technological complexes—the airlines, nuclear plants, chemical plants, dams, containerized cargo, and so forth—whose protection involves comprehensive monitoring and the installation of technical fixes that have nothing to do with routine surveillance of everyday life. This is actually the best, tough-minded advice from those who have studied the real prospects for terrorism: watch technological systems, not people's everyday activities.

In sum, the best strategy for an age in which terrorism has entered the picture is to attend to specific, very real circumstances of our vulnerability and correct them, taking steps that could, in fact, enhance rather than degrade our way of life. Is this not a better approach than fanning endless fears about terrorists and lobbing 500-pound bombs at strange neighborhoods in distant lands? Alas, this is probably not a great rallying cry: let us join together in a campaign to understand and systematically reduce our vulnerability, achieving new levels of resilience within the sociotechnical frame-

works of modern life. I realize that my plea would probably have little appeal on television talk shows.

The day after the 9/11 attack, I went to the university to teach a class of undergraduates in a course on law, values, and public policy. By then it was known pretty much who the hijackers were and who had instigated the attack. In my class that term, about a quarter of the students were Muslim, and a good number of those were of Middle Eastern origin. I began by asking everyone to express their thoughts and feelings about what had happened. There ensued a series of angry outbursts.

"Your people did this!" shouted a young man from the New York suburbs, pointing to a young woman wearing a head scarf.

"I'm as American as anybody in this room," she responded, fighting back tears, "and I hate the terrorists as much as you."

Echoing calls commonly heard on talk radio, some of the students exclaimed that America should just nuke all the capital cities in the Middle East and get it over with.

After about a half hour of this, I suggested that we turn to the readings for the day. It happened that we were wrapping up discussion of the *Oresteia* by Aeschylus. I'd assigned the book to raise the following question: How did people handle disputes before there was any system of law?

In the drama we behold Agamemnon's return from the Trojan War and a sequence of bloody murders that breaks out within the royal family. One killing leads to another within a moral order in which family members must enact retribution. Just as things are spinning out of control, the goddess Athena appears. She proclaims that the revenge killings have gone on long enough. From now on the city will be governed by the rule of law. There will be courts, trials, and juries within an enduring framework of civil order. For the spirits of revenge, the Furies, Athena creates a new role as the Eumenides, the kindly ones, asked to protect their new home, the city of Athens.

I asked my students, How would Aeschylus view the discussion we've been having today? Most of them got the point. Even when the crimes suffered are horrendous, acting out raw feelings of hatred may not be the best way to proceed. Perhaps there are more rational, more peaceful, more fruitful ways to confront these horrible problems and our deepest feelings about them.

I recognize that the body scholarship in technology studies is less profound than the dramas of Aeschylus. But it may contain ideas and proposals that point in some promising directions. Better the wisdom of Athena than the counsels of crazed vengeance our leaders still prefer.

Acknowledgment

An earlier version of this essay was given as the Tenth Annual Hans Rausing Lecture for the Department of History and Philosophy of Science, University of Cambridge, May 19, 2005.

Notes

1. Quoted in Thomas Homer-Dixon (2002).
2. The original text appeared in Langdon Winner (1975). The full quote is as follows: "The study of redundancy is one direction in which any future discussion of social complexity ought to investigate. In particular, it illuminates a whole category of action which has stood in the shadows of political thought for thousands of years but which now seems entirely relevant to the technological society—*sabotage*. A first rule, for example, might be: 'Find the critical but nonredundant parts of the system and sabotage (or protect) them according to your purposes'" (p. 69).
3. There is now a vast literature in this genre. See, for example, Langdon Winner (1986); Wiebe Bijker, Thomas Hughes, and Trevor Pinch (1987); Wiebe Bijker and John Law (1992); Donna Haraway (1997).
4. I expand on this point in Langdon Winner (2004).
5. See, for example, Joseph G. Morone and Edward J. Woodhouse (1986).
6. *The 9/11 Commission Report: Final Report of the National Commission on Terrorist Attacks upon the United States: Executive Summary,* http://www.9-11commission.gov/report/ 911Report_Exec.htm.
7. "Bomb Risk Forces NY Tower Rethink," BBC News, May 5, 2005, http://news.bbc.co.uk/1/hi/ world/americas/4515759.stm.
8. "College Student Admits Planting Box Cutters on Planes," CNN, October 17, 2003, http://www. cnn.com/2003/US/10/17/suspicious.baggage/.
9. "Student in Box-Cutter Case Gets Probation," Newmax, June 24, 2004, http://www.newsmax. com/archives/articles/2004/6/24/122102.shtml.
10. More than a year after the release of the final report of the 9/11 Commission, members of the commission, reassembled in a private group called the 9/11 Public Discourse Project, complained that few of the remedies they had proposed had been implemented. See Lara Jakes Jordan, "Sept. 11 Panel: U.S. Remains Unprepared," *Washington Post,* December 5, 2005. Other reports warning that U.S. approaches to terrorism are badly conceived include one written before the 9/11 attack, *Roadmap for National Security: Imperative for Change,* The National Commission on National Security/21 Century, February 15, 2001, http://www.google. com/url?sa=U&start=4&q=http://govinfo.library. unt.edu/nssg/PhaseIIIFR.pdf&e=912.

 Discussion Questions

1. What are the four "themes in social and political studies of technology" that are outlined by Winner in this excerpt? In your own words, use one or two sentences to describe each of these themes.
2. Identify examples from your own experience that illustrate the "technological style" that is described by Winner as having emerged in the U.S. since the 9/11 attacks.
3. What is a "normal accident?" How do you think this concept applies to military technologies?

 Supporting Activities

1. Read the wording of the Fourth Amendment of the U.S. Constitution. Conduct a class debate about whether, and in what ways, the protections contained in this amendment have been eroded since 2001. Provide specific examples to support your arguments. A good source for more information and for the text of this amendment can be found on the FindLaw site (http://lp.findlaw.com/).
2. Visit Langdon Winner's home page (http://www.langdonwinner.org/) and read some of his additional work, including his blog, *Technopolis*.
3. Watch the clip "The New Technology of War," available on the *Popular Mechanics* Web site (http://www.popularmechanics.com/blogs/technology_news/4221467.html). See also the cover article titled "Defending America" in the April 2006 issue of *Popular Mechanics* (Available: http://www.popularmechanics.com/technology/military_law/2530001.html).

 Additional Resources

1. See the full text of the 9/11 Commission Report (available: http://www.9-11commission.gov/report/911Report.pdf).
2. Refer to the additional resources dealing with surveillance listed at the end of "Section Seven: Perspectives on Communication Technology" of this book.
3. View a timeline and history of the Internet at the Web site of the Computer History Museum of Mountain View, California (http://www.computerhistory.org/internet_history/).
4. Watch the popular movie *Fat Man and Little Boy* (1989), a fictionalized account of the development of the first atomic bomb via the Manhattan Project. For a detailed account of the Manhattan Project, view the U.S. Department of Energy Office of History and Heritage Resources Web site (http://www.cfo.doe.gov/me70/manhattan/).
5. Visit the Stockholm International Peace Research Institute for comprehensive analyses of worldwide military expenditures, the various categories of military weapons, and the development of non-proliferation agreements (http://www.sipri.org/).

 Endnotes

1. Roland, Alex. 2009. War and Technology. Foreign Policy Research Institute. *Footnotes* (14 (2)). Available: http://www.fpri.org/footnotes/1402.200902.roland.wartechnology.html.

2. The Center for Arms Control and Non-Proliferation. 2008. *Global Military Spending.* Available: http://www.armscontrolcenter.org/policy/securityspending/articles/fy09_dod_request_global/.

3. Office of Management and Budget. (no date). *Department of Defense, President's 2009 Budget.* Available: http://www.whitehouse.gov/omb/budget/fy2009/defense.html.

4. Koizumi, Kei. 2008. "R&D in the FY 2009 Department of Defense Budget." In the American Association for the Advancement of Science *AAAS Report XXXIII, Research and Development FY 2009* (Chapter 5). Available: http://www.aaas.org/spp/rd/09pch5.htm.

5. Brzezinski, Zbigniew. March 25, 2007. "Terrorized by the 'War on Terror': How a Three-Word Mantra has Undermined America." *The Washington Post* (p. B01). Available: http://www.washingtonpost.com/wp-dyn/content/article/2007/03/23/AR2007032301613.html.

6. The phrase "military industrial complex" is most often associated with the farewell speech of President Dwight D. Eisenhower on January 17, 1961. View footage of this powerful message on YouTube at: http://www.youtube.com/watch?v=8y06NSBBRtY.

Perspectives on Workplace and Leisure Technologies

Technology has clearly transformed the workplace. The drudgery of manual labor has been significantly reduced, and worker productivity significantly increased, through the adoption of machinery and robotics. According to the U.S. Census Bureau, between 1977 and 2007 the manufacturing sector of the U.S. workforce shrank by nearly 40 percent, while manufacturing output increased by over *100 times*.[1,2] Clearly, more work is being done by fewer workers.

A more recent workforce transition concerns information technology (IT). Of the total productivity growth in the U.S. between 1995 and 2002, fully two-thirds can be directly linked to the adoption of IT, as described in a report from The Information Technology and Innovation Foundation.[3] This comprehensive report also links IT adoption to greater innovation, shallower economic downturns, higher quality goods and services, and better resource utilization. The effects of IT on the workplace have been steadily increasing for the past 50 years, and today there are virtually no segments of the workplace that are untouched by the impacts of IT.

While easy to dismiss as trite and insignificant, recreation is an important component of a healthy lifestyle. And recreation is an important segment of the economy as well. In 2001, Americans spent $64 billion in retail sporting goods stores.[4] The estimated total economic impact from outdoor recreation in the U.S. in 2005 was estimated at $730 billion.[5] Professional teams from the four "major" sports in the U.S. (baseball, football, basketball, and hockey) have a combined value of $12 billion.[6]

As with so many areas of innovation, technological development follows the money. Consider, for example, the progression of baseball bats from wood to aluminum to carbon fiber to carbon *nanotubes*.[7] Fishing rods have undergone a similar transformation, with nanotube models now available.[8] High-end bicycle frames made from carbon nanotubes have competed in the Tour de France.[9]

The point is, demands in the workplace and in the realm of leisure have provided a significant market to drive technological innovation, and neither the factory floor nor the golf course have looked the same since. What impacts can we expect technology to have in the workplace and on recreation in the future?

From Ford to Dell: Mass Production to Mass Customization

The following excerpt from Roger Alcaly's *The New Economy* considers how technology has historically and is currently radically transforming the way business is conducted. Case studies of two companies are presented: Ford Motor Company and Dell Computer. Both businesses leveraged the cutting-edge technology of their time to become powerhouses. Ford pioneered the use of automated assembly lines, and Dell pioneered the use of real-time information technology.

However, there are significant differences in how Ford and Dell applied their new technologies. Ford pursued a highly centralized structure in which the company itself controlled the technology. The decision to move parts and materials suppliers, machinists, and car distributors in-house was believed to simplify the manufacturing process and therefore result in cost savings. Ford also strived to reduce costs per unit by pursuing standardization. Dell, in sharp contrast, is using IT to outsource virtually all non-core aspects of its business and prides itself on built-to-order products.

Alcaly is particularly interested in whether the IT revolution and outsourcing, as implemented by Dell, can be applied to a "blue chip" company like Ford. Is a build-to-order model possible, or perhaps necessary, for such companies to survive? What would it mean for the businesses and consumers?

Roger Alcaly, who formerly taught economics at Columbia University, is a principal of Mount Lucas Management Corporation, an investment firm in Princeton, New Jersey. He is a regular contributor to *The New York Review of Books* and author of the 2003 book *The New Economy and What It Means for America's Future.*

From Ford to Dell: Mass Production to Mass Customization

By Roger Alcaly

Henry Ford developed mass production, the manufacturing model that held sway for most of the twentieth century, but the term "mass production" was apparently coined by an editor of the *Encyclopaedia Britannica* who in 1925 asked Ford to write an article for a three-volume supplement he was preparing. The piece first appeared as a feature story in a Sunday edition of *The New York Times* titled "Henry Ford Expounds Mass Production: Calls It the Focussing of the Principles of Power, Economy, Continuity, and Speed." Although the article was attributed to Ford, it was written by his spokesman, William Cameron, who later said that he "should be very much surprised to learn that [Henry Ford had] read it."[1]

Mass production originated as a new approach to making automobiles, but its influence was far more pervasive, demonstrating to all manufacturers how to produce efficiently for a broad market. As the *Britannica* article suggests, Ford was not shy about publicizing his innovative methods, and they spread rapidly throughout the economy, shifting attention to larger-scale production and spurring growth and productivity. "The Ford Motor Company," the historian David Hounshell writes, "educated the American technical community in the ways

"From Ford to Dell: Mass Production to Mass Customization" from *The New Economy: What It Is, How It Happened, and Why It is Likely to Last* by Roger Alcaly. Copyright © 2003 by Roger Alcaly. Reprinted by permission of Farrar, Straus & Giroux, LLC.

of mass production." Unlike other turn-of-the-century automakers who used skilled craftsmen to produce small quantities of expensive cars tailored to their customers' needs, Ford concentrated on producing large quantities of standardized products at low cost, and his success initially elicited caustic responses. In 1912, for example, an English automotive journal commented:

> It is highly to the credit of our English makers that they choose rather to maintain their reputation for high grade work than cheapen that reputation by the use of the inferior material and workmanship they would be obliged to employ to compete with American manufacturers of cheap cars.

A year later, Ford introduced his first moving assembly line at his Highland Park plant in Detroit and by 1914 was probably producing more cars than all English manufacturers combined. By the early 1920s mass-production techniques had spread throughout the U.S. automobile industry, tripling its annual output to more than 3 million cars, with Ford accounting for about two-thirds of the total. These methods also began to be used in producing electrically powered consumer durables such as washing machines, refrigerators, vacuum cleaners, and radios, as well as farm equipment and other products whose potential sales were large enough to justify the necessary investments in new factories and equipment.[2]

The key to mass production, Ford believed, was the "simplicity" of its constituent operations, a consequence of dividing the production process into a finely specified sequence of steps that could be carried out by unskilled or semi-skilled workers using specially designed limited-purpose equipment. Beyond repeatedly performing their specific tasks, assembly-line workers had no role in the operation. Thinking about issues such as product design, how the factories should be laid out, what each assembler should do, or scheduling deliveries of

materials and shipments of finished products was done by professionals: designers, industrial engineers, production engineers, and so on. Workers were discouraged from offering suggestions for making their own jobs more efficient. Even chores such as cleaning work areas, repairing equipment, or checking product quality were done by specialists, including housekeeping workers, equipment repairmen, and quality inspectors. And because production was geared to meet anticipated demand—that is, goods were "built-to-forecast" rather than to meet firm orders—and equipment could not readily be stopped and started, companies tended to accumulate massive inventories of final goods, materials, and work in progress.[3]

Carrying out the simple individual tasks of Fordist production required standardized parts of uniformly high quality that could be fit together easily without interrupting the assembly process, a need that few others recognized but one that Ford pursued with "near-religious zeal." Aided by improved machine tools that could work with hardened metals that would hold their shape, Ford-produced parts became increasingly homogeneous and easy to assemble, enabling the company to progressively routinize workers' tasks and speed the flow of work. It helped that Ford cars were designed to be easy to manufacture as well as easy to operate and repair, especially the Model T, which was introduced in 1908, the nineteenth model Henry Ford had built since the original Model A in 1903.

Before 1908 Ford cars had been assembled at a single station, frequently by one or two assemblers who worked an average of almost nine hours on each set of tasks, such as attaching the wheels, springs, motor, transmission, and generator to the chassis, before performing the same operations on another car. In this early setup, assemblers had to collect the parts needed for each phase of their work and file and smooth them so that they fit together. However, by the end of 1912, the last year before Ford began using the moving assembly line to carry the car in progress from worker to worker, the assembly process had been streamlined and the individual steps pared down so much that workers were spending less than 2.5 minutes on each set of tasks for which they were responsible. The moving assembly line cut the average "task cycle" in half, to about 1.2 minutes, and the time required to form an almost finished vehicle fell even more, from twelve and a half hours to about an hour and a half.

Ford's development of the moving assembly line to improve productivity in his plants illustrates a critical difference between his approach and that of Frederick Taylor, with whose scientific management it is often linked. Like Taylor, Ford and his engineers constantly sought to establish precise procedures and standards for performing most efficiently the tasks involved in producing automobiles. Indeed, Ford and other Detroit-based companies may have adopted many of the core principles of "Taylorism" before Taylor did. But, more fundamental, "the Ford approach was to eliminate labor by machinery," Hounshell concluded, "not, as the Taylorites customarily did, to take a given production process and improve the efficiency of the workers through time and motion study and a differential piecerate system of payment." In other words, "Ford engineers mechanized work processes and found workers to feed and tend their machines"; as a consequence, "the machine ultimately set the pace of work at Ford, not a piecerate or an established standard for a 'fair day's work.' This was the essence of the assembly line and all the machinery that fed it."[4]

By boosting productivity, assembly-line production allowed Ford to keep prices low, thus increasing sales and, because mass-production techniques were so effective in capturing economies of large-scale production, enabling it to reduce prices further as more cars were produced and unit costs fell. Between 1908, when the first Model Ts were produced, and the early 1920s, when more than 2 million were made,

the Model T's price fell by almost 70 percent after inflation. The assembly line was introduced at Ford's Highland Park plant in mid-1913 but was resisted at first by the workers. For the year as a whole, employment averaged 13,623, but only because nearly 65,000 workers were hired, enough to make up for more than 50,000 who left the company in frustration, out of boredom, or because they couldn't keep up with the pace of the line. The turnover rate averaged 370 percent for the year but was much higher in the months after the assembly line was installed. "So great was labor's distaste for the new machine system," a Ford biographer wrote, "that toward the close of 1913 every time the company wanted to add 100 men to its factory personnel, it was necessary to hire 963."[5]

Although Detroit was not yet a union town, the threat of unionization and work stoppages may have concerned Ford more than high turnover. High fixed costs and dedicated machinery made mass-production plants particularly vulnerable to strikes and disruptions, and the Wobblies—the Industrial Workers of the World, or IWW—had been active in Detroit in the spring of 1913, briefly stopping production at Studebaker. Whether reducing turnover or staving off the Wobblies and other unions was the main factor, Ford moved quickly to stabilize relations with his workers, establishing his famous "five-dollar day" in January 1914. Under the plan, workers would continue to earn a base wage of $2.34 per day, which had been set just three months earlier, but they could also qualify for supplements, boosting their daily pay to $5 or more. These bonuses were called "profit-sharing" payments, but they were based on a worker's "character" rather than his effectiveness. To determine who was worthy, the company established its intrusive Sociological Department, whose members visited workers every six months to ensure that they were leading "clean, sober, and industrious" lives, in "well lighted and ventilated" homes, located outside "congested and slum areas of the city," making it unlikely that they would waste the money in "riotous living."

The five-dollar day generated favorable publicity for the company, burnished Henry Ford's image as an industrial statesman, and, by raising workers' incomes, increased their buying power and thus their demand for other goods and services if not for cars. Business leaders initially denounced Ford as a utopian, a socialist, and "a traitor to his class," but by the 1920s many had come to appreciate the benefits of higher wages and profit sharing in raising morale, productivity, and aggregate demand and in gaining labor peace. High wages were an integral part of the philosophy of "welfare capitalism" that many leading companies adopted after World War I, and even though he eschewed general wage increases after 1919 and fought viciously against unionization of his company, Henry Ford continued to celebrate the advantages of greater pay, maintaining, for example, in *Today and Tomorrow,* which was published in 1926, that the "wage motive" was "the fundamental motive of our company." But higher wages only were justified, he believed, if they stimulated workers and managers to boost productivity and lower prices. "It is this thought of enlarging buying power by paying high wages and selling at low prices which is behind the prosperity of this country," he wrote. "If we set ourselves to the payment of wages, then we can find methods of manufacturing which will make high wages the cheapest of wages."[6]

Ford's obsessive quest to control production costs by mechanizing, standardizing, and simplifying the work process extended beyond his search for better ways to manufacture automobiles. He also sought to integrate assembly operations with many of the other steps involved in making and distributing cars, including producing the necessary steel, glass, and tires and transporting the raw materials and finished products to and from the Ford facilities. This vision was embodied in the mammoth Rouge production complex, built shortly after

World War I on a two-thousand-acre piece of land along the Rouge River in Dearborn, just outside Detroit. Rouge was the largest industrial complex in the world, an "industrial colossus" that employed almost 100,000 workers at its peak. Extreme and striking, a facility in which raw materials "came in one gate, while finished cars went out the other gate . . . completely eliminating the need for outside assistance," Rouge symbolized the possibilities of "vertical integration" that other companies sought to emulate. Ford even tried to add raw materials to the mix, maintaining a rubber plantation in Brazil and iron mines in Minnesota. He also had fleets of ships, railroad cars, and airplanes for carrying resources, equipment, and finished cars.[7]

Ford was motivated to integrate in this way because he was much more efficient than his suppliers and thus could profit from doing more things internally, but he also distrusted others and seemed to need to control everything himself. Whatever the benefits in the short term, the managerial difficulties of coordinating such large and diverse operations were equally great, especially for somebody who could not bear delegating authority. In addition, Ford's obsession with manufacturing may have caused him to neglect marketing and design. For almost twenty years, the company concentrated almost exclusively on the Model T, leaving it vulnerable to competition from General Motors, which had adopted Ford's production methods but also had created a far broader product line with annual model changes. In 1927 Ford was forced to stop producing the Model T and closed the Rouge complex for almost a year in order to develop new products. Fittingly, because it was so representative of its patriarch's strengths and weaknesses, Rouge was the setting for a bloody labor battle about a decade later in which the United Automobile Workers won the right to represent Ford workers, the last of the Big Three's employees to be organized.[8]

If Ford and Rouge are emblematic of the old business system, Dell Computer, which Michael Dell describes as *virtually* integrated," is representative of the new one. What he means, beyond the clever wordplay, is that Dell has succeeded by "focusing on delivering solutions and systems to customers" and "stitching together a business with partners that are treated *as if* they're inside the company," rather than by following Ford's example and trying to do everything itself. In other words, the company, which sells directly to its customers the computers that they specify, is largely a middleman, coordinating its selling and assembly of computers with the activities of outside suppliers, service technicians, and delivery firms such as Airborne Express and UPS. Virtual integration would not be possible without sophisticated information and communications technology. With it, Dell has been able to expand its direct-to-customer business model and become in less than twenty years the world's leading computer maker, with 2001 sales of approximately $30 billion and a market value, even at its low point on September 21, 2001, of more than $40 billion. It employs fewer than twenty thousand people directly but four or five times as many through the business it commits to its partners. Dell's superior efficiency was especially apparent during the 2000–2002 economic slump, when it slashed prices aggressively and gained market share, a strategy that may have helped drive Compaq and Hewlett-Packard, the second- and fourth-ranking computer manufacturers, to merge.[9]

To better appreciate how the system works, consider Dell's relationships with some of its vendors and big customers. Sony produces monitors for Dell's computers, and they are so reliable that Dell doesn't feel it has to test them or carry any buffer stocks. It doesn't even have to take delivery of the monitors. Instead, Michael Dell recounted, "we went to Sony and said, 'Hey, we're going to buy two or three mil-

lion of these monitors this year. Why don't we just pick them up every day as we need them?'" What actually happens is that Dell instructs "Airborne Express or UPS to come to Austin and pick up 10,000 computers a day and go over to the Sony factory in Mexico and pick up the corresponding number of monitors. Then while we're all sleeping, they match up the computers and the monitors, and deliver them to the customer." For Sony, the relationship with Dell is a large source of demand, and because Dell builds computers only in response to firm customer orders, its needs are relatively predictable, at least in the short term. Moreover, Dell's advanced data-sharing systems allow it to communicate this information to its suppliers, in some cases reporting its inventory levels, replacement needs, and delivery schedules hourly.

Similarly, because Dell maintains electronic records of customer orders, including the exact specifications of their computers and workstations, its technicians can pinpoint problems much more easily and precisely when complaints arise. And for large customers such as Boeing and Eastman Chemical, it often provides special services. Boeing has more than 100,000 Dell PCs, and to service its needs, Dell stationed roughly thirty people at the company who "look like Boeing's PC department" but are not employed by Boeing and probably are not even employed directly by Dell. Eastman Chemical, on the other hand, has developed unique software packages for its workstations, and Dell maintains in its factory a high-speed network and massive server loaded with the relevant software components, enabling it to equip Eastman's new computers during the assembly process with the particular software mix that each requires, saving the company roughly three hundred dollars per machine.[10]

One of the most obvious advantages of the Dell build-to-order system is that it substantially reduces the need for inventories, and some of the clearest evidence that companies have adopted such new operating methods can be seen in the decline in inventories throughout the economy over the last twenty years. Relative to sales, inventories in the goods-producing sectors of the economy have fallen by about 20 percent since the early 1980s, driven largely by the fall among durable-goods producers such as Dell and Ford, whose inventory-to-sales ratios dropped roughly 30 percent during this period. Curtailing inventories lowers businesses' operating costs, but it also appears to have helped reduce the volatility of economic growth and inflation, reinforcing the benefits of better monetary policy that has aided the economy since Paul Volcker became chairman of the Federal Reserve System in August 1979. Better inventory controls increase profits because less money is tied up in carrying inventories and because firms with lower inventories tend to link them to product lines that are selling well, making it likely that fewer items will become obsolete or have to be discounted or written off. For the U.S. durable-goods sector, the capital freed up by carrying fewer inventories is on the order of $500 billion, saving roughly $25 billion in annual carrying costs if financing rates are around 5 percent and more if they are higher.[11]

Progress in controlling inventories and managing supply chains has encouraged automakers and other businesses to think about capturing the even bigger payoffs that may be possible by further emulating Dell's methods. For example, automobile inventories are now about $100 billion, and McKinsey & Company consultants estimate they would be 60–80 percent lower if cars were built to order rather than in anticipation of future sales. According to Nissan, the resulting savings could be as much as thirty-six hundred dollars per car. The problem for the automakers, however, is that most auto plants do not make money unless they operate at 80 percent of capacity or higher. As a result, the potential advantages of building to order are likely to be eaten away by inefficiently small production runs unless demand can be spread out appropriately or production methods made flexible enough to accommodate lower volumes more effectively.[12]

In fact, Dell not only builds its computers solely in response to firm orders; it also encourages buyers to customize them to fit their own needs. (An ad that ran widely in the fall of 2000, for example, featured a typical teenager dressed in baggy pants and sneakers and slouched before his computer, telling readers, "Everyone at school bought these shoes and got this haircut, but my computer is 100% me.") Even if they don't customize their computers, however, Dell customers pay for them when they place their orders, giving the company free use of the money until it must pay its workers and suppliers for producing the machines. In the first few months of 2000, Dell's average float—prepayments that are temporarily available to the company—was about $1.5 billion, roughly two-thirds of its monthly sales. Assuming Dell earns 5 percent on the money, float of this magnitude contributes close to $100 million to its annual earnings, a further attraction to automakers and others not yet engaged in mass customization or able to get customers to prepay.

Dell is able to produce customized computers for a mass market because they can be built from a limited number of modular components that can be assembled quickly in response to customer specifications. And while automobile suppliers have been working closely with car companies to design and produce complete units for the manufacturers to assemble, including systems for braking, climate control, and car interiors, there may be limits to how far they can go, particularly since the United Automobile Workers remains strongly opposed to modularization because it would reduce even further the work done under their contracts with the Big Three automakers. The attractions are so great, however, that automakers are unlikely to stop trying to become more like Dell, transforming themselves into virtually integrated "brand owners" that simply design, engineer, and market cars, while outsourcing everything else. A Finnish engineering company currently makes Porsche Boxters, and even once-proud Rouge, which now houses only three thousand workers producing eight hundred Mustangs a day, is heading in that direction, undergoing a $2 billion face-lift designed to turn it into a flexible assembly plant of the future.[13]

Author Citations

1. David A. Hounshell, *From the American System to Mass Production, 1800–1932: The Development of Manufacturing Technology in the United States* (Baltimore: Johns Hopkins University Press, 1984), p. 1.

2. Ibid., pp. 260–261; and David C. Mowery and Nathan Rosenberg, *Paths of Innovation* (New York: Cambridge University Press, 1999); pp. 48–55, which quotes the magazine *Autocar*.

3. The discussion of mass production in the next few pages relies on James P. Womack, Daniel T. Jones, and Daniel Roos, *The Machine That Changed the World: The Story of Lean Production* (New York: Harper-Perennial, 1991), pp. 26–29.

4. Hounshell, *From the American System to Mass Production,* pp. 250–53.

5. Daniel M. G. Raff, "Wage Determination Theory and Five-Dollar Day at Ford," *Journal of Economic History* (June 1988), pp. 388–91; Hounshell, *From the American System to Mass Production,* pp. 256–59; and Irving Bernstein, *The Lean Years: A History of the American Worker, 1920–1933* (Boston: Houghton Mifflin, 1960), pp. 179–80. The Ford biographer is Keith Sward, *The Legend of Henry Ford*, who is quoted by Hounshell, p. 257.

6. See Henry Ford (in collaboration with Samuel Crowther), *Today and Tomorrow* (New York: Doubleday, Page & Company, 1926), pp. 8–10; Raff, "Wage Determination Theory," pp. 387–99; Hounshell, *From the American System to Mass Production,* pp. 258–59; Bernstein, *Lean Years*, pp. 179–81; and Stuart D. Brandes, *American Welfare Capitalism, 1880–1940* (Chicago: University of Chicago Press, 1976), pp. 88–89. According to Raff, Joseph Galamb, chief designer of the Model T and one of Henry Ford's close associates, recalled Ford saying he established the five-dollar day to ward off the Wobblies.

7. Womack, Jones, and Roos, *The Machine That Changed the World*, pp. 33–35, 38–39; and Hounshell, *From the American System to Mass Production,* pp. 267–68. The term "industrial colossus," which is from Allan Nevins and Frank Ernest Hill, *Ford: Expansion and Challenge, 1915–1933* (New York: Scribner, 1957), is quoted on p. 267 of Hounshell's book.

8. Mowery and Rosenberg, Paths of Innovation, pp. 54–55; and Irving Bernstein, *Turbulent Years: A History of the American Worker, 1933–1941* (Boston: Houghton Mifflin, 1969), pp. 734–51.

9. Joan Magretta, "The Power of Virtual Integration: An Interview with Dell Computer's Michael Dell," *Harvard Business Review* (March-April 1998), pp. 74–76; and John Swartz, "Dell Computer is in the Catbird Seat, for Now," *New York Times* (Sept. 11, 2001). The emphasis has been added to Michael Dell's remarks.

10. All the quoted remarks in this paragraph, as in the prior one, are Michael Dell's and are from the Margretta interview, pp. 76–79.

11. James Kahn, Margaret M. McConnell, and Gabriel Perez-Quiros, "On the Causes of the Increased Stability of the U.S. Economy," *Economic Policy Review*, Federal Reserve Bank of New York (May 2002), esp. pp. 184–87 and chart 3.

12. Mani Agrawal, T. V. Kumaresh, and Glenn A. Mercer, "The False Promise of Mass Communication," *McKinsey Quarterly* (2001); and "Mass Customization: A Long March," *Economist* (July 14, 2001), pp. 63–65.

13. "Incredible Shrinking Plants," *Economist* (Feb. 23, 2002); "All Yours," *Economist* (Arpil 1, 2000), pp. 57–58; and Fred Andrews, "Dell, It Turns Out, Has a Better Idea," *New York Times* (Jan 26, 2000).

Discussion Questions

1. Explain the difference between "vertical" and "virtual" integration. How has technology made possible both of these business models?
2. Alcaly suggests that car manufacturers are trying to follow in Dell's "build-to-order" footsteps. What do you see as major obstacles to this transition?
3. The economic landscape has changed considerably since the publication of *The New Economy* in 2003. Do you see Dell's business model as more or less relevant now compared to 2003, and why?
4. How do you see IT performing in an era of dwindling resources and a likely curbing of globalization?

 Supporting Activities

1. Research Frederick Winslow Taylor and his theory of Scientific Management. How is Scientific Management similar to, and different from, Ford's assembly line model?
2. The adoption of technology in the workplace, whether through automation or IT, has its critics. What are some objections raised to each of these technologies?
3. Find and briefly summarize one article from the popular press about Dell's business model.
4. Find and briefly summarize one article from the popular press about Ford's *current* business model.

 Additional Resources

1. Also cited in the Endnotes, but worth including here as well, is: Atkinson, Robert D., and McKay, Andrew S. 2007. *Digital prosperity: Understanding the benefits of the information technology revolution*. The Information Technology and Innovation Foundation.

 Endnotes

1. U.S. Census Bureau. 2009. *Economy-wide key statistics: 2007*. Available: http://factfinder.census. gov/servlet/IBQTable?_bm=y&-geo_id=D&-ds_name=EC0700A1&-_lang=en.
2. U.S. Census Bureau. June 2001. *1997 economic census: Statistics for all manufacturing establishments*. Available: http://www.census.gov/prod/ec97/97m31s-gs.pdf.
3. Atkinson, Robert D., and McKay, Andrew S. 2007. *Digital prosperity: Understanding the benefits of the information technology revolution*. The Information Technology and Innovation Foundation.
4. Andreff, Wladimir, and Szymański, Stefan (Eds.). 2006. *Handbook on the Economics of Sport*. Edward Elgar Publishing.
5. Outdoor Industry Association. 2006. *The active outdoor recreation economy: A $730 billion annual contribution to the US economy*. Available: http://outdoorindustry.org/images/researchfiles/ RecEconomypublic.pdf?26.
6. Lee, Soonhwan, and Chun, Hyosung. 2002. Economic values of professional sport franchises in the United States. *Sport Journal*. 5 (3). Available: http://www.thesportjournal.org/article/economic-values-professional-sport-franchises-united-states.

7. AllBusiness. 2006. *Nanotech goes to bat.* Available: http://www.allbusiness. com/sports-recreation/sports-games-outdoor-recreation-baseball/6344175-1.html.

8. TackleTour. 2005. *Get a sneak peek of AiRRUS applying "Nanotechnology" to their newest rods.* Available: http://www.tackletour.com/reviewairrus2006.html.

9. PEZCycling News. 2006. *PEZ-clusive test: BMC SLC01.* Available: http://www.pezcyclingnews.com/?pg= fullstory&id=3870.

Wild Promises: Anticipating Our Technological Future

In the previous nine sections, you have learned what technology is and the role technology plays in our lives. You have gained an appreciation for the impact technology has on us individually and collectively. Conversely, you have seen the role that people play in the process of technological development and adoption, and you (hopefully) recognize the responsibility we all share to become educated citizens and voters.

This last section looks at some technologies that aren't yet fully developed, but that have the potential to radically transform society as we know it. You are likely to be somewhat familiar with these technologies, but may not have given much thought to their potential impacts. These potential impacts are the focus of this section. The selected readings aren't intended to present an inclusive list of the most important emerging technologies, nor do they provide a highly technical treatise on the subjects included. However, each of these topics illustrates in a unique way the issues that arise in the early stages of technological development, as well as the attendant uncertainties. The objective of this section is to raise awareness about technological decision making prior to adoption.

How can we anticipate what technologies the future will hold and what their impacts will be? People who study such things have been labeled futurists. Futurists include scientists, economists, policy makers, executives, authors, and academics, all of whom have an interest in predicting and planning for the future. Forecasting future technologies is no easy task, and a variety of methods have been developed. One widely-used method is to *extrapolate* into the future based on trends observed in historical data. Another method solicits the opinions of experts in a variety of fields and seeks a consensus opinion, often with multiple blind iterations (known as the *Delphi technique*). Arriving at a consensus is often quite difficult, but the technique has proven to be worthwhile. Simulations, including mathematical, physical, or conceptual modeling, have also been employed. Scenario development, typically including best, worst, and most likely cases, is helpful in framing the range of future possibilities. Sometimes a combination of methods is used. These and other methods all have their strengths and weaknesses.

The topics covered in this section include robotics, space travel, and nanotechnology. In addition, the opening essay discusses the very idea of looking into the future. The difficulties inherent in predicting future technologies is not a good rationale for avoiding examination of these technological developments. We would argue that it's even more critical to gain an understanding of emerging technologies than it is to understand current technologies, because you have the ability to influence the adoption of future technologies. With this ability comes the responsibility as a citizen and voter to be informed about these issues.

The Future: What is the Problem?

Susan Greenfield acknowledges that for the past 100 years society has greatly benefited from scientific and technological advances. In her book, *Tomorrow's People*, she tries to predict what science and technology have in store for us over the next 100 years. Can we simply extrapolate the blistering pace of technological progress from the past and expect more of the same? What types of *unpredictable* technological developments should we anticipate? Will technologies of the future carry the same level of benefits and risks that prior technologies did?

Following the lead of Bill Joy, a prominent computer scientist and futurist, Greenfield highlights three broad and important categories of technologies: biotech, infotech, and nanotech (mirroring Joy's expressed concern about genetics, robotics, and nanotechnology in his *Wired* magazine article "Why the Future Doesn't Need Us"[1]). There have been tremendous accomplishments in these areas to date, and all three areas are poised for an explosion of scientific breakthroughs and a proliferation of mind-boggling technological advances that cannot be predicted based on past innovation. These new technologies are expected to dramatically increase in power and scope, as discussed in Section One, and may very well interact in synergistic ways beyond contemporary understanding. The questions should be asked: Knowing at least some of the potential risks, is it advisable to pursue these technologies? Do the benefits outweigh the risks? The technological optimist would obviously say yes.

Greenfield uses pop culture to make her point. For example, consider the evolution of Hollywood robotics, from HAL in *2001: A Space Odyssey* (1968) to the *Terminator* Series (1984, 1991, 2003, 2009). Early on, Hollywood "predicted" robots would be smarter and more powerful in 2001, and perhaps evil, but not substantially different from technology of the day and still in rather dull boxes. Later, Hollywood writers anticipated that robotics would have potential well beyond current technology and the Terminator was born. Interestingly, the time lapse between HAL and the first Terminator (16 years) is considerably shorter than the (current) duration of the Terminator franchise (25 years). Apparently, box office sales were enough to slow down and virtually halt robotic development!

Hollywood and Susan Greenfield are in agreement that future technological advances can't be predicted from past performance. What we'll likely get in the future is not simply a smaller, faster, more advanced version of what we have now, but something perhaps radically different, with unknowable unintended consequences. Perhaps the phrase "technological *revolution*" may not be hyperbole after all. This makes forecasting the future a very tricky endeavor indeed.

Susan Adele Greenfield (Baroness Greenfield) is a British scientist, writer, and member of the House of Lords. Her field of expertise is brain psychology, about which she has written for the popular press. She started the biotech companies Synaptica, BrainBoost, and Neurodiagnostics. Baroness Greenfield is Professor of Synaptic Pharmacology at Lincoln College, Oxford, and Director of the Royal Institution of Great Britain. In addition, she currently serves as Chancellor of Heriot-Watt University in Edinburgh.

The Future: What Is the Problem?

By Susan Greenfield

Look through an old album of sepia photographs from the early 1900s. There they are, our forebears, most usually posed in front of some cardboard Arcadian scene, doomed to manual or social drudgery and a rigid code of conduct and thought. Those placid, distant faces stare into a world, invisible and unknowable to us, of toothache, outside privies, stale sweat and certainty. 'The past is a foreign country,' mused L. P. Hartley in *The Go-Between*, 'they do things differently there.' Yet the mid-20th-century British prime minister Harold Macmillan, looking back over a long life to his Victorian childhood, once reminisced that the great watchword of the turn of the century was 'progress'. Progress—social, economic and above all scientific—was perceived as just that, the forward march of the human intellect, from which we would reap only benefits. And progress came from science.

In the 1950s the scientist knew everything. He (always he) was characterized in television advertisements as the white-coated authority, condescending to endorse 'scientifically' the latest washing powder. The very fact that there was television at all transformed not only people's lives but also the way they viewed the world beyond the confines of their own community. The chirpy, capped, short-trousered schoolboy of that era, voraciously swotting up endless facts that 'every schoolboy knows', was fascinated by the technological marvels of the Festival of Britain and the new world that science was making possible. Meanwhile penicillin was rescuing many from misery and early death, whilst the contraceptive pill, no longer just a

pipe dream, was about to revolutionize the outlook of, and for, women.

But the 20th century has surely taught us, among much else, that everything comes with a price; every schoolchild now knows that scientific and technological advances have colossal potential for both good and evil. Although the public have been aware, ever since Hiroshima, of the need to try to understand the implications of new scientific discoveries, it has only been in the last few decades of the previous century that the alarm bells have grown deafening. GM foods, mad cow disease and brain-scrambling mobile phones have compelled the most ostrich-like technophobe to question what might be happening in the remote and rarefied stratosphere of the laboratory. For science is increasingly not just on our minds but at the heart of our lives, encroaching upon everything that we hold dear: nutrition, reproduction, the climate, communication and education . . . The impact of science and technology on our existence, in the future, is no longer a whimsical excursion into science fiction.

Those sci-fi images of yesteryear now have an enchantingly amateurish glow. The Daleks in pursuit of Dr. Who, the politically correct crew in *Star Trek*—even that ultimate icon, from Stanley Kubrick's film *2001*, the psychopathic computer, HAL—are as far-fetched and unthreatening as the tin-foil outfits and staccato jerks of the marionettes in *Thunderbirds*. The human and humanoid characters, in most cases, think and act like we do. They have similar sets of values and expectations, and the bulk

From *Tomorrow's People* by Susan Greenfield. Copyright © 2004 by Susan Greenfield. Reprinted by permission of Susan Greenfield, via Brockman, Inc.

of the appeal depends on a good guys/bad guys plot. And that is how most people used to see the future—not chasing bandits around the galaxy so much as still being human in a world of souped-up, high-tech gadgetry—a gadgetry perhaps of interest to some anorak-kitted nerds, but for the majority of us reasonable everyday folk to be taken in our stride.

But now we face a future where science could actually change everyday life any day soon; many think such transformations are already under way. Yet there are some—let's dub them, without much originality, The Cynics—who do not see any point in dusting down the crystal ball. The chances are, glancing at the track records of our predecessors, that pretty much any prediction anyone makes now will be either impractical or uninspired.

Moreover, just because a technology is up and running doesn't mean to say it will become central to the daily grind. One late-19th-century prediction of the future, for example, was that everyone would travel around in hot-air balloons. And on the other hand, unknown, unimaginable technology can catch us unawares: a picture of a domestic scene 'in the future' drawn back in the 1950s shows all manner of gleaming appliances, but no computers, let alone anyone surfing the web. Even a glimmer of the priming technology just wasn't part of normal existence; it would have been a fairly impressive intellectual leap to conceptualize our 50-emails-a-day lifestyle from the standing start of clunky, expensive and essentially mechanical computers whirring and churning in their remote rarity in custom-made rooms of their own. And I remember a summer afternoon in the 1970s, lounging after a heavy lunch on a lawn with friends, when someone, a physicist, first mentioned the microchip—he prophesied that 'it will change all our lives'. The rest of us hadn't the vaguest idea what he was talking about.

The problem with thinking about the future, shrug The Cynics complacently, is that it is impossible to predict the big new scientific advances that underpin serious technological progress; meanwhile, how easy to be distracted by high-tech toys, the latest variation on an existing theme, amusing enough for escapist science fiction but not sufficiently innovative to restructure our entire existence and our seemingly impregnable mindset. Yet, as physicist Michio Kaku points out, the problem with extrapolating the future in the past—as with the hot-air balloon mass transport system—is that it hasn't been the scientists themselves making the predictions. Now they are in a very strong position to do so.

However, The Cynics have long placed a trip wire on the track of human progress, even when scientists have indulged in flights of fancy. They laughed at Christopher Columbus, derided Galileo, scoffed at Darwin and sneered at Freud. A curious feature of The Cynic's attitude is that he (and again it usually is he) thinks that science is on his side, backing up his sane voice of reason against the fantastic. In 1903 a *New York Times* editorial glibly wrote off Langley's attempts at flight: 'We hope that Professor Langley will not put his substantial greatness as a scientist in further peril by continuing to waste his time, and the money involved, in further airship experiments. Life is short, and he is capable of services to humanity incomparably greater than can be expected to result from trying to fly . . .' And a few decades later, in 1936, when technology had become much more part of life, Charles Lindbergh wrote to Harry Guggenheim of Robert Goddard's rocket research: 'I would much prefer to have Goddard interested in real scientific development than to have him primarily interested in more spectacular achievements which are of less real value.'

Even now one of the most popular quotes for after-dinner speeches has to be the famous prediction of Thomas Watson, Chairman of IBM, in 1943: 'I think there is a world market for maybe five computers.' And if you had suggested to our 1950s schoolboy that one day his, or her, 21st-century counterpart would have no idea what a slide rule was, or what log tables were all about, they would have thought you utterly crazy.

But it still does not follow that *this* time, *this* century should be any different, in terms of the revolutions in science and technology that come and go. Yes, as we shall see, we may well have the technology for a disease-free, hunger-free and even work-free existence. But then, too, the values, fears and hopes engendered in a chilly, smelly cottage on a bleak hillside would have produced an outlook very different from one based on a 20th-century upbringing in a centrally heated suburbia shimmering with shiny, chrome appliances and unforgiving neon lights. Yet we still have the same human brains as our very early ancestors, who stumbled uncomprehendingly around on the savannah some 100,000 years ago.

For the first time, however, our brains and bodies might be directly modified by electronic interfaces. For a second group, The Technophiles, such a prospect is welcome. The electrical engineer Kevin Warwick, for one, would welcome the prospect of heightened senses, sensations and muscle power that being a cyborg might bring—as we will see later. And cyber-guru Ray Kurzweil is gung-ho for the intimate embrace of silicon:

> There is a clear incentive to go down this path. Given a choice, people will prefer to keep their bones from crumbling, their skin supple, their life systems strong and vital. Improving our lives through neural implants on the mental level, and nanotechnology-enhanced bodies on the physical level, will be popular and compelling. It is another one of those slippery slopes—

> there is no obvious place to stop this progression until the human race has largely replaced the brains and bodies that evolution first provided.

Both Warwick and Kurzweil, not to mention other intellectual luminaries such as Marvin Minsky and Igor Aleksander, along with various futurologists such as Ian Pearson and Hans Moravec, all take it as read that another feature of future life will be conscious machines. Kurzweil's message is that our only future as a species will be to merge intimately with our technology: if you can't beat the robots, join them. So imagine a spectrum of beings, from pure carbon-based (as we humans are now) through the cyborg silicon-carbon hybrids that we could become to the ultimate— the vastly superior thinking silicon systems that will be Masters (and again they will have to be male) of the Universe.

It was actually because he was eavesdropping on a discussion between Kurzweil and the philosopher John Searle, concerning the very question of computer consciousness, that the co-founder and Chief Scientist of Sun Microsystems, Bill Joy, began to feel anxious about the direction in which future technology was heading. As an undisputed techno-mandarin, Joy created an enormous stir when he wrote of his urgent concern in the magazine *Wired*, in April 2000, in an article titled 'Why the future doesn't need us':

> The 21st-century technologies—genetics, nanotechnology, and robotics—are so powerful that they can spawn whole new classes of accidents and abuses. Most dangerously, for the first time, these accidents and abuses are widely within the reach of individuals and small groups. They will not require large facilities or rare raw materials. Knowledge alone will enable the use of them.

True, a critical difference between the technology of the 21st-century genetics, nanotechnology and robotics and that of the previous 100 years—darkening as they were with nuclear, biological and chemical doom—is that now it is no longer necessary to take over large facilities or access rare raw materials. Yet an even bigger change in the technology of the future, compared to that of the past, is that a nuclear bomb, though hideous in its potential, cannot self-replicate; but something that might—nanorobots—could soon be taking over the planet.

Just browse a few websites that are devoted to 'problems of preserving our civilization'. One worry, you will read, is that the manipulation of matter at the level of atoms, the nanotechnology that promises to be 'the manufacturing industry of the 21st century', will bring a new enemy—robots scaled down to the billionth of a metre that the nanolevel mandates, minuscule serfs who are focused on assembling copies of themselves. What might happen, one website asks, if such prolific yet single-minded operatives fell into the hands of even a lone terrorist? But then, of course, intelligent robots do not have to be small to be evil—just much cleverer than us. Common-or-garden human-sized machines might also soon be able to self-assemble, and, more importantly, to think autonomously.

Bill Joy had never thought of machines heretofore as having the ability to 'think'; now he is worried that they will, and in so doing lead us into a technology that may replace our species. He worries that humans will become so dependent on machines that we will let machines make decisions. And because these machines will be so much better than humans at working out the best course of action, soon we will capitulate entirely. Joy argues that, in any case, the problems will soon be so complex that humans will be incapable of grasping them. Considering that, in addition to greater mental

prowess, these silicon masterminds will have no need to sleep in, nor to hang out in bars, they will soon be way ahead of us, treating us as a lower species destined, as one website warns, to be 'used as domestic animals' or even 'kept in zoos'.

Kevin Warwick's predictions are similarly ominous: 'With intelligent machines we will not get a second chance. Once the first powerful machine, with an intelligence similar to that of a human, is switched on, we will most likely not get the opportunity to switch it back off again. We will have started a time bomb ticking on the human race, and we will be unable to switch it off.'

Equally nightmarish would be an elite minority of humans commanding large systems of machines, whilst the masses languish redundant. Either the elite will simply destroy this useless press of humanity or, in a more benign mood, generously brainwash them so that they give up reproducing and eventually make themselves extinct—it would be kindest to ensure that at all times the masses are universally content. They will be happy, but not free. It is a disturbing thought that these are the views of the Unabomber, Theodore Kaczynski; though he was obviously criminally insane, and no one would for a moment condone his actions, still Joy felt compelled to confront the sentiment that 'as we are downloaded into our own technology, our humanity will be lost'.

The coming Age of IT, then, offers a raft of possibilities from conscious automata to self-assembling autocrats to carbon-silicon hybrids. Extreme though such possibilities might seem, especially to The Cynics, it is very likely that a more modest version of carbon-silicon interfacing will feature in 21st-century life before too long. Soon computers will be invisible and ubiquitous—if not actually inside our bodies and brains then sprinkled throughout our clothes, in our spectacles and watches, and converting the most unlikely inanimate objects into 'smart' interactive gadgets.

The real problem is not what is technically feasible but the extent to which what is technically feasible can change our values. The gadgets of applied technology are the direct consequences of the big scientific breakthroughs of the previous century, and promise any day now to influence, with unprecedented intimacy, the previously independent, isolated inner world of the human mind. Yet this widespread availability of modern technology is, for some, a loud enough wake-up call for us to re-evaluate our priorities as a society. Bill Joy again: 'I think it is no exaggeration to say that we are on the cusp of the further perfection of extreme evil, an evil whose possibility spreads well beyond that which weapons of mass destruction bequeathed to the nation-states, on to a surprising and terrible empowerment of extreme individuals.'

But of course not all of this third group, The Technophobes, are scientists. Not surprisingly, and indeed more typically, non-scientists' fears are usually grounded in a more romantic view of life, but the fears are there nonetheless. In his Reith Lecture in 2000 Prince Charles summed up the worries of many: 'If literally nothing is held sacred anymore . . . what is there to prevent us treating our entire world as some 'great laboratory of life', with potentially disastrous long-term consequences?'

It may be a little unfair, and certainly incautious, to write off this type of view as simply that of latter-day Luddites, striving in vain to hold back progress with a misconceived vision of some golden bygone age when humans adhered to a Rousseau-like natural nobility, and no one died in childbirth, suffered poor housing, worked at mind-numbing manual tasks or froze to death . . . It's just that for many there is a very real fear that science, and the technology that it has spawned, have outpaced the checks

and balances we need for society to survive—indeed for life as we know it to continue at all.

In our growing knowledge of life, in biology, the trend for science to be slipping out of control appears already to be gaining an ever faster pace. The rigid hierarchy of a society segregated by biochemical and genetic manipulation, from intellectual 'alphas' down to 'epsilons' who operate the lifts, portrayed by Aldous Huxley in *Brave New World*, is now seen as a real future threat by many. Predictably, a morass of websites express serious concerns over genetics, for example: 'The path is open, bypassing the natural evolution, to design unusual creatures—from fairly useful to imagination-striking monsters.'

And we might well end up with 'designer' babies, potential geniuses or highly obedient and tough soldiers. But manipulation of genes allows further possibilities too; offset against the benefits of gene therapy and new types of medication and diagnostics, there are clones, artificial genes, germ-line engineering, and the tricky relationship of genetic profiling to insurance premiums and job applications. In any event, for The Technophobes, the question of basic survival seems far from certain; according to Bill Joy, the philosopher John Leslie puts the risk of human extinction at 30 per cent at the least. And the astronomer Martin Rees, in his latest book, *Our Final Century*, rates the chance as no better than odds on that civilization will avoid a catastrophic setback.

No one could really disagree with Aristotle that 'All men by nature desire to know'; the human brain has evolved to ask questions, and to survive by answering them. Science is simply the formal realization of our natural curiosity. Yet no one could fool themselves any longer that, as we stand on the cusp of this new century, we are travelling the simple path of 'progress'. Sure, for several generations now we have strived to balance the pay-off between 'unnatural' mechanization and a pain-free, hunger-free, longer-lasting existence; but now we face a future of interactive and highly personalized information technology, an intrusive but invisible nanotechnology, not to mention a sophisticated and powerful biotechnology, that could all conspire together to challenge how we think, what kind of individuals we are, and even whether each of us stays an individual at all.

For The Cynics the implications that this prospect poses, in all its horror and excitement, will be sensationalist hype at best and scaremongering at worst. They won't believe that science will ever be able to produce new types of fundamentally life-transforming technologies, and even if it were, they feel that humans are sufficiently wise and have an inbuilt sanity check to deal with any ethical, cultural or intellectual choices that might ensue. This attitude is not only questionable—in the light of the far more modest precedents that we have witnessed in technology over the last half century—but also chillingly complacent. Can we really afford to assume that humanity will be able to muddle through? And even if we did survive as the unique personalities we are now, in a world bristling with biotech, infotech and nanotech, can we still be sure that such passivity, just letting it all happen, will be the best way to optimize the benefits and reduce any ensuing risks?

Perhaps both Technophiles and Technophobes would agree on one very important issue that sets them aside from The Cynics: we must be proactive and set the agenda for what we want and need from such rapid technical advances; only then shall we, our children and our grandchildren come to have the best life possible. So first we need to evaluate the 21st-century technologies, and then unflinchingly open our minds to all possibilities . . .

Discussion Questions

1. Briefly describe the Cynic, the Technophile, and the Technophobe's view of the role of technology in the future. In which camp do you place yourself? These categories should sound familiar—they were presented in Section One. Has your answer to this question changed as a result of participation in this course?

2. Support or refute Bill Joy's contention, echoed by Greenfield, that robotics, nanotechnology, and genetics pose a fundamentally greater risk to humanity than do the previous generation's "big three" technological fears: biological, chemical, and nuclear.

3. Based on your knowledge of the emerging technologies highlighted in this article, which of these three technologies do you think will have the greatest impact on humanity as a whole? Do you see this impact as positive or negative? Explain your answer.

4. In your opinion, which aspect of humanity is in greatest need of a technological revolution?

 Supporting Activities

1. Identify an emerging technology that you think holds the greatest promise for humanity and learn more about it. At what stage of development is the technology? How soon is the technology expected to be "ready for prime time?"

2. Research and briefly report on some notable "futurist." What was his or her main contribution to the field?

3. Check out the Web site of the World Futurist Society www.wfs.org. Some parts of their journal, *The Futurist*, are available online at no cost. Briefly report on one thing you learned from the Web site.

4. Conduct the following group futuring activity:
   a. Identify a technology from one of the readings in this book.
   b. Determine a "preferred future" (or where you would like the United States to be with regard to technology policy in this area) for the year 2015.
   c. Identify (brainstorm) a variety of means, or policy options, for reaching that preferred future. Write down all ideas.
   d. After group discussion, select **two** of these policy options that you believe hold the most promise. Consider the feasibility of the options selected.
   e. Identify potential outcomes (both positive and negative) of implementing these two policies, including economic, environmental, moral/ethical, social, political and cultural outcomes.

5. Describe some hypothetical events that might disrupt the historic trends of technological development from the present day and continuing into the future. For example, what type of event might disrupt the trend of greater numbers of personal automobiles worldwide? Think of a particular technological context described in this book, examine current trends with regard to that technology, and then consider and describe the effects of disruptive events.

Additional Resources

1. Visit the Web site of the World Futurist Society (www.wfs.org).
2. Visit the Web site of the International Institute of Forecasters (www.forecasters.org).
3. Look for and read the series of books from prominent inventor, author, and futurist Ray Kurzweil: *The Age of Intelligent Machines* (1990), *The Age of Spiritual Machines* (1999), and *The Singularity is Near* (2005), all published by Penguin Books.
4. Watch the classic movie that really put Sci-Fi on the map: *2001: A Space Odyssey* (1967). The film won an Academy Award and has been deemed "culturally, historically, or aesthetically significant" by the Library of Congress.
5. Watch the movies in the Terminator Series: *The Terminator* (1984; recognized by the Library of Congress as "culturally, historically, or aesthetically significant"); *Terminator 2: Judgment Day* (1991; winner of four Academy Awards); and *Terminator 3: Rise of the Machines* (2003).

A Robot in Every Home

Who better than Bill Gates to predict the future of high-tech industry? After all, he was instrumental in guiding the first computer revolution that quite literally put a computer on every desk. If Bill Gates thinks a technology is "hot" you should probably listen.

And Mr. Gates thinks robotics is hot. Or rather, soon will be. Not surprisingly, he envisions a world in which "the PC will get up off the desktop and allow us to see, hear, touch, and manipulate objects in places where we are not physically present." This is already happening in a few niche applications, but Mr. Gates predicts that in the future robots will contribute to virtually every facet of society, including manufacturing, medicine, dangerous or mundane jobs, domestic chores, and *companionship* (mentioned twice in the article).

While he touts the potential of robotics, Mr. Gates is also quick to point out the technical challenges that remain. The remaining challenges, if you take the article at face value, would appear to be all technical, things like processor speed and storage, sensors, and—most importantly—clever algorithms. It's not surprising that a technophile like Bill Gates focuses on the remaining technical obstacles to widespread robotic integration. Perhaps it's equally unsurprising that Microsoft Corporation is stepping up to provide these clever algorithms with products like the concurrency and coordination runtime (CCR) environment and decentralized software services (DSS). Through these efforts, Microsoft hopes to "standardize" (a euphemism for "monopolize"?) the robotics software industry.

What is perhaps lacking in the article is a discussion of "why?" and, more importantly, a consideration of "why not?" Mr. Gates' tone is one of grateful inevitability, that robots will soon be with us and he just can't wait. He writes about asking robotics experts what they need in order to move forward, but doesn't mention asking anyone else how they feel about having advanced robotics. There's no mention of ethics, no weighing of the pros and cons of robotics—in fact, no acknowledgment that there may be negative considerations.

Bill Gates is cofounder of Microsoft Corporation and consistently ranks as one of the world's richest men. The Bill and Melinda Gates Foundation, founded in 2000, has a $35 billion endowment and focuses on improving health, reducing poverty, and increasing access to technology around the world.

A Robot in Every Home

By Bill Gates

The leader of the PC revolution predicts that the next hot field will be robotics

Imagine being present at the birth of a new industry. It is an industry based on groundbreaking new technologies, wherein a handful of well-established corporations sell highly specialized devices for business use and a fast-growing number of start-up companies produce innovative toys, gadgets for hobbyists and other interesting niche products. But it is also a highly fragmented industry with few common standards or platforms. Projects are complex, progress is slow, and practical applications are relatively rare. In fact, for all the excitement and

Reprinted by permission. Copyright © 2007 by Scientific American, Inc. All rights reserved.

promise, no one can say with any certainty when—or even if—this industry will achieve critical mass. If it does, though, it may well change the world.

Of course, the paragraph above could be a description of the computer industry during the mid-1970s, around the time that Paul Allen and I launched Microsoft. Back then, big, expensive mainframe computers ran the back-office operations for major companies, governmental departments and other institutions. Researchers at leading universities and industrial laboratories were creating the basic building blocks that would make the information age possible. Intel had just introduced the 8080 microprocessor, and Atari was selling the popular electronic game Pong. At homegrown computer clubs, enthusiasts struggled to figure out exactly what this new technology was good for.

But what I really have in mind is something much more contemporary: the emergence of the robotics industry, which is developing in much the same way that the computer business did 30 years ago. Think of the manufacturing robots currently used on automobile assembly lines as the equivalent of yesterday's mainframes. The industry's niche products include robotic arms that perform surgery, surveillance robots deployed in Iraq and Afghanistan that dispose of roadside bombs, and domestic robots that vacuum the floor. Electronics companies have made robotic toys that can imitate people or dogs or dinosaurs, and hobbyists are anxious to get their hands on the latest version of the Lego robotics system.

Meanwhile some of the world's best minds are trying to solve the toughest problems of robotics, such as visual recognition, navigation and machine learning. And they are succeeding. At the 2004 Defense Advanced Research Projects Agency (DARPA) Grand Challenge, a competition to produce the first robotic vehicle capable of navigating autonomously over a rugged 142-mile course through the Mojave Desert, the top competitor managed to travel just 7.4 miles before breaking down. In 2005, though, five vehicles covered the complete distance, and the race's winner did it at an average speed of 19.1 miles an hour. (In another intriguing parallel between the robotics and computer industries, DARPA also funded the work that led to the creation of Arpanet, the precursor to the Internet.)

What is more, the challenges facing the robotics industry are similar to those we tackled in computing three decades ago. Robotics companies have no standard operating software that could allow popular application programs to run in a variety of devices. The standardization of robotic processors and other hardware is limited, and very little of the programming code used in one machine can be applied to another. Whenever somebody wants to build a new robot, they usually have to start from square one.

Despite these difficulties, when I talk to people involved in robotics—from university researchers to entrepreneurs, hobbyists and high school students—the level of excitement and expectation reminds me so much of that time when Paul Allen and I looked at the convergence of new technologies and dreamed of the day when a computer would be on every desk and in every home. And as I look at the trends that are now starting to converge, I can envision a future in which robotic devices will become a nearly ubiquitous part of our day-to-day lives. I believe that technologies such as distributed computing, voice and visual recognition, and wireless broadband connectivity will open the door to a new generation of autonomous devices that enable computers to perform tasks in the physical world on our behalf. We may be on the verge of a new era, when the PC will get up off the desktop and allow us to see, hear, touch and manipulate objects in places where we are not physically present.

From Science Fiction to Reality

The word "robot" was popularized in 1921 by Czech playwright Karel Čapek, but people have envisioned creating robotlike devices for thousands of years. In Greek and Roman mythology, the gods of metalwork built mechanical servants made from gold. In the first century A.D., Heron of Alexandria—the great engineer credited with inventing the first steam engine—designed intriguing automatons, including one said to have the ability to talk. Leonardo da Vinci's 1495 sketch of a mechanical knight, which could sit up and move its arms and legs, is considered to be the first plan for a humanoid robot.

Over the past century, anthropomorphic machines have become familiar figures in popular culture through books such as Isaac Asimov's *I, Robot,* movies such as *Star Wars* and television shows such as *Star Trek*. The popularity of robots in fiction indicates that people are receptive to the idea that these machines will one day walk among us as helpers and even as companions. Nevertheless, although robots play a vital role in industries such as automobile manufacturing—where there is about one robot for every 10 workers—the fact is that we have a long way to go before real robots catch up with their science-fiction counterparts.

One reason for this gap is that it has been much harder than expected to enable computers and robots to sense their surrounding environment and to react quickly and accurately. It has proved extremely difficult to give robots the capabilities that humans take for granted—for example, the abilities to orient themselves with respect to the objects in a room, to respond to sounds and interpret speech, and to grasp objects of varying sizes, textures and fragility. Even something as simple as telling the difference between an open door and a window can be devilishly tricky for a robot.

But researchers are starting to find the answers. One trend that has helped them is the increasing availability of tremendous amounts of computer power. One megahertz of processing power, which cost more than $7,000 in 1970, can now be purchased for just pennies. The price of a megabit of storage has seen a similar decline. The access to cheap computing power has permitted scientists to work on many of the hard problems that are fundamental to making robots practical. Today, for example, voice-recognition programs can identify words quite well, but a far greater challenge will be building machines that can understand what those words mean in context. As computing capacity continues to expand, robot designers will have the processing power they need to tackle issues of ever greater complexity.

Another barrier to the development of robots has been the high cost of hardware, such as sensors that enable a robot to determine the distance to an object as well as motors and servos that allow the robot to manipulate an object with both strength and delicacy. But prices are dropping fast. Laser range finders that are used in robotics to measure distance with precision cost about $10,000 a few years ago; today they can be purchased for about $2,000. And new, more accurate sensors based on ultrawideband radar are available for even less.

Now robot builders can also add Global Positioning System chips, video cameras, array microphones (which are better than conventional microphones at distinguishing a voice from background noise) and a host of additional sensors for a reasonable expense. The resulting enhancement of capabilities, combined with expanded processing power and storage, allows today's robots to do things such as vacuum a room or help to defuse a roadside bomb—tasks that would have been impossible for commercially produced machines just a few years ago.

A BASIC Approach

In February 2004 I visited a number of leading universities, including Carnegie Mellon University, the Massachusetts Institute of Technology, Harvard University, Cornell University and the University of Illinois, to talk about the powerful role that computers can play in solving some of society's most pressing problems. My goal was to help students understand how exciting and important computer science can be, and I hoped to encourage a few of them to think about careers in technology. At each university, after delivering my speech, I had the opportunity to get a firsthand look at some of the most interesting research projects in the school's computer science department. Almost without exception, I was shown at least one project that involved robotics.

At that time, my colleagues at Microsoft were also hearing from people in academia and at commercial robotics firms who wondered if our company was doing any work in robotics that might help them with their own development efforts. We were not, so we decided to take a closer look. I asked Tandy Trower, a member of my strategic staff and a 25-year Microsoft veteran, to go on an extended fact-finding mission and to speak with people across the robotics community. What he found was universal enthusiasm for the potential of robotics, along with an industry-wide desire for tools that would make development easier. "Many see the robotics industry at a technological turning point where a move to PC architecture makes more and more sense," Tandy wrote in his report to me after his fact-finding mission. "As Red Whittaker, leader of [Carnegie Mellon's] entry in the DARPA Grand Challenge, recently indicated, the hardware capability is mostly there; now the issue is getting the software right."

Back in the early days of the personal computer, we realized that we needed an ingredient that would allow all of the pioneering work to achieve critical mass, to coalesce into a real industry capable of producing truly useful products on a commercial scale. What was needed, it turned out, was Microsoft BASIC. When we created this programming language in the 1970s, we provided the common foundation that enabled programs developed for one set of hardware to run on another. BASIC also made computer programming much easier, which brought more and more people into the industry. Although a great many individuals made essential contributions to the development of the personal computer, Microsoft BASIC was one of the key catalysts for the software and hardware innovations that made the PC revolution possible.

After reading Tandy's report, it seemed clear to me that before the robotics industry could make the same kind of quantum leap that the PC industry made 30 years ago, it, too, needed to find that missing ingredient. So I asked him to assemble a small team that would work with people in the robotics field to create a set of programming tools that would provide the essential plumbing so that anybody interested in robots with even the most basic understanding of computer programming could easily write robotic applications that would work with different kinds of hardware. The goal was to see if it was possible to provide the same kind of common, low-level foundation for integrating hardware and software into robot designs that Microsoft BASIC provided for computer programmers.

Tandy's robotics group has been able to draw on a number of advanced technologies developed by a team working under the direction of Craig Mundie, Microsoft's chief research and strategy officer. One such technology will help

Lego Mindstorms. A tool set for building and programming robots, has become the best-selling product in the history of the Lego Group, the Danish toy maker.

Source: ©2004 The Lego Group (*Lego Mindstorms*).

solve one of the most difficult problems facing robot designers: how to simultaneously handle all the data coming in from multiple sensors and send the appropriate commands to the robot's motors, a challenge known as concurrency. A conventional approach is to write a traditional, single-threaded program—a long loop that first reads all the data from the sensors, then processes this input and finally delivers output that determines the robot's behavior, before starting the loop all over again. The shortcomings are obvious: if your robot has fresh sensor data indicating that the machine is at the edge of a precipice, but the program is still at the bottom of the loop calculating trajectory and telling the wheels to turn faster based on previous sensor input, there is a good chance the robot will fall down the stairs before it can process the new information.

Concurrency is a challenge that extends beyond robotics. Today as more and more applications are written for distributed networks of computers, programmers have struggled to figure out how to efficiently orchestrate code running on many different servers at the same time. And as computers with a single processor are replaced by machines with multiple processors and "multicore" processors—integrated circuits with two or more processors joined together for enhanced performance—software designers will need a new way to program desktop applications and operating systems. To fully exploit the power of processors working in parallel, the new software must deal with the problem of concurrency.

One approach to handling concurrency is to write multi-threaded programs that allow data to travel along many paths. But as any developer who has written multithreaded code can tell you, this is one of the hardest tasks in programming. The answer that Craig's team has devised to the concurrency problem is something called the concurrency and coordination runtime (CCR). The CCR is a library of functions—sequences of software code that perform specific tasks—that makes it easy to write multithreaded applications that can coordinate a number of simultaneous activities. Designed to help programmers take advantage of the power of multicore and multiprocessor systems, the CCR turns out to be ideal for robotics as well. By drawing on this library to write their programs, robot designers can dramatically reduce the chances that one of their creations will run into a wall because its software is too busy sending output to its wheels to read input from its sensors.

In addition to tackling the problem of concurrency, the work that Craig's team has done will also simplify the writing of distributed robotic applications through a technology called decentralized software services (DSS). DSS enables developers to create applications in which the services—the parts of the program that read a sensor, say, or control a motor—operate as separate processes that can be orchestrated in much the same way that text, images and information from several servers are aggregated on a Web page. Because DSS allows software components to run in isolation from one another, if an individual component of a robot fails, it can be shut down and restarted—or even replaced—without having to reboot the machine. Combined with broadband wireless technology, this architecture makes it easy to monitor and adjust a robot from a remote location using a Web browser.

What is more, a DSS application controlling a robotic device does not have to reside entirely on the robot itself but can be distributed across more than one computer. As a result, the robot can be a relatively inexpensive device that delegates complex processing tasks to the high-performance hardware found on today's home PCs. I believe this advance will pave the way for an entirely new class of robots that are essentially mobile, wireless peripheral devices that tap into the power of desktop PCs to handle processing-intensive tasks such as visual recognition and navigation. And because these devices can be networked together, we can expect to see the emergence of groups of robots that can work in concert to achieve goals such as mapping the seafloor or planting crops.

These technologies are a key part of Microsoft Robotics Studio, a new software development kit built by Tandy's team. Microsoft Robotics Studio also includes tools that make it easier to create robotic applications using a wide range of programming languages. One example is a simulation tool that lets robot builders test their applications in a three-dimensional virtual environment before trying them out in the real world. Our goal for this release is to create an affordable, open platform that allows robot developers to readily integrate hardware and software into their designs.

Should We Call Them Robots?

How soon will robots become part of our day-to-day lives? According to the International Federation of Robotics, about two million personal robots were in use around the world in 2004, and another seven million will be installed by 2008. In South Korea the Ministry of Information and Communication hopes to put a robot in every home there by 2013. The Japanese Robot Association predicts that by 2025, the personal robot industry will be worth more than $50 billion a year worldwide, compared with about $5 billion today.

As with the PC industry in the 1970s, it is impossible to predict exactly what applications will drive this new industry. It seems quite likely, however, that robots will play an important role in providing physical assistance and even companionship for the elderly. Robotic devices will probably help people with disabilities get around and extend the strength and endurance of soldiers, construction workers and medical professionals. Robots will maintain dangerous industrial machines, handle hazardous materials and monitor remote oil pipelines. They will enable health care workers to diagnose and treat patients who may be thousands of miles away, and they will be a central feature of security systems and search-and-rescue operations.

Although a few of the robots of tomorrow may resemble the anthropomorphic devices seen in *Star Wars*, most will look nothing like the humanoid C-3PO. In fact, as mobile peripheral devices become more and more common, it may be increasingly difficult to say exactly what a robot is. Because the new machines will be so specialized and ubiquitous—and look so little like the two-legged automatons of science fiction—we probably will not even call them robots. But as these devices become affordable to consumers, they could have just as profound an impact on the way we work, communicate, learn and entertain ourselves as the PC has had over the past 30 years.

Discussion Questions

1. In your opinion, what are the pros to widespread adoption of robotics technologies? To help focus your response, consider the following applications:
   - "intelligent" robots in manufacturing
   - "intelligent" robots providing health care services
   - "intelligent" domestic servant robots
   - "intelligent" robots performing dangerous jobs
   - robot soldiers
   - hybrid human/robots

   Be sure to provide specific examples to illustrate your points.
2. For the applications described above, what do you see as cons? Again, be specific.
3. Are you in favor of public financial support for research and development of robotics technologies? Are you in favor of regulating private research and development? Explain your opinion.

 Supporting Activities

1. Write a short report about a "famous" real robot such as ASIMO, Stanley, or Sojourner.
2. Watch a movie in which a robot is an important figure. Write a one-page report that includes a brief summary but that primarily focuses on the issues raised with regard to robotic technology.
3. Check out the robotics research programs at the University of Southern California (http://www-robotics.usc.edu/); Johns Hopkins (http://lcsr.jhu.edu/); University of Texas at Austin (http://www.robotics.utexas.edu/); MIT (http://darbeloflab.mit.edu/node/28); and Harvard (http://hrl.harvard.edu/research/).

 Additional Resources

1. Microsoft's robotics software, Robotics Developer Studio, can be previewed at: http://msdn.microsoft.com/en-us/robotics/default.aspx.
2. For information about DARPA's Urban Challenge 2007 see: http://www.darpa.mil/grandchallenge/index.asp.

The Quest for Mars

It may seem that a reading about a manned mission to Mars would be the least relevant to this book's mission of exploring the relationship between technology and society. After all, how many of us will be directly affected if humankind colonizes another planet? Will space technology impact society as much as, say, robotics? Probably not. However, the study of the "business" of space travel can provide valuable insights into how society affects technology; that is, what are the social factors that result in the success of one technology over another? This article does just that.

You may be surprised that there are more presidents mentioned in this excerpt about Mars than there are astronauts. The success of a Mars mission appears to rest on the State of the Union speech rather than the state of rocket technology. Lambright alludes to a few technological challenges, including propulsion and closed biosphere engineering, but he makes it clear that the most critical components of a successful space exploration program are a supportive government and an interested citizenry.

A general conclusion can be drawn. Any "high-tech" endeavor (indeed, this is arguably the highest-tech endeavor ever undertaken by humankind) is inherently also a social endeavor requiring public support and considerable project management expertise. Its success or failure is in large part determined by quirks of history, politics, leadership, and popular whim, perhaps more so than on the technical gadgetry.

Let's put this theory to the test. In 1966, during the heyday of the Apollo program, NASA's budget represented 5.5 percent of the total Federal budget. By 2007, this percentage had dropped to 0.6 percent.[2] Clearly, governmental commitment to space exploration had waned. To put things into perspective, according to 1997 data consumers in the U.S. spent over three times the NASA budget on tobacco alone.[3] Clearly, public interest in and commitment to space exploration has diminished.

Rather than being discouraged by the nature of the decision-making process, we can be encouraged by the influential role that groups outside the political mainstream, in one case a group of college students, have had on building and sustaining an interest in a Mars mission. An understanding of the decision-making process will hopefully empower readers to get involved in causes they believe in strongly.

The Quest for Mars

By W. Henry Lambright and Debora L. VanNijnatten

The early twenty-first century stands as a watershed between the space program that was and the space program that will be. The past is highlighted by Apollo and by Neil Armstrong's epochal "one small step for [a] man . . . one giant leap for mankind." The future that could be is human spaceflight to Mars. As the moon highlights NASA's twentieth-century past, Mars stands as a symbol for what can come in the twenty-first century. It is an exciting and inspirational goal by which advocates can organize action and mobilize political support. For them the question is less *whether* an expedition to Mars will come than *when, how,* and *why.*

Through unmanned flights and related technological development, NASA is already

Lambright, W. Henry, ed. *Space Policy in the Twenty-First Century.* pp. 173, 185–197. © 2002 The Johns Hopkins University Press. Reprinted with permission of The Johns Hopkins University Press.

moving today toward human spaceflight to Mars, but the process is halting and fragmented. There was an earlier decision to send humans to Mars, but it lacked commitment. Whether the next decision will be sustained remains to be seen. Critical to doing so will be the creation of a coalition of support as substantial as the goal is large. If that coalition can be maintained, the decision to go to Mars will lead, not to a brief moment of glory as with Apollo, but eventually to a permanent presence on the Red Planet.

Implementating the Decision

If humanity is to go to Mars, there will have to be a major policy decision, given the organization and resource demands. However, even more complicated than getting a decision will be carrying it out. Implementing a Mars decision will involve a vast long-term coordination effort, far more ambitious than the Space Station. Given its relative resources, the United States will most likely be the lead nation, and NASA will be the responsible agency within the United States. A Mars endeavor can be best conceived as a multinational technical project, the largest in history, in which talent, money, and decisions are shared. All of this will make for enormous complexity and unprecedented management challenges. However, lessons—positive and negative—will undoubtedly have been learned from the Space Station.

In the 1960s, NASA was literally re-created for Apollo into a large research and development agency capable of managing a far-flung government, industry, and university team—in essence driving a national coalition. In the 1990s, NASA was consciously reinvented again, this time reducing its size in an effort to bring new economies and efficiencies in the interest of "better, faster, cheaper" space projects. On the assumption that especially bold programs re-

quire high-capacity agencies to manage them, the Mars program will almost certainly necessitate a third reinvention. NASA will likely be leader of a coalition that is unprecedented in size, involving both international partners and the private sector. Mars will require a twenty-first-century version of a "large-scale approach" to management. Faster, better, cheaper does not seem adequate to what is involved.

If NASA is to lead in a Mars program, it will have to divest itself of ongoing operational responsibilities for the Space Shuttle and the Space Station, the better to concentrate on the pioneering research and development required of a Mars mission. As Leib points out in chapter 4, maintaining and using the Space Station will be absorbing tasks for many years. However, they do not necessarily have to be tasks performed and paid for by NASA.

Fulfilling a Mars decision will require political and managerial skills of the highest order. The priority of a program can go up or down with an election, the economy, or a technological setback. It is critical that the management team buffer technical decisions from political interference even as political support is sought. The leaders of NASA and its institutional allies must hold to the goal in spite of shifting winds. There is no avoiding the conclusion that an organization that is weak politically cannot take humans to Mars.

Three Routes to Mars

Implementation can vary in speed. There can be small or large steps. How quickly to go depends on technology and politics. It also depends on the costs spacefaring nations and the public constituency underlying them are willing to bear and the risks they choose to endure.

There are three tracks to Mars that appear in the writings of present advocates: fast, mid-range, and gradual. The *fast track* is provided in the writings of Sagan and (especially) Zubrin. Zubrin calls his plan "Mars Direct." This approach omits the moon as an intermediary step. Zubrin calls the moon a "siren song,"[37] an unnecessary diversion. His rationale is if you want to go to Mars, go to Mars! He argues that the moon is so different from Mars that it would not provide a learning experience any better than Antarctica—or Wyoming, for that matter. Sagan agrees: "A lunar base wouldn't be a detour on the road to Mars, but a trap. We would use up [financial] resources and indefinitely delay going to Mars. Mars is much more exciting."[38]

Zubrin and other "fast trackers" espouse a "live off the land" philosophy. Instead of taking a huge amount of supplies and creating infrastructures along the way, they would fly to Mars as fast as possible and convert resources on Mars to facilitate living there and returning to Earth. Mars Direct, according to Zubrin, could be achieved with minimal new technology within ten years at a cost from $20 to $30 billion.[39]

The *mid-track* is seen in the Augustine and Stafford reports. They call for the moon as an interim step. They emphasize the moon is 250,000 miles away, a three-day journey achieved before. Men and women sent there can presumably return relatively easily if something goes wrong. Mars is 35 million miles from Earth when most proximate. The distance increases to 230 million miles when Earth and Mars are on opposite sides of the sun. That distance and the extra requirements it places on human beings and machines argue for more time, learning, and technological development, using the moon as a stepping stone.[40]

The *gradual track* has been proposed by Wesley Huntress, former Associate Administrator for Space Science at NASA and president of the American Astronautical Society. It provides an interim program for humans in space be-

yond the Space Station if the nation is not politically ready for the decision to go to Mars. That rationale is linked closely to space science. He lists three grand challenges in space science where human spaceflight is relevant:

First, to read the history and destiny of the solar system. How did it come to be, what is its fate and what does its origin and evolution imply for other planetary systems? Second, to look for evidence of life elsewhere in the solar system—at Mars, at Europa, wherever in the history of the solar system there has been liquid water; [and] third, to image and study planets around other stars. Ultimately, to find Earth-like planets in other planetary systems.

"The ultimate destination [for human exploration remains] the surface of Mars," he declares, "but the capability to accomplish that mission is developed and tested over time in less risky missions along a natural evolutionary technological pathway. It is not a Mars-or-bust program."[41]

What is the role of humans in accomplishing the space science goals? One is that they can ferry equipment from the Space Station to deeper space where they could build a large space telescope facility. Lagrangian points in space—where the gravity of Earth and the moon balance—allow for stable, relatively unattended equipment and are ideal for observation. However, they are more distant in space than the Space Station's low-Earth orbit. Hence, NASA could develop new capability to go beyond the Space Station to operate further out.

From astronomical operations at Lagrangian points, human beings could move progressively to more difficult tasks in space such as exploring asteroids. Thus, Huntress recommends going back to the moon for reasons of science as well as a spur to develop additional human spaceflight capabilities. Only after these efforts does he propose flight to Mars. Here also he takes a gradualist approach, suggesting that instead of a direct assault, a space station in Mars orbit be built to support operations to and from the surface. All of these steps reduce risk.[42]

Issues: Developing Technology

Each of these tracks has challenges in technological development. The trade-offs are excruciating. Huntress sacrifices speed for scientific payoff but also "buys time" to build support for a Mars decision after the Space Station is built. However, time is money. His plan requires developing a new shuttle to go from the Space Station to Lagrangian points, asteroids, and the moon. He also recommends a new space station around Mars. Choices, particularly those of pace, will be propelled in large part by what kind of trigger stimulates decision. The fastest-paced decisions, because they are more likely to cost more in the short-term and put human lives at greatest risk, will require the most dramatic triggers, the clearest decisions, and the most substantial political support.

Important lessons can be learned from Apollo, the Space Station, and other recent technological projects that can be applied to developing technology for Mars. For example, as Madison and McCurdy note, "Unlike the trip to the moon, which in eight years moved with ever increasing specificity from concept to execution, the Space Station effort for nine years languished in the design phase."[43] During this period approximately $10 billion was spent with little hardware actually being built. This was more than the original projected cost of the entire construction project. Needless to say, the 1984 goal of Reagan to build the Space Station within ten years was missed mightily. The lesson for advocates is to move as quickly as possible through the technology development phase. In this way, proponents can show progress, and opposition has less opportunity to mobilize.

Similarly, NASA is anticipating opposition in connection with an early unmanned mission to Mars—Mars Sample Return. Expecting environmental and health issues to be raised with receipt on Earth of samples, NASA plans to build a containment facility. Although sample return is perhaps a decade away, NASA has enlisted a consultant organization to help plan how to engage the public to deal with perceived risks.

Furthermore, one technology among many that will have to be developed during the implementation period is that of "closed loop ecological life systems." The Augustine panel pointed out that "air and water must be recycled and nourishing food produced within automated closed-cycle support systems." "However," the panel continued, "little is known about constructing reliable biospheres that can be depended upon for continuous automated production of food and organic materials and the removal of toxins and contaminants." Mars will entail long-duration spaceflight of a kind never experienced before. The Augustine panel called closed ecological systems among "the least understood and the most challenging" technologies to be developed in any Mars program.[44]

Another fateful technological development ahead pertains to propulsion. A decision will be made between conventional chemically based fuel or more advanced transportation technologies. The Stafford panel said unequivocally that while a trip to the moon with conventional fuel was possible, a nuclear-powered rocket was the preferred technology in the case of Mars, owing to far greater technical efficiency.[45] It behooves those who favor this technological approach to understand that environmentalists and arms control activists are likely to lobby against nuclear technology as they did against the nuclear-fueled *Cassini* mission. Opposition to means can prevent realization of the end.

Issues: The Human Factor

Each of the three routes to Mars will place unprecedented physical and psychological stress on humans. How little is known about such stress is unsettling. In 1991, for example, eight people entered and sealed the airlock on Biosphere 2 in Arizona for a two-year mission. The facility, while controversial and imperfect, did sustain eight humans for the full two years, along with 3,800 species of plants and animals. The crew also was able to produce about 80 percent of its food through intensive agricultural activities and to recycle 100 percent of the human and domestic animal wastes and 100 percent of the water in their environment. Increases in carbon dioxide levels and dropping oxygen levels were a constant threat, however. In addition, some species of plants and animals disappeared, and the biospherians had to struggle to maintain food production in the controlled environment. A number of the biospherians left the facility in a substantially weakened condition.[46]

At one point, a crewmember severed a fingertip in a threshing machine in the Biosphere 2 facility, had to leave it for a brief time to get treated, and then returned. Accidents and health problems in a Mars expedition will have to be treated where they occur. In an expedition to Mars, there will be unique health problems such as dangers from radiation, solar flares, and lack of normal gravity. In preparing for Mars, experience must be accumulated in telemedicine so that procedures can be communicated by experts on Earth to a doctor-astronaut in space and, if the doctor is the victim, to someone else. That a doctor can be a victim in a remote place is pointed up by a recent case where a doctor in Antarctica was diagnosed with possible cancer and could not be readily evacuated due to weather conditions. She had to treat herself as best she could.

Moreover, there are potential psychological traumas. A considerable body of research exists on the behavioral and performance problems associated with long-term isolation in polar locations, especially in Antarctica. Early studies found that Antarctic wintering-over parties experienced such effects as "absent-mindedness" and emotional disturbances.[47] The relatively brief experience of U.S. and Russian astronauts/cosmonauts on *Mir* suggests that psychological problems can be heightened by cultural differences. There is much speculation and concern about who should ultimately go to Mars in terms of personality, sex, marital status, and so forth. In Biosphere 2, individuals experienced "fits of apathy, listlessness, anger, callous aloofness, and fear."[48]

The Space Station will provide opportunity to learn much about technological and human factors in space. This is one of its chief purposes. However, there are limits to what it can teach, particularly if one of the more direct routes to Mars is selected. The extreme distance of Mars from Earth—35 million miles at its closest—will place singular demands on human endurance and psychology. If conventional chemical rockets are used, it will take 230 days one way and require surface stays of 500 days while the planets realign to expedite a return trip. While nuclear propulsion could provide more flexibility, according to the Stafford panel, explorers are very likely to be away from their home planet for well over two years.[49]

That is a major reason some Mars advocates believe the moon is an essential learning laboratory for technology and man. Establishing a lunar outpost "is needed to learn how to live and work on the surface of an alien planet," said the Augustine panel. "Particularly important will be the testing of habitats; closed ecological life support systems and remote space-rated power plants; learning to process and use indigenous materials; observing the effects of living in extreme heat, cold, and dust in low-gravity fields; and developing reliable systems to provide radiation protection and surface mobility for humans and robots through 300 hour-long days and nights."[50] The moon can provide lessons learned in coping with medical, psychological and socio-cultural problems. Similarly, the approach outlined by Huntress provides opportunities beyond the moon for learning to cope with human factors in deep space, far from home, in preparation for Mars.

Achieving the First Mars Landing

Still, when all is said and done, the first expedition to Mars will be a totally new experience. It will be daunting—more so if the fast track is the route, less so if the gradual track is used. An expedition will be preceded by years of unmanned expeditions to survey the planet on select optimal landing sites. The features of Mars are quite different from the moon and Earth. One-third the size of Earth, Mars has a diverse and rugged topography, with a volcano far higher than Mt. Everest and canyons as long as North America is wide. The atmosphere of Mars is mostly carbon dioxide, and there are periodic dust storms. These features require power systems, rover landers, rover vehicles, and habitats especially relevant to Mars.[51]

Landing humans on Mars will be one of the most awesome events in history. It will also be quite controversial. There may be religious groups that will object to the very idea of seeking life beyond Earth. However, the more influential protests are likely to come from environmentalists and scientists because the issue of extraterrestrial life is a double-edged sword. There are those who worry about the possibility of astronauts bringing back to Earth an "Andromeda Strain" that could infect the human species. Others worry that humans will contaminate Mars if there is bacterial life of some form

there. Such concerns will have to be taken seriously by advocates of a Mars expedition, and elaborate precautions made. Risks acceptable to advocates will likely not be acceptable to their critics.[52] As noted, long before this issue of contamination is raised in connection with humans, it will have to be resolved with a robotic Mars sample-return mission.

The Distant Future: Settling Mars

The Apollo expeditions to the moon lasted just three years, from 1969 to 1972. Our expectation is that once Mars is visited, the exploration will continue—because, as Sagan suggested, the Red Planet will prove inherently "exciting" in every way.

At first only those specifically trained to be explorers will go. But as resource-conversion techniques improve and biospheres enlarge, more and more people of varying backgrounds will someday go. Scientists will create research bases, much as they did in Antarctica. In the more distant future, people will actually travel to Mars as a place to live. Eventually, the first child will be born—a Martian![53]

As continuing habitation ensues, there will be increased pressures to "terraform" Mars. This is a debate so central to the issue of humans on Mars that it has already begun. Terraforming refers to planetary engineering, a technology development perspective on an extraordinary scale, remaking Mars in a manner fit for humanity.

At the founding meeting of the Mars Society, the single most disputed topic was terraforming. Two competing visions of Mars divided the activists. On the one side were those who saw Mars as the next frontier, much as the New World was a frontier after Columbus or the western United States was a frontier in the nineteenth century. They felt it was man's destiny to conquer and used terms such as "manifest destiny." The other side saw Mars as a pristine, almost sacred place to be protected—a new Eden. As a reporter who covered the meeting noted, "By the end of the debate, a lot of people are really quite cross—a remarkable thing, considering how far off, in both time and space, these martian issues are."[54] Another example at the initial Mars Society meeting was debate over the role of government. What should government do, if anything? How much—or little—government will be enough? Who will govern Mars? Toward whose ends? As the above disputes reveal, humans will transport to Mars issues over which they fight on Earth. The Mars Society meeting showed that while technology may advance rapidly, human nature and attitudes remain the same.

These debates within the activist group not only presage conflict in the future but also divide the activist camp at a time when activists provide energy for keeping Mars on the policy agenda. Any division in the activist group weakens the case for Mars and may delay the decision they want.

Conclusion

In the early twenty-first century, America and the world stand between the manned landing on the moon and a future human spaceflight to Mars. The Bush rhetoric of 1989 aside, there has been no sustained presidential decision to go to Mars; however, it seems likely that once the International Space Station has operated successfully for some period of time, pressures will mount for a decision by the president to announce a new manned mission for NASA.

As the Bush experience with SEI showed, presidential decision making is not enough. The 1989 decision was strategic in form but not in practice. The politics of the time were not ripe for anything other than the most incremental of decisions. What was missing was a broad politi-

cal constituency to support the goal. Decisions to launch large-scale technological programs require technical and political readiness—a readiness that is not present now.

A constituency is just starting to build. There is a grassroots movement led by the Mars Society, replete with a crusading leader, Robert Zubrin, who writes books and lectures around the country. There are other space associations with a Mars interest. It is thus possible that this grassroots advocacy will grow in years to come.

This will be the case especially if NASA is successful in its robotic flights to Mars. The 1999 loss of Mars probes has slowed down NASA's progress, but once resumed, robotic surveys of the Red Planet have the potential of speeding up unmanned exploration. As scouts, they can discover phenomena that can intrigue the public and focus increasing attention in the direction of Mars. Meanwhile, with the Space Station, astronauts will gather important experience in living and working in space in a multinational setting.

Goldin termed the quest for Mars a marathon, not a sprint.[55] A marathon, while much longer than a sprint, still has a pace and a direction. Getting off to a strong start and maintaining momentum require preparation, persistence, and substantial public entrepreneurship.

Apollo had a constituency born of Cold War competition. NASA managed a national priority in the 1960s, holding approximately 5 percent of the federal budget. If NASA had a similar priority in the 1990s, according to Goldin, its budget would have been $75 billion, rather than the less than $14 billion it averaged.[56]

To go to Mars may not require the crisis-born national priority of Apollo, a priority that made it an urgent, fast-track program; but it will require a far greater national priority than space now holds—even if "faster, better, cheaper" techniques are brought to bear. However, Mars will still require a large-scale technological and managerial approach, and when human beings are involved, expensive safety measures are essential. Moreover, new technologies will be needed. To get higher priority and attract meaningful political attention that lasts beyond a single decision, the grassroots movement has to grow into a more significant political force. Moreover, advocates must link Mars with politically relevant goals that attract and keep the favor of elected officials not only of the United States but also of its foreign partners.

There will be many motives for going to Mars, including those represented by the new Edenists and the terraformers, but the noblest motive lies in the intangible objective of learning more about humanity's place in the universe. Where did we come from? Where are we going? Are we alone? Moreover, getting to Mars represents a way of pulling nations together in a common, global enterprise that could capture the imagination of the world, contribute to peace, and help an Earth identity to coalesce.

The challenge for Mars advocates is to help technological progress and political opportunity to converge, to take advantage of events, discoveries, and particular personalities in office and turn them into occasions for action. Advocates have little choice today but to proceed incrementally. However, they can think strategically. With Mars as long-term objective, the programs leading to it, such as use of the Space Station as a laboratory for understanding stresses on humans in space and the Mars sample return, are significant efforts in themselves.

It is much easier to envision the technical steps to Mars—such as development of a new launch vehicle, improved biosphere technology, an outpost on the moon, training to deal with psychological effects of isolation, and so on— than to know what will trigger and sustain a sequence of goal-oriented decisions politically. Nevertheless, it seems inevitable that there eventually will be a decision to go, probably a multinational decision. Such a decision will give focus and pace to the overall effort. It will be followed by a host of implementing decisions, some big and some small, about technology, costs, risks, and organization. The process of accomplishment will therefore be uneven and immensely difficult. To use the metaphor of the marathon race, there may be occasions when the speed will slow, then pick up, only to slow again. At every major step, skeptics and dreamers will contest whether to continue. Exploration will compete with a score of more immediately pressing public missions. Yet if Sagan is correct, humanity is a species that "wonders" and, hence, "wanders."[57] The issue, therefore, becomes not whether but when a Mars mission will take place.

Author Citations

37. Robert Zubrin, *The Case for Mars* (New York: Touchstone, 1996), 135.
38. John Noble Wilford, *Mars Beckons* (New York: Knopf, 1990), 151.
39. Zubrin, *Case for Mars,* xix, 64.
40. See Advisory Committee on the Future of the U.S. Space Program, *Report* (Washington, DC: Government Printing Office, 1990); Thomas Stafford, Synthesis Group, *Report, America at the Threshold: America's Space Exploration Initiative* (Washington, DC: Government Printing Office, 1991).
41. Wesley T. Huntress Jr., "Grand Challenges for Space Exploration," *Space Times* 38, no. 3 (May–June, 1999): 4–13.
42. Ibid.
43. J. J. Madison and H. E. McCurdy, "Spending Without Results: Lessons from the Space Station Program," *Space Policy* 15, no. 4 (Nov. 1999): 213.
44. Advisory Committee on the Future of the Space Program, *Report*, 30.
45. Stafford, Synthesis Group, *Report,* 6.
46. "Biosphere 2 Status Report: Creating a Sustainable Agriculture for a Closed System," press release issued by Space Biospheres Ventures, September 1993: www.biospheres.org/sustagr.html.

47. C. S. Mullin, H. Connery, and F. Wouters, "A Psychological-Psychiatric Study of a IGY Station in Antarctica," project report, U.S. Navy, Bureau of Medicine and Surgery, Neuropsychiatric Division, 1958; C. S. Mullin and H. Connery, "Psychological Study of an Antarctic Station," *Armed Forces Medical Journal* 10 (1959): 290–96; C. S. Mullin, "Some Psychological Aspects of Isolated Antarctic Living," *American Journal of Psychiatry* 9 (1960): 362–26; and E. K. E. Gunderson, "Emotional Symptoms in Extremely Isolated Groups," *Archives of General Psychiatry* 9 (1963): 362–68. Other researchers have focused on the attributes of successful leadership of wintering-over expeditions, which is considered crucial; on interpersonal conflict and morale; on the incidence of mental disorders; on personality change; and on the higher levels of adaptability of single vs. married people. It has been argued by some that isolation is not all negative. At least at a limited degree, it can increase a person's ability to focus and sense of personal efficacy. The issue has to do with the limits of people. See P. Suedfeld, "Homo Invictus: The Indomitable Species," *Canadian Psychology* 38, no. 3 (August 1997): 164–73; P. Warshall, "Lessons from Biosphere 2: Ecodesign, Surprises and the Humanity of Gaian Thought," *Whole Earth Review* (Spring 1996).

48. P. Warshall, "Lessons from Biosphere 2," 27.

49. Stafford, Synthesis Group, *Report,* 4.

50. Advisory Committee on the Future of the Space Program, *Report,* 30.

51. Stafford, Synthesis Group, *Report,* 4.

52. The issue of contamination is discussed by Chyba in Chapter 7 of this volume.

53. Daniel Goldin, "Steps to Mars II," Conference Address, Washington, D.C., July 15, 1995.

54. Oliver Morton, "For the Love of Mars," *Discover* 20, no. 2 (February 1999), 69.

55. Goldin, "Steps to Mars II."

56. Quoted in Brian Berger, "How Far Away is Mars?" *Space News,* 19 July 1999.

57. Carl Sagan, *Pale Blue Dot: A Vision of the Human Future in Space* (New York: Ballantine, 1999), v, xiii.

Discussion Questions

1. The Apollo mission in the 1960s was undeniably driven by nationalism, or the desire to prove the technological superiority of the United States. In your opinion, is this a good motivator for a technological undertaking of this nature?
2. Explain the rationale behind the "faster, better, cheaper" attitude adopted by NASA in the mid 1990s.
3. Do you personally support space exploration, and in particular a manned mission to Mars? To help put your answer in more tangible terms, would you support this mission if it cost $20 billion? $100 billion? $250 billion? Put another way, would you favor space exploration over universal health care? Over higher funding for education? Over higher defense spending?
4. List and briefly describe the three "routes" to Mars. Identify each route's advocates, and the reasoning behind their advocacy.
5. Which side of the terraforming debate do you support? Do you see Mars as a new frontier to be conquered, or as a new Eden to be preserved? Justify your opinion.

 ## Supporting Activities

1. Chronicle all of the missions to Mars, including dates, missions, and accomplishments.
2. Find out when the most recent Space Shuttle flight was, and summarize its mission.
3. Check out three futuristic rocket propulsion schemes that are being considered for future long-distance space missions. A place to start looking is NASA's Advanced Space Transportation Program (for example: virtualskies.arc.nasa.gov/research/youDecide/advspactrans.html).
4. Summarize the findings of the Biosphere 2 experiment that are relevant for future Mars colonization.
5. Give some examples of a technology that "lost" to an inferior (or comparable) technology. One example is Betamax video cassettes.

 ## Additional Resources

1. View the video *Mars Underground*, which is a documentary about Robert Zubrin and his passion and advocacy for a Mars mission. Available from www.themarsunderground.com.
2. Visit the Web site of the Mars Society (www.marssociety.org), a Mars advocacy group.
3. Look at the resource provided by the private research group The SETI Institute (www.seti.org).
4. Watch the 1997 movie *Contact*, which explores the ethical and religious implications of the quest for extraterrestrial life.
5. Watch the 1969 movie *Andromeda Strain*, which is a fictional account of an extraterrestrial microbial infestation resulting from a returning spacecraft.

The Nanotechnology Revolution

Perhaps no area of technology holds the promise to radically transform society that nanotechnology does. Since 1959 when Richard Feynman first challenged the scientific community to create the field, nanotechnology has fascinated and mystified scientists, politicians, and the general public.[5]

What is nanotechnology? The field has evolved into two very different disciplines: mainstream nanotechnology and molecular nanotechnology. Mainstream nanotech, in summary, involves using conventional (although perhaps very advanced) tools and techniques to create very small things. And small things are useful indeed. This discipline is relatively mature, well understood, and its potential impact on society might be likened to the impact offered by newer, faster, smaller (but still conventional) computers. Molecular nanotech, by contrast, is the stuff of dreams.

Imagine the ability to manipulate individual molecules with essentially no limit to the variety and precision of your creations. With a molecular feedstock, common air or some ore, and a set of instructions, you can build an atomically perfect *anything*. No need for expensive and precise machinery. Sound fantastic? At this point molecular nanotechnology *is* pure fantasy. The "molecular assemblers" that will do all the molecular rearranging (remember, a pinhead contains several trillion molecules) have yet to be created. Some scientists are unconvinced that this type of molecular engineering is even possible. On the other hand, some scientists are convinced it's inevitable. Most politicians, responsible for much of the funding and regulating of nanotechnology research and development, can barely understand the concepts. The general public, for the most part, has no idea about any of it.

Should we as a society vigorously pursue molecular nanotechnology, or should we attempt to stop its development? What are the risks and benefits? Does the ability to target and repair individual cancers cells or virtually eliminate waste outweigh the risk of the "grey goo," a nanoweapon so relentless it simply consumes it enemy out of existence? Only a dialogue based on fact will lead us to the best decision, and fact can be hard to come by when the technology under discussion is only a dream in someone's mind.

Adam Keiper is a Fellow at the Ethics and Public Policy Center and Director of EPPC's program on Science, Technology, and Society. He is also the editor of *The New Atlantis*, EPPC's journal about the ethical, political, and social implications of technological advancement. Mr. Keiper has a degree in political science from American University and has worked on Capitol Hill.

The Nanotechnology Revolution

By Adam Keiper

The English chemist John Dalton first proposed the scientific theory of the atom two hundred years ago. Since then we have seen chemists come to understand the elements and their interactions, we have seen engineers make and use new materials to improve our lives, we have seen physicists demonstrate that even atoms are divisible, and we have seen warriors unleash the power of the atomic nucleus. In these two centuries we have amassed an enormous understanding of—and wielded an increasing control over—the fundamental units of matter.

Today, in the young field of nanotechnology, scientists and engineers are taking control

From *The New Atlantis, Number 2, Summer 2003* by Adam Keiper. Copyright © 2003 by The New Atlantis. Reprinted by permission. Please see www.TheNewAtlantis.com for more information.

of atoms and molecules individually, manipulating them and putting them to use with an extraordinary degree of precision. Word of the promise of nanotechnology is spreading rapidly, and the air is thick with news of nanotech breakthroughs. Governments and businesses are investing billions of dollars in nanotechnology R&D, and political alliances and battle lines are starting to form. Public awareness of nanotech is clearly on the rise, too, partly because references to it are becoming more common in popular culture—with mentions in movies (like *The Hulk* and *The Tuxedo*), books (including last year's Michael Crichton bestseller, *Prey*), video games (such as the "Metal Gear Solid" series), and television (most notably in various incarnations of Star Trek).

Yet there remains a great deal of confusion about just what nanotechnology is, both among the ordinary people whose lives will be changed by the new science, and among the policy-makers who wittingly or unwittingly will help steer its course. Unsurprisingly, some of the confusion is actually caused by the increased attention—sensationalistic reporting and creative license have done little to prepare society for the hard decisions that the development of nanotechnology will make necessary.

Much of the confusion, however, comes from the scientists and engineers themselves, because they apply the name "nanotechnology" to two different things—that is, to two distinct but related fields of research, one with the potential to improve today's world, the other with the potential to utterly remake or even destroy it. The meaning that nanotechnology holds for our future depends on which definition of the word "nanotechnology" pans out. Thus any understanding of the implications of nanotechnology must begin by sorting out its history and its strange dual meaning.

Mainstream Nanotechnology

Nanotechnology got going in the second half of the twentieth century, although a few scientists had done related work earlier. For instance, as part of an 1871 thought experiment, the Scottish physicist James Clerk Maxwell imagined extremely tiny "demons" that could redirect atoms one at a time. And M.I.T. professor Arthur Robert von Hippel (born in 1898 and still alive today) became interested in molecular design as early as the 1930s; he coined the term "molecular engineering" in the 1960s. [Dr. Hippel passed away a few months after this article was published.]

Usually, though, the credit for inspiring nanotechnology goes to a lecture by Richard Phillips Feynman, a brilliant Caltech physicist who later won a Nobel Prize for "fundamental work in quantum electrodynamics." He is best remembered today for his clear and quirky classroom lectures and for his critical role on the presidential commission that investigated the *Challenger* accident. On the evening of December 29, 1959, Feynman delivered an after-dinner lecture at the annual meeting of the American Physical Society; in that talk, called "There's Plenty of Room at the Bottom," Feynman proposed work in a field "in which little has been done, but in which an enormous amount can be done in principle."*

"What I want to talk about," Feynman said, "is the problem of manipulating and controlling things on a small scale. As soon as I mention this, people tell me about miniaturization, and how far it has progressed today . . . But that's nothing; that's the most primitive, halting step in the direction I intend to discuss."

Feynman described how the entire *Encyclopaedia Britannica* could be written on the head of a pin, and how all the world's books could fit in a pamphlet. Such remarkable reductions could be done as "a simple reproduction of the original pictures, engravings, and everything else on a small scale without loss of resolution." Yet it was possible to get smaller still: if you converted all the world's books into an efficient computer code instead of just reduced pictures, you could store "all the information that man has carefully accumulated in all the books in the world . . . in a cube of material one two-hundredth of an inch wide—which is the barest piece of dust that can be made out by the human eye. So there is *plenty* of room at the bottom! Don't tell me about microfilm!" He boldly declared that "the principles of physics, as far as I can see, do not speak against the possibility of maneuvering things atom by atom"—in fact, Feynman saw atomic manipulation as inevitable, "a development which I think cannot be avoided."

In his lecture, Feynman pointed out several avenues for research that would later come to define nanotechnology, such as making computers much smaller and therefore faster, and making "mechanical surgeons" that could travel to trouble spots inside the body. Feynman admitted that he didn't have a clear conception of how such tiny machines might be used or created, but to help get things going, he offered two prizes: $1,000 to the first person to make a working electric motor that was no bigger than one sixty-fourth of an inch on any side, and another $1,000 to the first person to shrink a page of text to 1/25,000 its size—the dimension necessary to fit the *Encyclopaedia Britannica* on the head of a pin. (He awarded the former prize in 1960, the latter in 1985.)

Although Feynman's lecture is, in retrospect, remembered as a major event, it didn't make much of a splash in the world of science at the time. Research in the direction he suggested didn't begin immediately, and nanotechnology was slow to take off. Feynman himself didn't use the word "nanotechnology" in his lecture; in fact, the word didn't exist until 15 years later, when Norio Taniguchi of the Tokyo University of Science suggested it to describe technology that strives for precision at the level of about one nanometer.

A nanometer is one billionth of a meter. The prefix "nano-" comes from the Greek word *nanos*, meaning dwarf. (Scientists originally used the prefix just to indicate "very small," as in "nanoplankton," but it now means one-billionth, just as "milli-" means one-thousandth, and "micro-" means one-millionth.) If a nanometer were somehow magnified to appear as long as the nose on your face, then a red blood cell would appear the size of the Empire State Building, a human hair would be about two or three miles wide, one of your fingers would span the continental United States, and a normal person would be about as tall as six or seven planet Earths piled atop one another.

In 1981, scientists gained a sophisticated new tool powerful enough to allow them to see single atoms with unprecedented clarity. This device, the scanning tunneling microscope, uses a tiny electric current and a very fine needle to detect the height of individual atoms. The images taken with these microscopes look like tumulose alien landscapes—and researchers learned how to rearrange those landscapes, once they discovered that the scanning tunneling microscope could also be used to pick up, move, and precisely place atoms, one at a time. The first dramatic demonstration of this power came in 1990 when a team of IBM physicists revealed that they had, the year before, spelled out the letters "IBM" using *35 individual atoms* of xenon. In 1991, the same research team built an "atomic switch," an important step in the development of nanoscale computing.

Another breakthrough came with the discovery of new shapes for molecules of carbon, the quintessential element of life. In 1985, researchers reported the discovery of the "bucky-ball," a lovely round molecule consisting of 60 carbon atoms. This led in turn to the 1991 discovery of a related molecular shape known as the "carbon nanotube"; these nanotubes are about 100 times stronger than steel but just a sixth of the weight, and they have unusual heat and conductivity characteristics that guarantee they will be important to high technology in the coming years.

But these exciting discoveries are the exception rather than the rule: most of what passes for nanotechnology nowadays is really just materials science. Mainstream nanotechnology, as practiced by hundreds of companies, is merely the intellectual offspring of conventional chemical engineering and our new nanoscale powers. The basis of most research in mainstream nanotech is the fact that some materials have peculiar or useful properties when pulverized into nanoscale particles or otherwise rearranged.

Seen this way, mainstream nanotechnology isn't truly new; we've been unwitting nanotechnologists for centuries. One official from the National Science Foundation told Congress that photography, of all things, is a subset of nanotechnology—and a "relatively old" one at that! But if the term "nanotechnology" is to be used that loosely, why not reach much further back into history? Renaissance artists used paints and glazes that got their appealing color and iridescence from nanoparticles. The ancients, too, found uses for nanoparticles of soot. On and on it goes, back through the ages.

A great many of today's mainstream nanotechnologists are simply following in that tradition, using modern techniques to make tiny particles and then finding uses for them. Among the products that now incorporate nanoparticles are: some new paints and sunscreens, certain lines of stain- and water-repellent clothing,

a few kinds of anti-reflective and anti-fogging glass, and some tennis equipment. Cosmetics companies are starting to use nanoparticles in their products, and pharmaceuticals companies are researching ways to improve drug delivery through nanotech. Within a few years, nanotechnology will most likely be available in self-cleaning windows and flat-screen TVs. Improvements in computing, energy, and medical diagnosis and treatment are likely as well.

In short, mainstream nanotechnology is an interesting field, with some impressive possibilities for improving our lives with better materials and tools. But that's just half the story: there's another side to nanotechnology, one that promises much more extreme, and perhaps dangerous, changes.

Molecular Manufacturing

This more radical form of nanotechnology originated in the mind of an M.I.T. undergraduate in the mid-1970s. Kim Eric Drexler was specializing in theories of space travel and space colonization in college when he first thought of using DNA to make computers. But why stop there? He soon realized that the biological "machinery" already responsible for the full diversity of life on Earth could be adapted to build nonliving products upon command. Molecule-sized machines, originally derived from those found in nature, could be used to manufacture just about anything man wished. *Anything*.

Drexler, who began to develop these theories before he'd heard of Feynman's lecture, first published his ideas in a 1981 journal article. Five years later, he brought the notion of molecular manufacturing to the general public with his book *Engines of Creation*. An astonishingly original work of futurism, *Engines* presented Drexler's nanotech theories and pointed out how nanotechnology would revolutionize other areas of science and technology—leading to breakthroughs in medicine, artificial intelligence, and the conquest of space.

At the heart of Drexler's vision for molecular manufacturing was a kind of nanomachine called an "assembler," which can "place atoms in almost any reasonable arrangement," thus allowing us to "build almost anything that the laws of nature allow to exist." It would take millions and millions of assemblers to make a product big enough for us to use—so in order for molecular manufacturing to work, assemblers must be capable of replicating themselves; as each "generation" of assemblers replicated itself, the overall number of assemblers would grow exponentially.

In one of the most striking passages of Drexler's book, he describes how molecular manufacturing could be used to build—to *grow*, really—a large rocket engine. Replicating assemblers would be pumped into a vat, and all the plans for the rocket engine would be stored on a single "seed." With the addition of fuel for the assemblers and raw materials for the construction, the engine would be completed in "less than a day" and would require "almost no human attention." The final product would be "a seamless thing, gemlike," light and strong—instead of a clunky, "massive piece of welded and bolted metal." If you wanted, you could "exploit nanotechnology more deeply" by building engines that repair themselves, or that "take different shapes under different operating conditions."

Drexler further imagined how nanotechnology could completely reshape everyday life. "It should be no great trick, for example, to make everything from dishes to carpets self-cleaning, and household air permanently fresh." Fresh food—"genuine meat, grain, vegetables, and so forth"—could be produced in the home. Suits made with nanotechnology could be used for virtual reality, simulating "most of the sights and sensations of an entire environment." And nanotechnology could make "some form" of telepathy "as possible as telephony."

Such powers seem like magic, a comparison that Drexler acknowledged: nanotechnology, he wrote, could make possible a device that "might aptly be called a 'genie machine.'" In a later book, he described in general terms how such a machine might be designed. Other writers, following in Drexler's footsteps, have imagined other grant-any-wish tools—like "utility fog," a theoretical swarm of tiny robots that could "simulate the physical existence of almost any object" and can thus "act as shelter, clothing, telephone, computer, and automobile." As envisioned by John Storrs Hall, the techie who dreamed the stuff up, the utility fog "that was your clothing becomes your bath water and then your bed" [J. Storrs Hall, "Utility Fog: The Stuff That Dreams Are Made Of," in Nanotechnology: Molecular Speculations on Global Abundance, B.C. Crandall, ed.].

Clearly, the Drexlerian notion of nanotechnology differs vastly from the nanotech products of today. Compare, for instance, how the two divergent visions of nanotechnology would differently affect one small aspect of human life: cosmetics. Mainstream nanotechnology will soon be used by cosmetics companies to help their current products—makeup, lotions, sunscreen, and so forth—last longer and work better. But if Drexler's version of nanotechnology were to come to fruition, the beauty industry would be revolutionized: nanomachines could precisely adjust your hair and skin color to your liking; wrinkles could be smoothed and excess fat removed; one writer suggests it would even

become possible to mold the face and body to whatever shape might be desired. Each person who cared to could achieve his or her own ideal of physical perfection or, for that matter, whatever frightening or gruesome effect they wanted. Many who never liked their own youth-

ful appearance will opt instead to copy some popular model or other sex symbol. It could become very confusing, with dozens of pop-idol look-alikes crowding the parks and boulevards of our future metropolis. Some may not relish the prospect, but we may never see the last of the Elvis clones. [Source: Richard Crawford, "Cosmetic Nanosurgery," in Nanotechnology: Molecular Speculations on Global Abundance, B.C. Crandall, ed.]

So while mainstream nanotech gives you better eyeshadow, Drexler's nanotech gives you a whole new face—yet these two technologies of profoundly different potential share one name. "If research on waterproof fabric coatings is 'nanotechnology,' then the term has become almost meaningless," Drexler told *Wired News* in June. Drexler himself now talks about his kind of nanotech as "molecular nanotechnology" and "molecular manufacturing." Other names have been suggested, too: one observer has argued that Drexler should start using the ugly word "mechutechnology." But for most people, one umbrella term describes both the mainstream approach and Drexler's more radical vision.

But is Drexler's nanotechnology realistically possible? Will we truly be able to watch houses build themselves from the ground up, to transform garbage into steak, to populate the world with Elvis look-alikes? Drexler's book *Engines of Creation* is an extraordinary exercise in prolepsis: he meticulously refutes every technical objection he can anticipate. Will thermal vibrations make his molecular machines impossible? (No.) What about radiation? (No.) Quantum uncertainty? (No!) To shore up his technical arguments for the feasibility of his vision, he further expanded on his ideas in the world's first nanotechnology textbook. *Nanosystems* (1992), a dense volume that grew out of a class he taught at Stanford, is crammed with equations and diagrams and designs for molecular ma-

chines, and it has gone far to put Drexler's nanotechnology on sound technical footing.

To date, no scientist or engineer has been able to make a rock-solid argument showing the impossibility of molecular manufacturing as Drexler envisions it. A few critics have challenged Drexler on technical points, most prominently Richard Errett Smalley, the Rice University chemist who won a Nobel Prize for discovering the new class of carbon molecules that includes buckyballs and carbon nanotubes. In 1999, in written testimony to a congressional subcommittee, Smalley claimed that Drexler's version of nanotechnology is "just a dream" and "will always remain a fantasy" because "there are simple facts of nature that prevent it from ever becoming a reality." [Testimony available in PDF format.]

When these claims were repeated in a 2001 article in *Scientific American* and again in public this year, Drexler and his allies responded with strongly worded public letters, accusing Smalley of basing his challenge on a straw man. Without getting into the technical details of the dispute, the essence of Drexler's response is devastating: If "atomically precise structures" are "fundamentally unfeasible, then so is life" itself, he wrote. Since enzymes and ribosomes and other molecular "machines" work in nature, man-made molecular machines should work, too.

Drexler and his supporters have made short shrift of other critics as well. Yet if no one has mounted a serious and sustained challenge to demonstrate a fatal flaw, or even a major error, in Drexler's vision of nanotechnology, why is it so often disparaged by those involved in mainstream nanotech? Molecular manufacturing has been called pseudoscience, science fiction, and unrealistic utopianism, and Eric Drexler himself has suffered repeated ad hominem attacks.

One reason for the animosity of the mainstreamers is their fear that Drexler's talk of the great boon and bane of nanotechnology will cast a pall over their own modest research—giving nanotech a reputation for being fantastical or hazardous.

A second explanation for why mainstream nanotech experts pooh-pooh Drexler is that they simply don't know what they're talking about. Drexler's kind of nanotechnology is so newfangled that it doesn't fit neatly into any single division of modern science or technology. (That fact actually caused difficulties when Drexler tried to obtain his Ph.D. at M.I.T.; he was eventually awarded an interdisciplinary degree—the world's first doctorate in nanotechnology.) It's difficult to find "appropriate critiques of nanotechnology designs," Drexler wrote in a 2001 article in *Scientific American*, since "many researchers whose work seems relevant are actually the wrong experts—they are excellent in their discipline but have little expertise in systems engineering. The shortage of molecular systems engineers will probably be a limiting factor in the speed with which nanotechnology can be developed."

No doubt some of the criticism of Drexler's nanotechnology is rooted in this important fact: nobody knows how to make the key component of his molecular manufacturing system, the assembler. Although Drexler and his supporters have come up with lots of designs for molecular machines and plans for how they would function, there still isn't any way to make them real. When someone figures out how to make the miniscule workhorses of molecular manufacturing—the critical moment of discovery that Drexler calls "the assembler breakthrough"—the rest may quickly fall into place, and the world could be transformed abruptly and forever.

Nanomedicine

Some people find Eric Drexler's vision of the nanotech future so compelling that they embrace it with religious fervor. This is not a new observation; a 1989 *Economist* article about Drexler spoke of his "gospel of nanotechnology" ["The Invisible Factory," *The Economist*, December 9, 1989]. The 1995 book *Nano* by Ed Regis includes an entire chapter called "Brother Eric's Nanotech Revival," describing the sense of awe that Drexler's lectures would inspire in members of the audience: "There was a veiled feeling of being one of the Elect, the Select, the Knowledgeable, the Chosen."

A half-century ago, philosopher and technology critic Jacques Ellul argued that the rise of technology leads to the decline of traditional spirituality, as man transfers "his sense of the sacred . . . to technique itself." We develop a "worship of technique," Ellul said, and we associate our technology with a "feeling of the sacred." Drexler's nanotechnology is perfectly suited to arouse religious enthusiasm. It involves incredible, invisible powers. The all-important "assembler breakthrough" is akin to a Second Coming or a Judgment Day. And there's even an afterlife: cryonics.

Nanotechnology is especially appealing to those in the growing ranks of what Charles T. Rubin, in the previous issue of *The New Atlantis*, usefully dubbed the "extinctionist project": the transhumanists, posthumanists, extropians, and others who seek to completely remake human nature. Nanotechnology is central to their vision of a future of agelessness, immortality, and rebirth.

They place their hopes in nanomedicine, a field that would repair or improve the body from the inside out, with a precision and delicacy far greater than that of the finest surgical instruments available today. Science fiction envisioned tiny internal medical procedures long ago; in the 1966 movie *Fantastic Voyage*, a medical staff boards an experimental submarine which is then drastically miniaturized and injected into a patient in order to destroy a deadly blood clot. Of course, miniaturizing humans is preposterous, but in the 1960s it was hard to imagine any other way to make tiny machines intelligent enough to reach and repair damage inside the body. But nanomachines are certainly small enough, and with programmed instructions, they can be smart, too.

The world's leading expert on nanomedicine is Robert A. Freitas, Jr., a polymath with a law degree who worked on numerous space-related projects before becoming involved in nanotechnology. Currently employed as a researcher at the nanotech firm Zyvex, he is one of only a handful of people who can claim to have made major theoretical contributions to Drexlerian nanotechnology.

Freitas is currently several years into the writing of an exhaustive four-volume series called *Nanomedicine*, the first technical work on the subject. In the first massive volume (published in 1999), he offers technical speculations on how nanorobots might navigate, sense their surroundings, and move through the body; how they might detect problems and communicate with one another; and how they might change shape and obtain energy. The second volume of *Nanomedicine*, due out this year, will examine "biocompatibility"—how nanorobots might interact with the body, especially the immune system.

Many of the tools of nanomedicine could be used for either therapy or enhancement. Take, for example, the "respirocyte," an artificial red blood cell about which Freitas has theorized. Respirocytes, capable of delivering oxygen hundreds of times more efficiently than real red blood cells, would be invaluable in the treatment of various respiratory and cardiovascular disorders, or as a substitute for real blood during transfusions. But they would also have "a variety of sports, veterinary, battlefield and other applications"; they could be used to boost a mountain climber's endurance, to help a diver hold his breath for hours, or to enable a soldier to fight harder.

And the respirocyte is among the simplest medical nanomachines imaginable. Others might be able to repair cells and fix damaged DNA; to remove toxins, clean out cholesterol, and eliminate scar tissue; to destroy cancer cells and fight countless diseases. And the same nanotechnology that keeps your body healthy can indefinitely stave off senescence. The process of aging, Drexler argued in *Engines of Creation*, is "fundamentally no different from any other physical disorder," so cell repairing nanomachines should, in theory, be able to halt aging or reverse it. You can pick the age you want to be—in fact, you can play mix and match: give yourself the distinguished hairline of a fifty-year-old, the sturdy frame of a thirty-year-old, the lusty libido of a twenty-year-old, and the keen eyesight of a ten-year-old.

Even the Grim Reaper is in for tough times: Death may already be "slave to Fate, Chance, kings, and desperate men," but in the age of nanotechnology, Death will increasingly obey the whims of Tom, Dick, and Harry, too. Molecular machines will bridge the gap between living matter and nonliving matter, making the border between life and death much fuzzier. In the age of nanotechnology, a person might intentionally put himself into stasis, perhaps to "time travel" dreamlessly into the future, or to wait out a centuries-long interstellar voyage. Even today, hundreds of people of sufficient means are making plans to freeze themselves in hopes that nanotech will someday restore them; these people are willing to shell out big bucks to cryonics companies that promise to preserve their corpses, or some meaningful fraction thereof, until the prospect of reanimation becomes realistic.

There are, however, some foreseeable limits to nanomedicine. While nanomachines might one day be able to restore and maintain the body, there is no guarantee that they'll be able to keep the *mind* intact. Some brain damage can be physically fixed, but lost memories and personality—the brain's software (figuratively speaking)—will be irretrievable. If bits of your mind are lost, "repair machines could no more restore them than art conservators could restore a tapestry from stirred ash," as Drexler has said. But of course many of those engaged in the extinctionist project have a solution in the works: they seek to reduce the mind to software (literally) so the contents of your brain can be as downloadable and fungible tomorrow as digital video and music are today.

How Soon?

Estimates on how long we have to wait for major breakthroughs in nanotechnology vary greatly. Robert Freitas told one interviewer that the kind of nanomedicine he envisions is "at least 10 to 20 years away"; in a different interview he put the number at 40 years. Another nanotech expert says molecular manufacturing is 20 or 30 years away. We'll have to wait at least ten years before we can ride in "superintelligent" airplanes enhanced with nanotechnology, according to a Boeing executive. An all-purpose nanotech entertainment system could "arrive on the scene around the year 2020," according to one writer [John Papiewski, "The Companion: A Very Personal Computer," in *Nanotechnology: Molecular Speculations on Global Abundance*, B.C. Crandall, ed.]. The British Ministry of Defense says nanotech won't hit its stride any earlier than 20 or 30 years from now, but a Canadian expert says it will start to dramatically change our lives in the next 10 to 20 years. Ray Kurzweil, the technologist, predicts in his book *The Age of Spiritual Machines* that nanotech will be used in manufacturing by 2019—and that by 2049, smart swarms and nanotech food will be feasible. The U.S. government projects that the worldwide nanotechnology market will exceed $1 trillion by 2015, although one group opposed to nanotechnology puts it more ominously: by 2015, the controllers of nanotechnology "will be the ruling force in the world economy" ["The Big Down," ETC Group, p. 43].

While there have been a few indications of progress in nanotechnology in the past two or three years, the present booming interest in all things "nano" is bound to quicken the pace of discovery. In the U.S., so many states are subsidizing nanotech research that a *New York Times* reporter whose job was to read governors' "State of the State" speeches in 2001 found herself asking: "Are there enough nanotechnological researchers to go around?" Governments in Europe and Asia are also putting money into nanotech, including Switzerland, Germany, Britain, China—and even Iran.

Businesses around the world are spending heavily on mainstream nanotech, pouring more than $3 billion into nanotech R&D this year alone, according to one estimate. A recent survey showed that "13 of the top 30 Dow component companies discuss nanotechnology on their websites." But all the nanotech buzz is destined to attract con artists and frauds, too. Some companies doing work completely unrelated to nanotechnology have incorporated "nano" into their names, in hopes of getting money from gullible investors caught up in the hype. And earlier this year, a major conference on nanotech was canceled under mysterious circumstances; it now appears that the whole thing was a scam to get money from the attendees.

If anything is likely to dampen the nanotech boom, it is the prospect of regulation. In the past year, mainstream nanotech has suddenly come under scrutiny from researchers and activists worried that nanoparticles could endanger public health or harm the environment. So far, there has been very little precautionary research on the safety of nanoparticles; indeed, when Rice University's Center for Biological and Environmental Nanotechnology conducted a survey of the scientific literature relating to nanoparticles—"a field with more than 12,000 citations a year"—they found *no* documented research on the risks of nanoparticles. Vicki L. Colvin, the Center's director, told Congress last April that the safety of nanoparticles should be determined through immediate and thorough tests. "From asbestos to DDT we have, as a society, paid an enormous price for not evaluating toxicological and ecosystem impacts before industries develop," she said. Her organization has started investigating nanoparticle safety, and in July the main U.S. lobbying group for the nanotechnology industry (the NanoBusiness Alliance) announced that it, too, would start studying the health and environmental safety of nanoparticles. Similar inquiries have begun in Britain and the European Union.

Beyond the Gray Goo

The health and environmental threats posed by mainstream nanotech are far less frightening than the hypothetical dangers of the Drexlerian flavor of nanotech. In an infamous article in *Wired* magazine in 2000, technologist Bill Joy made the case for halting nano-research because of the possibility that we might wipe out all life on Earth. Joy's article stirred up a hor-

net's nest of controversy, even though the idea had been around for a long time: the apocalypse he described was based on a theory that had first been suggested more than a decade earlier in *Engines of Creation*.

For molecular manufacturing to work, Drexler's assemblers would have to replicate themselves, just as tiny organisms make duplicates of themselves. But what if something went wrong—what if the replication spiraled out of control? Speed-breeding assemblers could devour all life on Earth in short order. According to *Engines of Creation*, "among the cognoscenti of nanotechnology"—presumably meaning the author and his friends—"this threat has become known as the 'gray goo problem'":

> *Though masses of uncontrolled replicators need not be gray or gooey, the term "gray goo" emphasizes that replicators able to obliterate life might be less inspiring than a single species of crabgrass. They might be "superior" in an evolutionary sense . . . The gray goo threat makes one thing perfectly clear: we cannot afford certain kinds of accidents with replicating assemblers. Gray goo would surely be a depressing ending to our human adventure on Earth, far worse than mere fire or ice, and one that could stem from a simple laboratory accident . . . We must not let a single replicating assembler of the wrong kind be loosed on an unprepared world.*

In time, Drexler backed away from the gray goo scenario, reasoning that no one would design a self-replicating assembler capable of surviving in nature. "Consider cars," he wrote in 1990. "To work, they require gasoline, oil, brake fluid, and so forth. No mere accident could enable a car to forage in the wild and refuel from tree sap . . . It would be likewise with simple replicators designed to work in vats of assembler fluid"—no right-minded engineer would create replicators that could exist in the wild.

But a terrorist might. Or an enemy nation. Biosphere-destroying self-replicators may not arise as the result of an inadvertent scientific slip-up, but they might be designed intentionally by those seeking to bring destruction or wreak havoc.

In the wake of Bill Joy's screed and the gray goo frenzy it inspired, Robert Freitas, the nanomedicine expert, wrote the first serious, technical analysis of the gray goo scenario. His paper—to which he gave the whimsical title "Some Limits to Global Ecophagy by Biovorous Nanoreplicators, with Public Policy Recommendations"—made estimates and calculations relating to the speed of replication and the rate of dispersal of self-replicators in the wild. If certain unlikely conditions are arranged just right, it is theoretically possible, Freitas found, for self-replicators to destroy the planet's entire biosphere in under three hours—but such a high-speed attack would instantly cause a massive spike in temperature, alerting authorities to the situation and allowing them to respond. Conversely, it is theoretically possible for biosphere-eating self-replicators to create an almost undetectably small increase in temperature—but then it would take them twenty months to complete their task, leaving plenty of time to observe the destruction and organize a defense.

Instead of going through all the trouble of designing self-replicators that could eat everything, why not design some that could make a more focused attack? "The classic example," Freitas says, "is tire rubber and asphalt tar binder; cars, trucks and airplanes roll on roads and tarmacs worldwide." Imagine the damage to the global economy if all the world's roads became soup overnight. "Other vectors with similar properties include cotton, polyester or other uniform textiles, insulation on electrical wiring, and paper money."

And though Freitas doesn't say as much, it seems possible that self-replicating nanobots could be designed to target and destroy a specific species. Perhaps they could be tailored to attack only humans—or just specific groups of humans, or just a specific individual. Nanoweapons could be smarter than conventional biological weapons, with a more precise lethality and potential to cause diseases unlike any seen before. What's more, nanotechnology could also be used to aid in the manufacture and targeting of conventional bioweapons. (There has also been some recent speculation that nanotechnology could be combined with nuclear weaponry. Analysts at the Acronym Institute for Disarmament Diplomacy and *Jane's Chem-Bio Web* have theorized that nanotechnology could play a part in the creation of so-called "fourth-generation" nukes with small, low-yield warheads. But they apparently confuse nanotechnology with microtechnology, and they make confusing and contradictory assumptions about how the technologies needed to enable fourth-generation nukes will evolve.)

Aside from nanotech's potential as a weapon of mass destruction, it could also make possible totally novel forms of violence and oppression. Nanotechnology could theoretically be used to make mind-control systems, invisible and mobile eavesdropping devices, or unimaginably horrific tools of torture. Yes, it's true that defensive applications of nanotechnology would develop alongside offensive ones, but that hardly mitigates the potential for enormities and catastrophes.

To save the world, Bill Joy argues that we must relinquish our pursuit of nanotech knowledge. He recommends international treaties and a verification regime. But that would be exceedingly difficult, since nanotechnology isn't just a science of the small, it's also a *small science*: it doesn't require giant equipment or big laboratories or gigantic budgets, and most of the work is conducted in small labs distributed around the world rather than in a few centralized behemoth facilities. Scientists wishing to hide their nano-tech research programs could easily disguise them as other projects in chemistry or physics. The allure of nanotechnology is so great that relinquishment could only work if it were enforced through "detailed, universal policing on a totalitarian scale," as Eric Drexler has worried, or if some horrible nanotech-related disaster shocked the world into giving up on nano.

No callow cheerleader for the nanotech revolution, Drexler in 1986 co-founded the Foresight Institute, a California-based nonprofit organization "formed to help prepare society for anticipated advanced technologies," especially nanotechnology. Among the Institute's projects is a set of proposed "Foresight Guidelines on Molecular Nanotechnology," first drafted in 1999. The guidelines forbid the creation of nanobots capable of "replication in a natural, uncontrolled environment," and provide several other principles for nanotechnologists. According to the Foresight website, the Guidelines "might eventually be enforced via a variety of means, possibly including lab certifications, randomized open inspections, professional society guidelines and peer pressure, insurance requirements and policies, stiff legal and economic penalties for violations, and other sanctions."

The Politics of Nanotech

So far, no nanotech businesses have adopted the Foresight Guidelines—after all, most firms are working on mainstream nanotech, not the riskier kind. Besides, nanotech companies have no motivation to regulate themselves, since it seems unlikely that they will be regulated by government any time soon. But this may change as the politics of nanotechnology begin to take shape.

Some agencies in the federal government have been involved in nanotechnology since at least the early 1980s, most notably the U.S. Na-

val Research Laboratory. By 1997, the federal government was annually investing $116 million in nanotech; that figure had doubled by 1999.

In 2000, the Clinton Administration pushed for more subsidies for nanotech and the creation of a National Nanotechnology Initiative (NNI) that would coordinate the nanotech work of six different agencies. President Clinton alluded to nanotechnology in that January's State of the Union Address, when he spoke of "materials ten times stronger than steel at a fraction of the weight, and—this is unbelievable to me—molecular computers the size of a teardrop with the power of today's fastest supercomputers." His administration worked hard to sell the proposal to Congress; as one official from the Clinton White House told *Scientific American*, "You need to come up with new, exciting, cutting-edge, at-the-frontier things in order to convince the budget- and policy-making apparatus to give you more money."

Congress couldn't resist, and the NNI was approved with an initial budget of $422 million. President Bush, in the first year of his administration, asked for another hundred million dollars for nanotech, and added another handful of agencies to the NNI. Bush's budget proposals for FY2003 and FY2004 further boosted the nanotech budget—despite the flagging economy and the war on terrorism. (In fact, some NNI proponents have used the war on terrorism to make the case for increasing nanotech funding; they say nanotech research can help build tools to detect weapons of mass destruction.)

Flush with nanotech cash, the National Science Foundation recently started a program to teach high school and elementary school students about nanotechnology, "with introduction to preliminary concepts as early as kindergarten," according to the *Christian Science Monitor*. "Business, industry, and higher-education leaders agree, saying early education gives students a jump on a job market many expect to blossom in the future."

Perhaps the most prominent federal entity under the NNI umbrella is the Department of Defense, which in May unveiled its new $50 million Institute for Soldier Nanotechnologies at M.I.T. The Institute, which treats soldiers as "integrated platform systems" rather than human beings, will bring together M.I.T. scientists, military officers, and researchers from private industry to develop lighter, stronger clothes and equipment for the Army. Some of the projects being suggested include an "exoskeleton" or "dynamic armor," which could become hard or soft at a soldier's command, and other clothes that could store energy—like the energy wasted in every footstep—and employ it later to give the soldier superhuman strength. All the technologies being developed at the Institute—like all other nanotech projects publicly acknowledged by the Defense Department—are essentially defensive, not offensive, in nature, so they are unlikely to incite opposition.

At the same time, because the benefits of nanotechnology are still largely uncertain, there is not yet a natural constituency for nanotech legislation—except for the nanotech companies themselves. They are represented by the New York-based NanoBusiness Alliance, a trade group founded in 2001 by F. Mark Modzelewski, who acts as the Alliance's executive director. Modzelewski, who modeled his group after the Biotechnology Industry Organization, was a low-ranking official in the Clinton Administration—which hasn't stopped him from making Newt Gingrich, that starry-eyed technophile, the Alliance's honorary chairman. Gingrich told the *Forbes/Wolfe Nanotech Report* that he believes that "those countries that master the process of nanoscale manufacturing and engineering will have a huge job boom over the next twenty years, just like aviation and computing companies in the last forty years, and just as railroad, steam engine and textile companies were decisive in the nineteenth century."

Since the politics of nanotechnology are still immature, there is no prominent opponent of nanotechnology in the nation's capital or even a unifying rationale for such opposition. The most organized opposition to nanotechnology has come from the ETC Group, a liberal Canadian environmental outfit that has published a series of harshly critical reports on nanotechnology—some of them detailed and provocative. In late July, Greenpeace issued its first report on nanotechnology, with ambiguous conclusions. [Available in PDF.] A few other environmentalist groups have spoken out against nanotechnology, but there hasn't yet been any movement comparable to the massive international campaigns against genetically modified foods. It is safe to speculate that these leftist groups will in time coalesce into an anti-nanotech front, using the rhetoric of anti-corporatism and environmental extremism to make their case. They will likely be opposed by the techno-libertarian and patient advocacy groups who presently support human cloning and embryonic stem cell research, and by the mainstream political establishment, at both the national and state levels, which sees nanotech as a way to boost the economy.

Just as there is no prominent figure in Washington arguing against nanotechnology, there is currently no prominent advocate of Eric Drexler's radical vision of nanotechnology. The closest thing to such an advocate may be Glenn Harlan Reynolds, a law professor from the University of Tennessee, whose Instapundit website and online columns are read by many Washingtonians. Reynolds frequently discusses nanotechnology, and when he does, he openly supports Drexler's ideas. (He also serves on the board of the Foresight Institute.) Reynolds is one of the few writers who understands both the workings of government and the basic theories of nanotechnology, which makes him useful to readers in the nation's capital.

If still unformed, however, there is reason to believe that public debate about nanotech is about to take off—with two new nanotech organizations founded in just the past year. The Center for Responsible Nanotechnology, run by a social activist and a nanosystems theorist, has been cranking out publications since January. "What we want," says Chris Phoenix, one of the Center's founders, "is to see molecular nanotechnology policy developed and implemented with a care appropriate to its powerful and probably transformative nature." And two Washingtonians—a futurist and an antitrust lawyer—are in the process of launching the Nanotechnology Policy Forum to improve the quality of public discourse about nanotech. They intend to host events every few months, and to stay scrupulously evenhanded: the advisory panel planned for the organization will include both friends and foes of nanotech—as well as present and former congressmen.

Congress also seems slightly more attuned to the need for debate about nanotechnology. Plans are afoot in both the House and the Senate to fund studies of the social, economic, and environmental implications of nanotechnology.

Also, legislation currently wending its way through Congress would establish "grand challenges" for nanotechnology: long-term objectives akin to President Kennedy's goal of putting a man on the Moon. While it isn't at all clear at this stage that nanotechnology can capture the imagination of the public like the Moon missions did, there is one obvious goal that would make an excellent "grand challenge"—a goal presently overlooked in all the millions of federal dollars going to nanotech: the assembler breakthrough. And just as the Apollo missions to the Moon were preceded by missions with incremental goals (achieved by the Mercury and Gemini programs), an ambitious nanotechnol-

ogy project aspiring to make the world's first assembler could also set intermediate goals, like the creation of a basic nanoscale computer or a nanoscale robotic arm. But the National Nanotechnology Initiative is so focused on developing mainstream nanotech that Drexler's nanotechnology has found neither a great advocate nor a great critic.

The Challenge Ahead

One Congressman, speaking on the House floor on May 7 of this year, said that nanotechnology may "create levels of intelligence that may be our protector, may be our competitor, or may simply regard us as pets. Or it may change our definition of what it is to be a human being." He said this with no indication of outrage or regret; he didn't rail against the prospect of a posthuman future; he expressed no aversion to life as a pet. Instead, he said that we need to talk about these issues, "to see how we can deal" with them, and to "get input from a wide range of society."

One proposal now under consideration is to create an advisory committee of "nonscientific and nontechnical" Americans to make recommendations about nanotechnology. This provision was inspired by the testimony of technology critic Langdon Winner before a House committee in April. "Congress should seek to create ways in which small panels of ordinary, disinterested citizens, selected in much the same way that we now choose juries in cases of law, [could] be assembled to examine important societal issues about nanotechnology," Winner said. The panels would listen to news and arguments, "deliberate on their findings, and write reports offering policy advice."

This sort of citizen panel would admittedly be an excellent gesture, a symbol of the fact that technological progress doesn't take place in a vacuum—that science and technology affect society as a whole and must remain subject to political oversight. But if the goal is really to inform the public and to get ordinary citizens to think about the implications of nanotechnology, a few citizen panels writing obscure reports won't have much effect. Nanotechnology education is most needed in newsrooms across the country and in the halls of the Capitol itself: We need reporters who know what they're talking about and who ask the right questions, and we need political leaders who can guide us through the confusing and potentially perilous times ahead.

This much seems clear: If molecular nanotechnology ever becomes a reality, we can expect massive social disruptions. As for the nature of these disruptions, we can, at best, only speculate.

First, we will hear complaints that the benefits of the new technology aren't being shared equitably; that the poor are being left out. But that problem will quickly fade away, as usually happens in our innovative market economy. (Think of the notorious "digital divide" of the 1990s, for instance; it's now all but gone.)

Second, we will reorganize our society and economy, shifting workers, eliminating jobs, and completely restructuring entire industries. We will hear questions about how our character will change: Will the abundance made possible by molecular manufacturing cause us to slip into hedonistic excess? Or might it have the reverse effect, making us *less* materialistic? Will life become so easy for us that it loses all meaning, or is it in our nature to keep seeking new challenges? (These questions may be as groundless as the "Leisure Question" that had social scientists wringing their hands a few decades ago, worrying about what we would do with all our free time in the age of automation and computers.)

Third, we will have to confront the "extinctionist" challenge and decide who we are. Nanotechnology raises many of the same ethical issues as biotechnology, and indeed the two techniques overlap. How much will we tinker with and revise our bodies? Will we choose a future as men or machines? Will we be able to use nanotechnology without drowning in nanotechnology, losing ourselves in nanotechnology, *becoming* nanotechnology?

And finally, we will be charged with rethinking our place in the universe. Our new powers of precision and perfection could lead us to a deeper appreciation for life—or they could make us lose all respect for the imperfect world we inhabit and the imperfect beings we have always been. The era of nanotechnology may be one of hubris and overreach, where we use our godlike powers to make the world anew. Is there room for wonder in a future where atoms march at our command?

Public debate about these matters will surely stay much lower to the ground—with arguments about where best to invest nanotech resources or about the quantifiable dangers of nanotechnology to the health and well-being of man and nature. Those who care about the deeper questions—about what nanotechnology means for human nature—must also master the details, both political and scientific. And they must offer not only lamentations for the disruptions and dehumanization that nanotechnology might cause, but a sensible vision of how nanotechnology might do some practical good—or even stir the very wonder that could be diminished by rearranging the smallest parts without seeing the whole.

*The online version of this article, which contains numerous links to citations and additional resources, is available at: http://www.thenewatlantis.com/publications/the-nanotechnology-revolution.

Discussion Questions

1. Do you support the development of molecular nanotechnology? Why or why not?
2. In your opinion, do you think that nanotechnology is a fundamentally different technology than, say, nuclear or chemical-based technologies? Are the risks and benefits fundamentally greater? Should nanotechnology be treated differently than other technologies (e.g., be regulated, supported, etc.)?
3. Briefly describe the role of a molecular assembler.

 Supporting Activities

1. Find some examples of commercially available products that use conventional nanotechnology. Also identify some anticipated future applications.
2. Briefly articulate the arguments that have been given against molecular nanotechnology. The leading critic is Richard Smalley.

 Additional Resources

1. K. Eric Drexler's Web site (www.e-drexler.com) contains, among other things, some short animations on what molecular nanotechnology might look like. His seminal book *Engines of Creation* is available to read online at: www.wowio.com/users/product.asp?BookId=503.
2. The Center for Responsible Nanotechnology: http://www.crnano.org/index.html.
3. The National Nanotechnology Initiative (http://www.nano.gov/html/centers/home_centers.html) was created in 2001 to coordinate the nanotechnology work done across federally funded agencies.
4. IBM's nanotechnology research group can be found at: http://domino.research.ibm.com/comm/research.nsf/pages/r.nanotech.html.
5. Rensselaer Polytechnic Institute has a nanotechnology research program: http://www.rpi.edu/research/nanotechnology/index.html.

 Endnotes

1. Joy, Bill. 2000. "Why Technology Doesn't Need Us." *Wired*. 8 (4): 238–262. Available: www.wired.com/wired/archive/8.04/joy.html.
2. Wikipedia. (2009). *NASA budget*. Available: http://en.wikipedia.org/wiki/NASA_budget.
3. Braastad, Richard. 1997. *Putting NASA's budget in perspective*. Available: http://www.richardb.us/nasa.html#table2.
4. Feynman, Richard. 1960. *There's plenty of room at the bottom*. Engineering and Science. Available: http://www.zyvex.com/nanotech/feynman.html.